THE DEVIL WALKS

Anne Fine

GALAXY PLUS

First published in Great Britain in 2011
by Doubleday, an imprint of
Random House Children's Books
This Large Print edition published 2011
by AudioGO Ltd
by arrangement with
Random House Children's Books

ISBN: 978 1445 874944

British Library Cataloguing in Publication Data available

Printed and bound in Great Britain by
TJ International Ltd

As certain as the sun behind the Downs
And quite as plain to see, the Devil walks.

John Betjeman

For AJMW

Part 1

1

Right from the very beginning, my life was strange. It didn't seem that way to me, of course. I'm sure, deep down, everyone in the world believes their life rolls on the way lives are supposed to go and it's the others who are off the track. But mine was the most peculiar start because of the way I'd been raised.

It was—oh, put it bluntly, Daniel!—halfway to mad.

My mother was no raving lunatic. Perhaps if she'd screeched and torn her clothes and wailed at the moon, then people would have noticed earlier and everything would have been different. But, no. My mother was the quietest soul. Or so I thought. As far back as I could remember, she moved with calm tranquillity around my room.

My sick room, I should say.

For, from the moment I was old enough to understand the words she said, she had been telling me that I was very ill indeed. And I believed her. Why shouldn't I? I had no reason not to trust her word. So I spent most of my growing years slumped against pillows. I was allowed to rise and totter unsteadily along the landing to the chill room that housed the water closet; but she would clutch my arm to steady me. (You too would have felt dizzy after so many hours in bed.) Sometimes in summer, when the lawn was bright with daisies, I'd be allowed to cling to the banisters and come downstairs—'Oh, slowly, slowly, Daniel! Take care not to fall!'—till suddenly I could feel the brush of air against my thin, pale shins, and smell the heady lilac.

As soon as I'd been settled in the wicker chair under the pear tree, rugs would be wrapped around my legs again. But at least I'd be out, seeing full skies, not just that poky square of light forcing its way through the grime coating on my small back window.

Mostly, though, I was kept in bed through all those endless days and years. Hour after hour my mother sat at my side, quietly crocheting the intricately layered collars of lace she wrapped in whispering sheets of tissue and sent to Manchester, where they were sold through ladies' catalogues to pay our rent. Sometimes I'd drift into sleep, and wake to find her gone. Or, when I was alone, I'd fall into a dream, then open my eyes to find she was beside me, her little ivory tools twisting and tugging at the dangling lace. I felt as if I dreamed her very comings and goings—but then

4

again, I spent so much time bobbing on the fringe of sleep that I lost touch with what was really happening and what was not. Often the dreams seemed real, but solid objects in my room appeared mere fancies of my own: the carved oak wardrobe and the paintings on the wall, my mother's beautiful old doll's house and the books on the shelf.

Those books. Without them I would have gone mad. I couldn't swim or walk, so others swam for me up crocodile-infested rivers, and strode over ice caps. I can't remember how I learned to read. I have a memory of my mother's pointing finger, and two fat creatures dressed in tartan shirts and scarlet trews—could they have been Bear and Badger?—who walked beside me through the alphabet and into nursery stories.

But by the time that I was of an age to come to a sense of myself—I'm Daniel Thomas Cunningham, and Liliana Cunningham's only son—Badger and Bear had vanished. Now many of the volumes by my bed were carried up from book shelves in the rooms below, and only then if I made mardy faces, and begged for hours against my mother's strictures that all the mould grown thick on their dank covers would ruin what was left of my ragged lungs.

Then, one day, chaos fell upon our house. I heard the knock on the back door, and that was strange because delivery boys usually came in the morning, and there were rarely any other packages unless my mother had sent off for satin to replace a fading gown. Under my window I heard a flurry of voices, as though more than one person down there on our back step was whipping up a bother.

5

'No, truly, Mrs Cunningham. You must come! Just for a moment. No further than your own front gate!'

'Mrs Cunningham, I beg you! We must insist.'

'You will be glad when you've seen what we have come to show you.'

Confused, my mother must have stepped out and followed them a very few steps around the path that led to the front of our house.

It was enough. The next thing I heard was the back door shutting behind her and the rasp as the night bolt slid across.

Someone I didn't know was in the house.

2

I struggled upright in my bed. Outside, I could still hear my mother's protests, each one more faint. 'What are you so determined to show me? Why should I come with you? What's anything on the street to do with me?' But I could hear footfalls—heavy, hurrying footfalls—coming up the stairs, and then doors opening along the hall.

Suddenly, there in the doorway stood a man. Though he looked young enough, his hair and beard were streaked with silver, and he was carrying a leather bag in such a businesslike fashion that I sensed at once he came for some honest purpose, and felt less frightened than before.

'So,' he said, 'it seems the whispering of all the ladies of the town is right. We have an invalid.'

I learned my manners out of books. But they

must have been none the worse for that, for when I whipped up the courage to greet him with the words, 'Good morning, sir. Are you a doctor come to visit me?' he beamed with pleasure.

'You have a voice, then.'

'Yes, sir.'

I felt that, by answering so promptly, I'd earned the right to ask a question of my own. 'Where have they taken my mother? Was all that commotion on the step simply a ruse to get her out of the house, and you inside it?'

He smiled again. 'And you have wits as well!'

Clearly he didn't think he had much time. Striding towards the bed, he took my arm and raised it from the covers. Pulling his watch out of his waistcoat pocket, he closed his fingers around my wrist and asked me civilly, 'And what's the name of your sickness? Can you tell me?'

I shook my head. 'I only know I've been this way as long as I can remember.'

Frowning, he indicated I should open my mouth, so he could peer inside. He listened to my heart and made me breathe more and more deeply. He asked me to cough, then leaned me forward in the bed and asked me to cough again. Pulling back the covers, he tapped my knees and pinched my toes. 'You feel that, then?'

'I do!'

I heard a rush of footsteps up the garden path, and others following. There was a noise I knew to be the door knob being wrenched, first to one side, then the other. I heard my mother's cries: 'What have you done? Am I locked out of my own home? Unbolt this door! Unbolt this door!' And other voices, still determined to soothe her: 'Come, Mrs

8

Cunningham. Be clear on this: no one intends you any harm.'

As if our home were still as peaceful as a country field, the doctor said to me, 'Can you get out of bed?'

I look back now, and part of me still wonders if it was some small bud of suspicion of my own that made me seize this chance to do exactly what the doctor asked, rather than make an effort to protest at the way he and his helpmeets had tricked my mother out of her own house. For, choosing to ignore the fluster outside, I carefully swung myself round and let my stick-thin legs search for the chill of the floor. The doctor held out an arm so I could steady myself, and I slid off the bed, gradually unfolding to my full height, not far short of the doctor's own.

'And can you walk?'

'Yes, I can walk.'

I made my way across the room towards the window. If I had had more strength, I would have raised the sash so I could lean out to console my sobbing mother. Instead, I turned to face the doctor, who was staring at me in astonishment.

'Why, boy, there's absolutely nothing wrong with you!'

'My mother says—'

He pressed a finger to his lips to silence me. 'I think perhaps we shouldn't talk of Mrs Cunningham—not till this mystery's solved.'

As if the mere mention of my mother had reminded him she was another problem, he strode across and slid the window up higher than I had ever seen it go. Cool air billowed round the room as he leaned out to send some wordless message to

9

those gathered below. Then he drew in his head and glanced about. 'Now, have you clothes?'

What did he think? That I was some neglected creature raised in a cave? 'Yes. I have clothes.'

But when we looked inside the wardrobe it was clear that there was nothing fit for any useful purpose. The only shoes I had were for a child far younger than myself. There was a jacket but, when it was spread, I found I could no longer squeeze so much as a fist into its narrow sleeves. In any case, I was distracted by the voices outside.

'Hold her more gently!'

'Come away, dear! No sense in struggling. You'll see your dear son soon enough. Just come away now. Quietly. Quietly.'

After a short search through my few belongings, my visitor gave up and sighed. 'The dressing gown will be enough. Tie the belt firmly around you, and we'll be gone.'

3

'Gone?'

It was the simplest of ideas, and yet it made me tremble. What had I thought? That all of life lay in the pages of books? I scoured the room for reasons to be excused from something so terrifying: the world that lay beyond our garden hedge.

'But what about my mother?'

The doctor shook his head. 'Yes. What indeed?' Then, as though brushing an unhappy question aside, he asked me suddenly, 'So, young man, do you have a name?'

'Daniel.'

He put his hand out gravely. 'And I am Doctor Marlow.'

I knew enough to shake it and answer forthrightly, 'I'm pleased to meet you, sir.'

I saw him brush aside the faintest look of puzzlement before he said, 'Well, Daniel, you'll admit this is the rudest interruption of the tranquil life you and your mother have shared. So it may be a good few days before she can pick up the threads again. Meanwhile, you can't be left alone.' He looked around. 'So, tell me, is there any small comfort in this room that we can take along with us?'

I glanced about. This little room was my world. I knew the pictures on the walls as well—no, better—than I knew the view from the window. In any case, I think it can't yet have occurred to me that paintings can, in one quick move, be unhooked from one wall and then as easily hung on another. Since Old Father Time had yet to offer me a reason to take much interest in him, I had no hankering to keep the clock. Indeed, in the whole room, apart from the story books, only one thing had ever filled my hours with pleasure. And that was no 'small comfort', but would take the strength of two grown men to carry out.

I shrugged.

The doctor pressed me. 'Nothing in this room is precious to you?'

'Only the doll's house.'

'The doll's house?' He looked confused, as if his earlier diagnosis might have been mistaken and there was truly something wrong with me. But then I pointed to the shrouded shape he must have taken for a piece of furniture my mother was protecting from the dust.

He raised a corner of the sheet that covered it. 'This?'

I nodded.

Curious, he whipped off the pale green cloth. And there the doll's house stood in all its glory.

The look of faint surprise that first came over his face—a strange choice for a boy!—shaded to admiration as he bent down to peer at it more closely. For the doll's house was perfect, from the tiny hard-boiled beads of scarlet paint mimicking roses spilling over the portico, up the carved pear-wood coils of miniature ivy clinging to its walls, past the tall windows and the topmost parapet, up to the steep grey slopes of all its curiously shaped roofs and high chimneys.

'Truly a labour of love,' he murmured. 'Even to make the shell of this beauty must have taken an age!'

He put out a hand. I thought he was about to search for the hook that, once unlatched, allowed the front to swing wide to reveal the rooms and staircases inside; the secret spaces and the fading wallpapers. Perhaps, I thought, he'd even reach in to pull out some tiny embroidered chair from one of the cluttered attics he'd expose, so he could more easily admire the almost-invisible stitching and see how even its needle-thin wooden legs were polished to a gleam.

But then it clearly struck him that, till the shock of his arrival, this doll's house must have been my whole wide world. Sharply he drew back his hand, as if he realized that to prise it open and finger anything inside would be like trampling in a private place.

Rising to his full height and stepping back, he said with soft courtesy, 'Precious, indeed! And far too valuable to be moved on a whim. But I'll make sure that no harm comes to it while you're away.'

13

Then, gently as my mother would have done, he took my arm and led me carefully through the door.

4

Nothing seemed odd to me about our destination: the doctor's own house. He was the only person I had met, the one who'd uprooted me, so it seemed natural that he should usher me to his own front door and introduce my shaking and enfeebled self to his astonished wife and wide-eyed daughters. Who else could I have pestered over the following days with endless questions: 'Where is my mother?' 'When can I see her?' 'Has she no message for me?' Questions to which he'd manage to give no answer before Mrs Marlow rushed in to bustle me away to the kitchen or dining room and beg me to eat. 'You've managed to grow tall; but now you must grow *strong*.'

No, stranger to me by far than my apparent adoption was the house itself. To someone who'd been hidden away, it was like moving out of some crepuscular world into a flood of colour: the morning light that shone through the red diamond-shaped panes set in the hall window to hurl long, glowing ruby lozenges across the tiled floor; the sparkling chandeliers; the Chinese rugs on which the patterns were so rich and strange they seemed to swirl; the gleams of light along the burnished banisters.

And the sheer strangeness of living in a house beset with voices. Where once I'd heard only the soft, soft shuffle of my mother's approach, now my ears rang all day with the new sounds of family life: doors endlessly opening and closing, the gong that rang for every meal, the motherly commands: 'Cecilia! Is this your cloak? Do you think Kathleen and Molly have nothing better to do than pick up after you?' 'Sophie! No need to stamp your way from room to room.' 'Mary, your kitten is loose again! Look in the lane.'

But Mrs Marlow was kindness itself to me, and put herself and her two elder daughters into a frenzy of sewing until I had a set of clothes to wear. Now, for the first time, I was encouraged to set foot outside the house—at first with someone's arm around me for support; then, as days passed, more steadily on my own. Beside me pranced the Marlows' youngest daughter. 'Daniel, catch up! Why must you keep on stopping?' But there was so much to be seen: carriages bowling past beyond the hedge, raising a storm of dust; droplets of rain that glistened on wet grass; Sophie's pet rabbit.

'Daniel! Come on! Come on!'

And so my small world grew a little, day by day, along with the strength in my legs. 'Soon you'll be coming with me to the Dame School,' Sophie

16

teased. 'We'll have to fold you up to fit you at a desk.'

'I might have lived a go-nowhere life,' I would admit to her. 'But I am not a know-nothing boy.'

But Sophie didn't care to learn whether I knew the names of capital cities or river ports. No, she was curious about the other aspects of my life. And though her sisters, Mary and Cecilia, obeyed their mother's order not to belabour me with questions, no sooner were the doctor and Mrs Marlow out of any room than Sophie would set about me. Had I read this book, or that? Could I paint landscapes and horses? If I was weak from lying in my bed, was I left unattended when I was bathing, or had my mother stayed at my side, and even washed me?

In leaped her sisters. 'Hush, Sophie!'

'For shame!'

But she'd ignore their warning frowns and press on with her endless inquisitions.

'Have you more names than Daniel?'

'Yes. Thomas.'

She gave the name a moment's kind consideration, and then pressed on. 'And what year were you born?'

I told her and she counted on her fingers. 'Why, then, you're four years older than I am almost to the day! And less than a year stands between you and Mary.'

I smiled. 'And so Cecilia outranks us all.'

'Cecilia?' Sophie waved a dismissive hand towards her eldest sister. 'Why, she is almost old enough to take a husband!'

Out tumbled more remonstrances. 'Sophie!'

'Button your silly beak!'

But still the questions would persist. One day, while we were sitting by the fire, out of the blue Sophie asked, 'Daniel, have you a father?'

I glanced at Mary and Cecilia. But it was clear that, on this matter at least, they were as curious as their sister and couldn't bring themselves to step in and silence her. They simply lowered their heads over their stitching and hoped to hear an answer.

So I did my best. 'My mother never happily mentioned him. But once, when I pestered her into a flurry, she told me that he had gone off to Glory just before my birth.'

Sophie looked baffled. 'Gone off to Glory?'

Hastily Mary whispered, 'That means he died.'

'Oh.' Sophie turned back to me. 'Well, have you no relatives? No aunts or uncles? No cousins?'

I made to shake my head, but something stopped me. What can it be about upheaval, both of mind and body? A drop falls in a tub of water that's been sitting for years, and it will cause no more than one small ripple on the surface. But drag that tub from one place to another, and you'll have stirred its depths. For suddenly there rose a memory of crawling along the landing as a tiny child and seeing, through some half-open bedroom door, my mother kneeling in prayer. Into my mind there came a muffled echo of her whispering voice, begging the Lord to keep safe her precious boy Daniel and his Uncle Se—

How had she meant to finish? Now I was so much older, more than one name sprang to mind. Sebastian? Selwyn? Septimus? But in the flash of childish recollection, all I knew was that she had turned to see me in the doorway and, with a face as white as bone, had broken off her prayer at once.

5

Was this real memory? Or just a fragment of a dream swept back by the disturbance of my removal into this house? When I had asked my mother about our family, she'd always said that we had none. And yet she had deceived me about my health. Why not at other times? And so, to be as truthful as I could, all that I said to Sophie was, 'I think my mother was a quiet soul from no sort of family.'

'No family.' I watched her pondering. 'But surely, at least, there must have been *visitors* to your house.'

I thought back to all the knockings on the door before the one that had changed everything. 'Yes, there were visitors. The butcher's boy came every Thursday morning. And Martin from the grocery knocked twice a week, and sometimes more if anything had been forgotten. But other than that . . .'

'No friends like us?' There was a look of perfect horror on her face. 'No proper company at all?'

I grinned at her. 'Is it so hard for you to think that someone could stay alive without the nourishing company of Sophie Marlow?'

She reached out to tug my hair. 'Don't tease! Don't tease!'

And out more questions came. Did I speak French? And had I ever seen a real live mouse? And did I wish I had a younger sister, just like her?

Now it was Mrs Marlow who came to the rescue, beckoning me out of the room to ask a question of her own.

'Daniel, now that you're strong enough to walk to church with us, I have to ask. Are you a Christian?'

I wasn't quite sure where the answer lay. I knew I said my prayers, and did not steal, and tried not to lie or envy. But as for what she meant . . .

She saw the confusion on my face. 'Are you baptized?'

So once again I took the chance to ask the question I had asked a hundred ways in the last weeks. 'Can I not go and ask my mother? She will know the answer!'

As usual at these moments, kind Mrs Marlow stirred uncomfortably in her chair and offered no response except to say, 'The parson claims he has no record of your baptism. But he assures me there will be no blasphemy in making sure.'

And so early next morning I was taken into church, quietly and privately, to be baptized. And

20

though I stood like any other supplicant of God's grace, my eyes were drawn by all the wonders around me: the stained-glass pictures of saints, the huge brass eagle holding a massive Bible on spread wings, statues of angels, vast stone tombs.

How much of life I'd missed! On the walk out of the church I felt Sophie tug me back, out of her mother's hearing. 'Now at last we can be assured you are no heathen!' All the way home she teased. Once we were through the door she snatched up one of my new boots. I chased her up one staircase and down the other, until she threw herself onto a sofa, panting. Hurling the boot at me, she cried, 'See? You have hunted me round the house so fast I can barely breathe! Oh, how could you *possibly* have been foolish enough to think you were so ill you had to lead your life locked away?'

It seemed to me the reason was obvious. 'Because that's what I was told.'

Sophie leaned forward eagerly. 'But Father says there's nothing wrong with you. Even your legs are strong—and will grow more and more so, now that you use them.'

'Then I expect my mother, even though she was mistaken—'

Clearly she had no time for any explanation of this sort. 'Your *mother*? But Kathleen says it's common knowledge in the town that your poor mother's insane.'

This was too much for Mary and Cecilia. They rushed to tell their sister, 'Hush, Sophie! Have more discretion!'

'And more charity!'

'But it is *true*.' And though Mary caught Sophie's arm and, with Cecilia's help, began to pull

21

her forcibly towards the door, their younger sister turned back. 'Think, Daniel! Why *else* should she have got it into her head to entomb you?'

I watched the door closing behind the three of them and forced myself to push away unease and tell myself that, though Mary and Cecilia were trying to be kind, truly it was preposterous to drag poor Sophie from the room after so silly an announcement. I could agree my mother had arranged our life in a way that was inexplicable. And it was hard to brush away the creeping realization that all my childhood had been stolen away. Sophie's had been one big and colourful plum pudding of a life, stuffed with a million sights and sounds and feelings; my own had been thin gruel. And yet my mother and I had not been unhappy. I had been comfortable with her. And though I'd sometimes had the sense she felt bad luck was stalking her, my mother had been comfortable with me.

Could it be *possible* she was insane?

Insane?

No, not that, surely! Never!

6

Sophie came back a short while later, tear-stained and chastened, flanked by her two stern sisters. They stood like guards as she apologized. 'Daniel, I'm sorry. I had no right to say what I did. It was pure foolishness. I won't speak out of turn again.'

But how could she help it? It seems the tale of my discovery had been by far the most intriguing story the townspeople had heard for years. Every few days Sophie spooned out more gleanings of kitchen gossip. 'Kathleen says that the sweep was here this morning. And he was telling her that, though you've been with us for several weeks, Mrs Parker is *still* inventing reasons to visit all her friends and boast to them that she was the first to catch sight of you.'

Over her shoulder I saw her sisters' gathering frowns. But Sophie was warming to her story. 'And

Mrs Parker says that, though you must have lived in Hawthorn Cottage almost since you were born, it's not till she was passing by your garden one afternoon last summer—'

'Stooping to peer through some thin patch in the hedge?' Mary suggested tartly.

Ignoring the interruption, Sophie kept on, '—that she first spotted you, slumped in a wheeled chair in the shade, shrouded with blankets. She thought you must be some young visitor come to stay quietly with Mrs Cunningham until your health was restored. But then she happened to catch sight of you again a few weeks later.'

Just at that moment, Dr Marlow came into the room. Clearly he'd caught the last few words because he too broke in, echoing Mary's suspicions. 'Spotted the poor boy through some small hole she herself dutifully bored through the hawthorn hedge, I have no doubt.'

But Sophie was too taken up with telling me the story to be derailed. 'She thought it very odd. After all, nobody came to visit you. And you appeared to be getting neither worse nor better—'

'Ah,' interrupted Dr Marlow. 'If only I could come to my own diagnoses with as much speed and confidence as Mrs Parker.'

I burst out laughing. I couldn't help it. It seemed to me, who'd only ever had my mother's solemn company, that sitting here in this enormous room buzzing with family members rushing in and out, teasing and interrupting one another, scolding and quarrelling and joking, felt rather as if I'd been swept into the pages of one of those books I'd read so often just to pass the hours. I don't believe I would have been surprised if Dr Marlow had

24

suddenly declared we were about to take canoes and paddle up the Amazon, or pile into a wicker basket under some giant air balloon and set off over the Channel for France.

My laughter quietened when I realized that Dr Marlow was watching me. On his face was that same bewildered look I'd seen in my own bedroom when we first shook hands, and then again quite often since I'd moved into his house. Only a few minutes later, when the girls fell to arguing over a colour match for one of Mary's silks, he took the chance to beckon me out of the room.

Did he have news for me about my mother? Or had I taken some false step in this, my brand-new life? My heart began to thump. Freshly reminded that I was not safely one of his warm and merry family, I slid off the little fireside stool and made for the door.

Dr Marlow was waiting for me out in the hall. Laying an arm round my shoulders he said, 'Come to my study. I want to have a quiet word.'

I couldn't help but burst out with my worries. 'Have I done something wrong?'

He laughed. 'No, nothing wrong.' His tone turned graver. 'But there is something I'd like to understand.'

So into the study we went, and first he made me comfortable in a chair, then pulled his own closer till our knees almost touched. He seemed at a loss to know how to begin. Finally he sighed. 'No way to beat about this bush,' he said. 'Daniel, I tell you bluntly that there's something about you that has been puzzling me greatly.'

I waited.

It seemed a good long time before he spoke

25

again. 'If what I understand about your former life is true, then all these last years you've been as good as locked away from health and air and cheery companionship.'

That didn't seem quite right. 'But I did have my mother for company.'

He took small care to hide his poor opinion of that. 'And yet, here in our noisy and disordered household, you seem to fit in well.'

Since I was baffled, silence lay between us.

'Perhaps *too* well?' he suggested after a moment.

'*Too* well?'

He smiled. 'Sophie brings you her rabbit, and you're lost in wonder, running your fingers through its fur as if you'd never felt the like.'

'Indeed I hadn't, sir. Not on a living creature.'

'We walk with you down to the stream. You stop to stare at every cow.'

'They seem so *huge*. So much more *weighty* than they look in books. And when Sophie leaned across the fence to pat one—why, *dust* flew out of it!'

He smiled. 'Sunsets distract you utterly.'

'I never saw such skies before. My room faced north.'

'In short, over the past weeks I've watched you discovering the world as if you were a child in petticoats: the first rainstorm on your head; the first time you came down the stairs without the aid of the banister. Why, when I caught you peering into one of Kathleen's pots, watching the porridge bubble, I swear you looked just as entranced as if you stared into the Elixir of Life.' He spread his hands. 'Everything's fresh to you, Daniel.

Everything's new'—suddenly he leaned toward me—'except for *people*.'

'People?'

As though embarrassed now, he studied the backs of his fingers. 'I mean to say, if you'd met *nobody*, where did you learn so civilly, right from the start, to address a man like myself as "Sir" and my dear wife as "Madam" or "Mrs Marlow"? Where did you learn to hear a tease and recognize it for what it was? Why were you never discountenanced by all my daughters forever rushing out of one door and in another, with Sophie tugging at your mop of hair to get your attention?' Again he spread his hands. 'And so, Daniel, stuck in that room with only your mother for company, how did you ever learn to be so comfortable in a family?'

I made a guess. 'From books?'

But he looked unconvinced. 'Oh, I can see how reading could teach you to *understand* the world and how it works. You say yourself that there are cows in books—though nowhere near so weighty and so dusty as the real thing! But people are harder to understand than simple cows. And there is something in the sheer ease of how, from the very start, you fitted in with us, how you spoke up at meals, how you teased Sophie, how you were first to know when Mary was irritated, or Cecilia was tired . . .'

I loved the man so much already that I was delighted to find an answer for him.

'Oh, that! Oh, that is nothing. I have always lived *that* sort of life. Only I lived it all inside the doll's house!'

27

7

The doctor stared at me across the desk. 'Inside the doll's house?'

And so I told him everything: how I would wait to see the fringe of light thrown by my mother's candle flicker beneath my door as she went past at night; how I'd slide quietly out of bed and crawl across to the doll's house. Sated with sleep all day, I'd often spend the whole of a moonlit night creating dramas in my miniature world, spinning out tales of all sorts, from glorious adventures to small domestic scenes, with everything cut down to size except the passions of my characters. I told him all about Mrs Golightly, carved thin as a wooden peg but dressed in snow-white finery; about Rubiana, the delicate doll with blue eyes and tumbling hair and the beginnings of a pout on rosy-painted cheeks. 'I'll show you all of them

28

when I go home.' Excited by the memory, I carried on, describing Topper the dog—too big and clumsy to fit easily in the doll's house, worn bald in places, but still good to bark a warning whenever my imagined stories needed it. And Hal, the doll who was a prince until the day I had lost patience with the endless run of royal tales I was inventing, and snapped off his crown.

He smiled. 'Aha! So young, and yet already a republican!'

Not fully understanding him, I took it for a tease and carried on. 'I didn't want my mother to know that I'd been out of bed. So the next day I waited till the butcher's boy was hammering on the door, then, as my mother hurried away, begged her to pass Hal to me. I knew she'd be too flustered to notice any change in him. When she came back I cried that I had dropped him out of bed and broken his crown.'

The memory of my mother sitting close to me, all calm and quiet, swept back in force. I had a sudden longing to be there again, in my old life, safe in my bed. My tears rose, and my stomach gripped so tightly that I could barely breathe. Could this be homesickness—a feeling, up till then, I'd only read about in books?

It seemed ungrateful to tell this kind and generous man how much I wanted to be back with my own mother in my own bleak home. But I did manage to blurt out, 'And she was good to me! That very afternoon she put aside her own work to crochet a tiny scarlet beret to hide the scar on Hal's head!'

He sat back, giving me time to brush away my tears before he went on with his questions. 'So,

29

Daniel, when there were stories in which a young man like yourself could play the hero, this doll called Hal took the part?'

I blushed. 'Sometimes.'

He shook his head in wonder. 'And so you learned to live among real people simply from your imagination and a fine doll's house that your mother bought for you.'

I knew enough about the games boys were supposed to play. 'The doll's house wasn't bought for me,' I told him hastily. 'It was my mother's when she was a child. It's called High Gates and is a perfect model of the house where she was born. It simply happened to be in the room into which she moved my bed.'

'So,' he said dryly, 'almost a storeroom both in size *and* in purpose.'

Was he suggesting that my mother had packed me away inside that small back room as if I too were simply some random and unwieldy legacy from her own past? I burned to defend her. 'She had good reason to move my bed in there! Back when I was a baby, it seems my crib was in the larger room that overlooks the street. But when I asked if I could go back there so I'd have more to see, my mother said that its bay windows made the place "a veritable cave of winds", and I'd be more at risk.'

Another wry look crossed the doctor's face. 'As much, perhaps, from the curiosity of people passing by as from the icy draughts?'

I'd never realized it until that moment. But he was right, of course. That was the reason why, the moment I was grown enough to pull myself up at the window, my mother had moved me into that

30

tiny, sunless back room.

And why she would not let me back again.

Strange that a little detail like that could have such a ring of truth. Now, suddenly, the idea that my mother might be mad no longer seemed quite so preposterous. It was a sickening feeling, as if my already unsettled world had shifted yet again. I think that I felt dizzy. But Dr Marlow was still staring at me gravely. And we were alone. So now that the idea had finally forced its way through all the barriers I'd carefully put up against it, I had to ask him.

'Please, Doctor Marlow, is it true what people in the town are saying about my mother?'

He reddened with vexation. 'The people of this town should keep their opinions to themselves!' He tried to calm himself. 'But if they're gossiping out of turn, perhaps you should tell me what is being said.'

I hung my head. 'That she is . . .'

Now that I feared it might be true, I couldn't say it.

He prompted, 'Is . . . ?'

I found that I could barely whisper it. 'That she is quite insane.'

The silence seemed to last a hundred years. And then the most that he could offer was, 'Your mother is not well at all.'

My tears began to fall. I felt such *guilt*. What could I have been *thinking*? How could I possibly have spent so many of the hours since we were parted laughing and learning new card games, and chasing Sophie up and down the stairs? I should have been beside my mother through all the days—and all the nights if need be. How could I

31

blandly have assumed that she'd recover from the shock of my removal as quickly and easily as I'd recovered from my change of circumstance? What had I *thought*? That she would weep for a while to have her strange plan to raise me as an invalid thwarted by neighbours' cunning, then dry her tears and agree that it would be more sensible to let me enter the world?

Had I believed our problem would be swept away by this short time apart? I was a *fool*.

Flushed with the closest I had ever come to anger, I hissed at Dr Marlow, 'What have we *done*? My mother must be mad with grief to have lost sight of me! Why have you let me abandon her like this?'

He stretched out a hand to calm me. 'Daniel, don't think this way.'

I reared back out of reach. 'No! You must take me with you to the hospital! I have to see her!'

'Not yet. She isn't ready.'

But I was burning with frustration. 'She *must* be ready! She *cannot* be so crazed she wouldn't be cheered to see me.'

He was adamant. 'Daniel, her mind is hectic. It's on a tightrope. Take my word for it, this way is better. If you love your mother—as I know you do—then you must trust me, and you must be patient.'

He was a doctor. And he and his family had been good to me. I tried to calm myself. 'You promise me that she'll be well again?'

He took his time to answer. And even then all he would say was, 'You're a smart boy—certainly smart enough to understand that's not a promise I can offer you. What I will say is that as soon as I'm confident that seeing you will not disturb her even more I'll take you with me.'

It was the most I could get out of him. And so I settled for that. And maybe I was a shallow and ungrateful son. But I was younger then, and must forgive myself for letting all the comforts and amusements of the doctor's house, and the kind thoughts and care of its inhabitants, quickly distract me till, once again, all of the townspeople who saw me clambering over fences with Sophie, or whispered behind their hands about me as I walked around the town with Mrs Marlow, carrying her parcels, could easily be forgiven for thinking me a happy and untroubled boy.

8

A few days passed, and then a fever swept across our town. All the next week we hardly saw anything of Dr Marlow except for his tailcoat as he hurried from the house, or his wan face as he came home to snatch a meal. For safety's sake he ate alone. 'Don't you come near me, girls! No, nor you, Daniel! Not for a moment. I am a walking pest house!'

I thought him very brave, and wondered if, when I was old enough, I'd study to be a doctor. It would seem odd to switch from spending the first part of my life being an invalid to spending the rest of it working to cure them. But since Cecilia and Mary's tutor had thrown up his hands at what he called 'the yawning gaps' in my poor education, and Mrs Marlow herself had started me on daily lessons, I'd come to realize that one day soon I'd have to earn my living.

So next time I saw Dr Marlow snatching up his bag, I leaned over the banisters and called to him, 'Can I come with you? Can I be of help?'

He turned his face up and laughed. 'I tell you, Daniel, if anyone could go round the town this week in perfect confidence, it would be you.'

'How so?'

'Look at yourself!' he told me. 'If there's a sturdier constitution within twenty miles I'd be astonished. How many children could grow to your age with no fresh air or exercise without their mother even once having to send for a doctor to try to keep them from death's door?'

I'd never thought of things that way. While I was mulling it over he added, 'If you've a mind to be useful, then help my poor wife keep Sophie amused while she's cooped up away from this infection. I'm told the child's already half wild with boredom, and Mary and Cecilia are complaining that they can't read more than a page, or sew a stitch, before she bothers them.'

I thought back to the long and empty hours that I'd once had to fill. 'Suppose the doll's house was carried here?'

'Your doll's house?' He beamed. 'You would allow that?'

'If it would help.'

'Then I'll arrange its carriage here this very afternoon!'

With a wave he was gone. And less than two hours later I heard the rattle of a wagon in the street. I hurried down the stairs and held the door while two men in green smocks brought in their burden, shrouded by its faded green dustsheet.

Gently they set it down on the tiled floor and whipped off the cover.

Behind me, I heard a squeal of delight. 'A doll's house?' Already Sophie was rushing across the hall towards it. 'Oh, wonderful! What joy!' She skidded to a halt. 'Oh, look! It's perfect! Do the windows open? Oh, Daniel, is it really yours? And are there dolls inside?'

Mary ran after her to pull her back. 'Sophie! Perhaps Daniel would prefer you not to poke your fingers into the only token he has of his old home.'

I'm sure she didn't mean so brutally to remind me of how I'd been uprooted. Still, her words came as a shock. I stared at the doll's house. Here, out of the night shadows, it looked less like the miniature world that it had always been to me and more like the plaything of a child.

Sophie kept pestering. 'Oh, Daniel. It's a darling little home! Look at the tiny painted rosebuds around the door. May I just peep inside? Oh, Daniel, please!'

I stepped back, giving her room to drop to her knees in front of it. She lifted the latch that swung the front open. 'Look! Here's a whole tumble! A sailor and a milkmaid and two princesses. A sweet boy clown. Two swarthy brigands!' Clearly the men in smocks had tipped the dolls they found beside the small house into it before they carried out their load. Sophie was squealing with glee. 'And here's a little bald dog! Poor thing. I'm going to call him Popsy!'

'His name is Topper,' I corrected her.

She looked up, mortified at her presumption. 'Oh, Daniel. I'm so sorry. Of course you've already given them names.'

'It doesn't matter. They are only here so you can play with them.'

'But you must teach me who they are.'

So I ran through their names, and left her opening all the doors and peering into the tiny papered bedrooms. 'This is Hal's room! No! It'll be where Rubiana sleeps. I'll put her in the bed right now. She's tired after her journey.' If Sophie's quick inventions could help her pass the hours, then I was glad. And when Mrs Marlow came back from her own errands of mercy round the stricken town, I told her I'd be happy for the doll's house to be put anywhere Sophie chose.

9

And so the doll's house was put by the bay window in the morning room. Could Sophie have been more content? All through the last busy days before those strong enough to triumph over the fever had started to recover, Sophie played with the dolls she had found tumbled in the little house. Hearing her make the worn dog Topper bark in a fury at pretty Rubiana's teasing, or uncrowned Hal knock fiercely at a door, I'd think how often I myself had crouched in moonlight inventing the very same sorts of silly plots and childish conversations, and I was glad that only spiders had been close enough to blush on my behalf.

If Sophie caught me passing the open door she'd call to me to take a turn with one of the dolls. One morning there was no escape. 'Now, you be Topper.' She thrust him into my hand, and waved the stiff peg doll towards him. 'And Topper must growl horribly because he has a deadly fear of Mrs Hawthorn here.'

'Mrs Golightly,' I corrected her.

Her cheeks went pink. 'I'm sorry, Daniel. That was stupid of me.'

She seemed so flustered I was curious. 'How is it stupid, Sophie?'

'Because—because . . .' Panicking, she fell upon my mercy. 'You see, we only saw her over the garden gate. We didn't know her *real* name.'

I couldn't think what she was talking about. The dolls had never been outside.

Sophie pressed on. 'We meant no disrespect. We simply saw your mother walking in the garden, and since your house is known as Hawthorn Cottage we called her Mrs Hawthorn to ourselves. We didn't know your name was Cunningham.'

I was still baffled. 'Sophie, who are we talking about? My mother, or a peg doll?'

'Well, both, of course,' she said.

'Both?'

She looked surprised that I myself could be so stupid. 'Well, look! She is the mirror image.'

I looked at the peg doll and saw it for the very first time: that same tense, upright look; the same dark eyes that drilled out from a lean face; a studied carefulness about the dress. I suppose I'd thought that all the peg dolls in the world must look this way. (If there'd not been so many illustrations in my story books, I might have thought that all the mothers in the world did too.)

But it made sense. For, if the doll's house had been designed to look exactly like the home in

39

which she'd been raised, what was so strange about the dolls inside it resembling people in the family? Perhaps my mother had, over the years, grown to look just like one of the grandmothers I must have had—though this was something that I might have learned only through brutishness, since any question to my mother about her childhood or her family was met with floods of bitter tears, or long pale silence.

Sophie was staring at me with such anxiety that, simply to tease her back to confidence, I asked, 'And did you and your sisters spend *many* hours peeping over our garden gate? Perhaps you should have ventured down the alley and spied at your Mrs Hawthorn much more easily through the hole Mrs Parker bored in our hedge.'

Giggling, Sophie reached for my hand to pull it down. 'Come, Daniel. Act your part. How can a dog put his full mind to barking when he is floating in the air?'

And so I joined her in the game and I enjoyed it. But the mere mention of Mrs Parker had set young Sophie's mind on a fresh tack. Over the next couple of hours her tongue ran loose. She told me how the ladies of our town had always found my mother strange—a woman alone, who kept no company and clearly sought none. But after I'd been spotted in the garden, the whispering began afresh. The butcher's boy had sworn that there was far more meat in his deliveries than would suit just one widow—

'Not just one widow,' I interrupted Sophie solemnly. 'One wooden, peg-thin widow.'

'Oh, don't torment me!' Sophie squealed, and went on to tell how Mrs Parker and Miss Gott had drummed up a deputation to speak to her father and insist he go to see the pale young invalid who'd been seen sitting in the wicker chair. 'Perhaps his family can't afford a visit from a doctor,' they'd said. 'But you mustn't mind that, because the two of us will undertake to pay the bills if you think you can help the child.'

So Dr Marlow had knocked on our door and doffed his hat. It seemed my mother had been graciousness itself until she finally understood who Sophie's father was and why he'd come. Then her eyes flashed and she'd closed the door in his face.

'Truly? My mother shut the door in Dr Marlow's face?'

'It was the talk of the town! And after that, of course, people began to wonder if she was in her senses. It was a matter of days before the plan was hatched to lure her from the house for long enough for Papa to sneak inside and take a peep at you.'

I felt a flurry of conflicting thoughts. I cannot say that I was sorry I had been—what was the word? Rescued? Set free?—from my confinement in that tiny room. And yet I knew my mother's sense of deep intrusion. Feeling so much for her, I couldn't help but think myself disloyal. That's probably why I tried to make a joke of something so important it had derailed my mother's life. 'Sophie, you are a perfect *mine* of information. If I should ever want to know anything at all about myself, I shall know where to turn.'

'You're teasing me again. Back to the game!'

*   *   *

Not all her gossip was as orderly as on that afternoon. Since she was kept inside as strictly as the rest of us during those weeks of sickness, most of her news came fresh from the kitchen, where she would spend long hours haunting poor Kathleen as she cooked, or pestering Molly to let her sweep the floors or lay the fires. We'd play for half an hour or so, and then she'd tell me, 'Today there were mandarin oranges in the market. And we shall have one each after our lunch.' Or, 'There's a collection to buy Mr Mackay a wooden leg after his accident.'

One morning she flew through the green baize door between the kitchen and the hall as if she were on skates. 'Daniel! Kathleen has told me that your house is taken!'

'Taken?' I had a vision of Hawthorn Cottage being lifted onto a carriage and wheeled away. 'How, taken?'

'It's let again. It has been rented out to a new family. And Mrs Parker says there are four children, one for each year of the marriage.'

Crossing the hall with a vase of fresh blooms, Mrs Marlow broke step. 'Sophie!'

Sophie said stubbornly, 'But it is *true*. And Mrs Parker swears she has already seen the whole tribe tumbling around the garden.'

I couldn't understand what she was telling me. While she rushed off to pass the news on to Cecilia and Mary, I took the chance to follow Mrs Marlow into the conservatory. Shutting the door between ourselves and the rest of the family, I said, 'How can the house belong to others now? It is my *home*.'

Mrs Marlow drew breath and shook her head at

me sadly. 'No, Daniel. Not if your mother has failed to pay the quarter's rent.'

'But I thought I'd live there for ever. I thought that I was only staying here until my mother was well again, and then we'd—' My knees began to falter in the old, old way. I tried so hard to finish. 'And then together she and I would—'

I saw the pity in Mrs Marlow's eyes and I broke off. So many warning signs and gentle hints—all stubbornly ignored. I had been stupid. My mother could no longer keep a roof over our heads. Not only was my old life over, but it would never return, and for the first time since I'd been led from Hawthorn Cottage into the Marlows' home, I truly realized what was happening.

Then I burst into noisy, jerking sobs. What sort of fool was I? Up till that moment I'd been doing little more than play a part, like one of the dolls in my imagined stories. My mother had been carried off, and over and over I had set my face against all possible grim futures. Blandly, I'd sunk back into waterlogged calm. I might have had bad dreams, but waking each morning, I'd clearly found some way to bundle up the fright and the anxieties—the storms of grief I felt—and tidy them away as if they were no more than nightclothes to be neatly tucked beneath my pillow.

I lay in Mrs Marlow's arms and wept. The girls crept in and were sent out again, first to fetch blankets to wrap around my shoulders, and then again to leave the two of us in peace while Mrs Marlow stroked my head and wiped my tears and tried to hug me back into some sense that there was comfort in the world.

I cried until I couldn't cry a single tear more.

43

Then I was led to bed, and tucked in tight, and Mrs Marlow stayed in the chair beside me until I slept.

10

Why did I set myself in front of the doll's house next morning? Sophie was not yet pestering me to play a part. Could it have been because I felt back in my former skin: unsteady on my feet, light-headed from my hours of weeping?

There was a tap on the door. Sophie peeped in and, with a gentleness that I can only think must have been laid on her as a charge by her kind mother, asked me, 'Shall I leave you to yourself? Or would you like company?'

'I don't know what I want.'

But still I patted the rug beside me. Sophie crept in and reached for Topper, still her favourite. I picked up Hal, and off we went into some spiralling adventure of Sophie's invention. Lost fortunes and a kidnapped brother? I can remember little of the story until the moment Sophie walked one of the brigands through each room in turn, in search of some hidden will she was insisting would make young Hal rich.

Her brigand took his search to heart. He tumbled chairs, up-ended beds, and, though too tall, stormed up the attic stairs, poking his head in every room. Then Sophie pushed him up the last few steps that served no purpose since they came to a dead end.

I fretted as his stiff arms brushed the faded wallpaper. 'No point in sending him up there.'

'He's headed for the roof.'

'What, through the attic ceiling?'

'No,' she insisted. 'Through the sliding panel.'

'What sliding panel?'

But her quick, prying fingers were already showing me. There, where I'd always thought there was some tiny flaw in the design—steps leading up to nowhere—Sophie had found an explanation. 'See? The square above him slides across.'

I was astonished. I could remember using my tiny fingers to prise at it so often from all sides when I was small. It never shifted. Sophie had come at the problem quite a different way and used a thumb to push it to the side.

Back it had slid. Already she had squeezed her brigand through to make him clamber out. He scaled the iron ladder to search among the chimney pots, then leaned over the highest parapet to search some more.

'He'll not find any will and testament tucked in the ivy,' I scoffed. 'The wind and weather would have shredded it.'

She was determined to follow her own story.

'Not if it's wrapped in oilcloth and tucked in some hollow.'

So on we went, until her story drew to its close, the brigand hunted down. I started gathering the dolls together.

'No, no!' she said, distraught. 'We must arrange for his escape, or he'll swing from the gallows.'

Knowing the gong would sound for lunch at any moment, I said, 'Why don't we simply make the judge transport him?'

'Too harsh by far!' cried my soft-hearted companion.

'Then we must leave him kicking his heels in gaol—at least while we put the doll's house to rights after his clumsy visit.'

I set the little chairs and tables on their feet while she picked up the tiny black and scarlet logs her villain had spilled from the grate.

'Lucky he didn't start a fire!' I teased.

But he had caused some damage in the doll's house. A pin had sprung up from the long thin padded seat under the drawing-room window.

Sophie put in her hand. 'I'll push that back.'

I tried to stop her, but I was too late. Her thumb had bent it.

'Bother!' she said. 'Oh, well. I'll pick out the pin. Then we can straighten it and try again.'

'Leave it to me,' I begged. But Sophie was too quick. Using her fingernails as pincers, she tugged. Again, she was too hasty. Out sprang another pin, and then another.

The long top of the padded window seat was lifting suddenly, like a lid.

11

'What's this?'

Reaching inside, Sophie pulled out a doll I'd never seen. Like Mrs Golightly, he'd been whittled from wood, almost a peg doll. He was a mischievous-looking lad with lank dark hair that fell over sharp eyes, and he was dressed in thick black clerical skirts far, far too long for him.

She handed him to me. 'Is he a *choirboy*? And how is he supposed to walk, hobbled with skirts like these?'

I shrugged, as much at a loss as she was to explain his peculiar garb. And it felt strange to think that all those hours I had played alone, this doll had been so close, practically under my fingers, almost as though he had been hiding there, listening and waiting.

She snatched him back. 'I'll not leave him like

that! I think it very cruel of someone'—and here she looked at me suspiciously—'to dress him in such a way, and nail him in a window seat that might as well serve as a coffin.'

I laughed. 'Come, Sophie. Perhaps, like me, he had to sit for ever in a wicker chair or in his bed. Perhaps these skirts were wrapped so thickly round his poor lame legs to keep them warm.'

She wasn't amused. 'You were not lame. And I expect that neither is he.'

I teased, 'So you're a doctor now!'

Just then the lunch gong rang and Mary appeared in the doorway. 'Mother says both of you must come at once.'

Regretfully Sophie laid down the doll. 'I shall say no to pudding,' she announced, 'so I can make him something more sensible to wear through our adventures.'

Of course her love of jellied fruit won out against compassion for a wooden doll. She sat as long, and ate as much as I did, and my appetite had been the wonder of the house; even Cook praised me. But Sophie did remember to beg some velvet scraps from Mary's work box along with her small sharp scissors and, as soon as lunch was done, she fell to her task.

I watched her spread the velvet scraps beside the doll. 'Shall his new breeches be blue or green?'

She took some time to choose, pushing at the doll's skirts so she could better measure the length of his legs. I heard her gasp. Then, snatching him from the floor, she quickly turned away. Only a moment passed before, as if she'd suddenly become possessed of sleight of hand, she thrust a different doll towards me.

49

Yes. Another doll entirely!

But not that, either. No, not quite. For here were the same face, the same eyes and the same lock of hair that fell across the forehead. This was the same boy grown into a man, but the green eyes gazed out with a more piercing look and the thin smile had curdled into something sourer—closer, I thought uneasily, to satisfied spite than simple mischief.

As I watched, Sophie flipped the doll over. The boy was back. She flipped the doll again. The skirts swept down and there, once more, was the grown man.

'Two dolls for one! Daniel, have you seen *anything* so clever?'

I didn't answer. I was miles away, back in a book of fairy tales I'd had to beg my mother to take out of my room each night because it gave me such bad dreams. There was an illustration at the front. If I looked at the picture one way up, then it was Snow White with her tumbling ebony locks smiling at me. Twist the book upside down and the same picture showed a different face entirely. Lace frills around Snow White's neck had now become her wicked stepmother's greying hair. The ebony curls had turned themselves into dark scallops around the old queen's neck. Through the strange alchemy of the artist's skill, only the eyes, viewed upside down, stayed eyes. Everything else—eyebrows, age lines around the neck, lips and the shadows of the chin—became some other. How many hours had I sat in bed, haunted, twisting the book this way and that, just as now Sophie flipped this most unusual doll first one way, then the other?

'Don't keep on doing that, Sophie! Leave it be!'

I had surprised myself, and she had never heard me be so sharp with her. Her small face crumpled and her lower lip shook. Then, as if suddenly resentful of my tone, she flipped the boy to show the man again and thrust him in my face.

I'll swear her voice became a snarl. 'I'll do exactly as I choose!'

Even more startled than I, poor Sophie threw the doll down on the rug as if it scorched her. Her eyes stared and she suddenly looked scared to death.

'Sophie?' I put a hand out. She was trembling. 'Sophie?'

'I'm sorry, Daniel! I didn't mean to speak like that!'

I had to comfort her. 'I didn't for a moment think those were your *own* words.'

It was as if she actually believed me. 'Really?'

She looked so anxious that I thought it best to keep up the pretence. 'No, not for a moment.' I forced myself to laugh. 'I took it you'd forgotten that our game was over, and had become your fierce brigand once again.'

She was still pale. 'Come on,' I tempted her. 'Let's start again. Begin another story.'

'Another story, yes.'

She reached for safe little Rubiana with her pink cheeks and bright blue eyes. I chose from the rest of the dolls. I look back now and I no longer think it curious that, offered a doll with two fresh faces, I still turned my back and picked up poor balding Topper, who could do nothing more than scratch and bark.

We set off with as much invention as we could muster, but within minutes all enthusiasm melted away. Sophie threw Rubiana aside. 'Daniel, let's leave the doll's house for another day.'

'Yes,' I agreed at once. 'Another day.'

It was a long time before that day came.

12

No doubt Mrs Marlow spoke to her husband about my storm of weeping, because early one morning, shortly after the fever had left town, he rapped on the door to my room.

'Awake, Daniel? I've a couple of calls to make down by the quarry; but then I'll keep my promise and come back to take you with me to the hospital to see your mother.'

I rushed to dress myself, all the time wondering what she would think to see me look so different. Now, there was colour in my cheeks. My legs were stronger and I stood up straight. In the new jacket that had been made for me I looked quite the young man of health and sense.

But when I said as much to Mrs Marlow, she drew me aside. 'Daniel, you mustn't be too disappointed with this meeting. Your mother is not well. If she were half herself she wouldn't still be in the hospital. And Doctor Marlow says the nurses can't persuade her to eat more than a few scraps. Her face is very drawn, he says. You will be shocked.'

I kept a sober look, and nodded to show that I'd been listening. But, deep inside, my heart was singing because I knew the moment my mother saw me standing there, she would be well again. She'd take me in her arms, her spirits soaring, and make an effort to return to her old self. Soon she'd be bringing out her lace-making tools and earning our living again. Perhaps the Marlows would allow her to take my bedroom for a week or two, while I slept on the couch in the doctor's study. And then, when they were both assured she was quite well, we would go off together and find another place to live, as good as Hawthorn Cottage. Better.

'Daniel!'

The doctor was at the door. I flung my arms round Mrs Marlow, and ran from the house. Together, Dr Marlow and I walked through the town and out the other side, further than I had ever ventured with Mrs Marlow or the girls before the fever had corralled us all. Mostly we walked in silence, and more than once I had the feeling that Dr Marlow had drawn breath to speak and then thought better of it, while I was busy trying to control my rising excitement.

At the town's edge we reached the sign that pointed to Langley Hospital, but the doctor kept on.

I stopped. 'Why are we going further?'

'Further?'

I pointed to the sign he'd just walked past. 'Are there more visits to make before I see my mother?'

He understood at last. 'No, Daniel. She's not there.'

'You said that she was in the hospital.'

'And so she is. But there's more than one sort of hospital, and she's in another.'

'Where?'

'Further along. A little out of town.'

We walked for what seemed half an hour or more. Suddenly, we were off the road and into what he told me was a beech wood. Maybe it was the fact that this was the first true wildness I had ever seen that made it such a gloomy place. We'd only gone a little way between the trees before I had the feeling that I was in a strange world out of fairy tales. Birds screeched and fluttered. I could hear the rasp of leaves, and scuttling in the undergrowth.

'It feels like stepping into one of those stories on the shelf.'

'I only wish it were!' he answered before, instantly regretting his words, he stopped in his tracks to grip me by the shoulders. 'Did my wife warn you?'

A chill ran over me. 'She said my mother was much changed.'

'A good deal changed. You might not recognize her. She has been very ill.'

I flared up. 'Maybe she would have been a whole lot better if your kindness had stretched to letting me visit her!'

Taking my arm, he led me to a tree stump and made me sit at his side. 'You're wrong. Naturally you think of your mother as the gentle soul who sat beside your bed, and brought your meals, and helped you out into the garden, and back again. But, Daniel, that was your mother while she was managing to keep your life the way she wanted it: shut down, shut in—yes, shut away from everything.'

It seemed a harsh way to describe a woman caring for her son. But since I now knew there was nothing wrong with me, how could I argue with him? I sat sullen and silent.

He kept on. 'At first we took her to the hospital that you and I just passed. I thought—so did the nurses—that once we'd explained to her that you were safe, she would calm down. She heard every word I said—that you'd come back to her as soon as she'd accepted that you weren't ill and needn't waste another minute of your precious life locked away from the world.'

He let out a sad sigh. 'But still she raved.'

I felt as if I couldn't properly know the word. '*Raved*, did you say?'

He was insistent. 'Yes, she screeched and spat. Tore at her clothes. Spun like a dervish—even flew at our faces with her fingernails and cursed us.'

'*Cursed* you? My *mother*?'

'Believe what I'm telling you, Daniel. We are not dealing with the mother you know. She acted like a woman unhinged. It reached the stage where bolts were put on her door, and none of the nurses dared go in without two sturdy janitors to keep them safe. We tried for weeks. The trays of food we left were hurled around the room. The crockery was broken. The other patients were kept awake all night because of her howls—'

'My mother *howled*?'

56

'The nurses said it was like listening to a wolf bay at the moon.'

I covered my ears. 'No, I can't bear this. Don't say any more!'

He used his strength to pull my hands away and told me, almost angrily, 'Now can you see why I've been waiting so long to take you to see her? I must be the only doctor in these parts who blessed the coming of fever to his own town, because it gave me one more small excuse to keep a boy from his mother.'

Seeing my tears splash on my knees, he slid a comforting arm around my shoulders. 'And now I've told you the truth, perhaps we should sit quietly while you decide if you'd prefer to take my advice—heartfelt advice, Daniel!—to turn for home. It will not do you any good to see your mother.'

He broke off. It was as if he had to force himself to finish what he had to say.

'And I no longer think that it will do your mother any good to see you.'

13

And so we sat there on that mossy stump, while I thought stubbornly he must be wrong. Try as I might, it was impossible to imagine my mother tearing her gown and slapping at her nurses, or hurling so much as a reel of thread onto the floor. Do I sound mad if I say that it suddenly occurred to me that Dr Marlow might be making up this terrible story so he could keep me in his family? He had no son of his own. I was an amiable and sensible lad. Perhaps, between them, he and his wife had hatched a plot to steal me from my mother and keep her locked up in her turn. Or perhaps Mrs Marlow didn't realize what her husband planned. Perhaps—

My head spun. I stood up. 'I know you think I'm foolish to persist. But I won't rest until I've seen her.'

He rose in turn. 'No, Daniel. I admire your courage. But I must warn you, this will be a dreadful day for you.'

'It is already,' I said ruefully. And on we walked through the beech wood until we came across a cart track, which we turned to follow. Soon, through the thinning trees, I caught sight of a dark, forbidding building.

'Is that the place?'

He nodded. We walked on, past a leaning sign that said *Haldstone Asylum*, past outhouses and stables, through a stone arch and then across a cobbled courtyard sprung with thin weeds.

We reached a massive studded door. While I stood waiting, Dr Marlow tugged the bell. Far off inside we heard a jangling. It seemed an age till we heard footsteps. The door opened and a woman as round as a ball, wearing a dark blue uniform, greeted the doctor cheerfully enough. 'Ah! Come again to see your patient?' She looked at me and her expression changed. 'Is this . . . ?'

'Yes, this is Mrs Cunningham's son.'

The information sounded like a warning. The matron looked me up and down, then turned away saying, 'Perhaps the two of you would give us just a few moments?'

I wondered if she meant to scuttle off to warn the other nurses: 'Quick! Rip Mrs Cunningham's skirts, strew broken crockery around her room, and poke her with her needles till she howls.' Or perhaps I'd been told nothing but the honest truth, and as a kindness to me the matron meant to rush ahead and force my maddened mother into decent clothing, and sweep up the messes around her—

even wipe her tear-stained cheeks—to save me from a little of the shock.

'We'll wait in here till Matron comes for us,' said Dr Marlow. Clearly he knew the building well, because he ushered me into a waiting room. Cold ashes lay in the grate, and over the mantelpiece there was a painting of a cloudy sky over blue hills. 'Take a chair, Daniel.'

We waited without speaking until a nurse put her head round the door. 'Ready?'

We followed her. I'd never in my life opened my eyes under water in any river; but there was a dismal greenness to the corridor down which we walked that made me think of drowning. On either side were doors. To the left, some were ajar. I turned to see a nurse empty a chamber pot into a sluice, and passed another room in which there was a cluttered desk.

But on the other side, all of the doors were rimmed with iron and were shut. Their bolts were shot across, and from inside I could hear dismal noises—mutterings and groans, or sounds of weeping.

I felt my anger rising. 'My mother—is she locked away like this?'

'Hush, Daniel.'

I bit my lip and kept walking. We turned a corner and I almost stepped in what I took to be a trail of oil leaking beneath a door.

Dr Marlow stopped short. 'Curses!'

He took my arm and tried to push me through a door on the other side. 'Daniel, you must stay out from underfoot till this grim matter's sorted.'

I couldn't think what he was making so much fuss about. 'My mother spilled oil once when she

60

was trying to ease a stiff hinge on the doll's-house door. And all she did was—'

But he was staring at me as if I were an idiot. So I looked down again.

Red oil?

Blood.

14

I don't believe I'd seen blood spilled before, except on the coloured plates in my adventure books. Appalled, I let him push me into the room across the corridor. The door swung closed behind me as I heard him call, 'Nurse! Any nurse! Come to James Harper's cell!'

His *cell*? The very word had stopped my heart. I heard the bolt grind as the doctor tugged it back, and then the scurry of footsteps. There came the most almighty clang as the door shut behind him and his willing helpers, while into me crept the dread fear that he'd deceived me and the blood that I'd seen trickling across the flagstones had been my mother's.

Even before the voices quieted, I'd hurried back into the corridor to listen.

I heard the doctor say, 'Now, steady, Jim. Be

strong. The stitching will take time. And it will hurt.' I heard a man's voice moan, and then the doctor spoke again. 'Oh, Jim. Why must you constantly be trying to cheat your Maker out of a little of the time he wants to keep you on earth?'

My heart stopped banging and my breathing slowed. Filled with relief, I crept back into the room, and for the first time looked around. It seemed half office, half study. Along two of the walls stood wooden cabinets, all neatly labelled: *Ab–An, An–Av, Av–Be*, and on and on, drawer by drawer, around the room.

I drew near only one. *Co–Cu*.

There would be nothing in that cabinet to interest me, I was convinced of that. Wasn't my mother undergoing treatment? If there was any file on her, then surely someone would be poring over it, trying to make sense of the strange events that so mistakenly had brought her here.

So, then. No harm in looking.

I pulled the neat brass handle. The drawer swung out, and there it was at the back—a file so freshly labelled it sprang up at me.

Cunningham, Liliana.

I drew it out and carried it to the desk. I knew that I was courting trouble, but desperation got the upper hand. I tried to calm myself with the idea that, when Dr Marlow came back, I would have time to shut the file and turn it face down on the desk. He was unlikely even to glance at it; and if he did, he would assume it had been lying there all along.

I sat in the big leather chair and shuffled quickly through the sheets of paper in the file. Liliana Cunningham: her age and height and weight and hair colour, and then page after page of pulse rates and temperatures. Daily accounts of what food had been offered. (The corresponding spaces for what she'd actually eaten had been left blank. Was she determined to *starve*?) Tucked behind these there was a written account of her distress: . . . *frenzied and distraught . . . seized by the most impregnable illusion . . . sure she must keep her son from some old evil that is threatening him . . . imprisoned only for his own good . . . cannot be comforted, cannot be convinced . . .*

I turned to the last loose page. And there it was: *Next of kin: In disturbed sleep, the patient mutters constantly of someone the nurses understand to be a brother. And yet, once woken, she refuses to divulge his name, or say a word about her family.*

So was it possible? Had my strange wisp of memory been, not a dream, but some true flash of remembrance? Had I an *uncle*?

I heard the door knob rattle. Slamming shut the file, I swung the chair around to try to make it look as if I'd spent the time staring out of the window.

In came the doctor, letting down his sleeves. 'Well, thank the Lord that's done.' He looked me over as I swung to face him, then, mistaking my distress, he teased me gently. 'We share the work, I see. I stitch the wounds. You do the trembling.'

The instant his words were out, he tried to snatch them back. 'Forgive me, Daniel! In the distraction I had forgotten for a moment why you are here with me.'

At any other time I might have taken comfort in the fact that he'd gone halfway to mistaking me for some companionable son. But on that morning only my mother—'frenzied and distraught'—was in my mind.

Dr Marlow stepped closer and gripped me by the shoulder. 'Not changed your mind? No one would blame you. No one on God's good earth!'

I shook my head. If my poor mother *could not be comforted, could not be convinced*, then I had even more reason to seek her out. My education may have had no order to it, but I had learned enough to believe that no one is truly threatened by ancient evils. There is foul luck and there is foul behaviour; and misery and trouble will stem from both. But neither come from inhuman, brooding sources who store it up to tip it over you. Perhaps, I thought, if I stand tall before my troubled mother, healthy and steady, I will be able to rid her of her mad ideas. She might regain her senses.

'No, I've not changed my mind. I want to see her.'

So we moved on along the corridor and, rounding a corner, stopped at the first door. Dr Marlow raised a hand as if to tap on it, and then a puzzled look came on his face. He turned to Matron, who was hurrying after us, holding the frock coat he had left behind. 'Why is the bolt drawn across?' he asked. 'I ordered that Mrs Cunningham should always have someone inside with her, to mind her through her anguish.'

'Indeed she does,' said Matron. 'But when you called for a nurse, Sara heard first and ran to help, shooting the bolt behind her. Your Mrs Cunningham has been alone no longer than the time it took to stitch James Harper's arm.'

Nodding, the doctor slid back the bolt. 'Be brave,' he whispered, then went ahead of me into the room.

But he had no idea how brave you have to be to see, over a shoulder, the stick-thin shadow of your mother with her neck awry, slung from a bar on the window by a short noose that she has fashioned with her own skilled fingers from the lace trimmings on her tattered dress.

*   *   *

I have no memory of being hustled out, or heaving up the breakfast that Mrs Marlow had insisted I shovel into myself before I faced the day. I have no memory of being led away down that grim, sunless corridor into another room and being begged to take a sip of spirits. I have no memory of being bundled onto a passing cart and driven home, given a sleeping draught and put to bed.

The only things that I recall are things I overheard. Sara, the nurse, wailing in horror and guilt at having given her patient the opportunity to put an end to her unhappy life. The matron tearfully explaining to Dr Marlow how very determined my mother had been that she'd not see me. 'If you'll no longer let me protect my son,' she'd kept on crying to the nurses around her, 'how can I look in his face?'

And my last recollection of that day is of the doctor himself, murmuring to his wife across my bed as he watched over me.

'There's a black memory for a poor boy to carry all his life—his mother hanging from the window bars, with staring eyes and no more flesh on her than a peg doll.'

15

I've just one echo in my mind from all the days that followed, and that's of Dr Marlow murmuring to his wife, 'There's more than one sort of fever.'

And I was burning up, though whether from grief or guilt I couldn't say. I had strange fancies in which each time plump, comfortable Mrs Marlow, waiting so patiently beside my bed, let her head droop towards sleep, she'd suddenly assume the thin, drained aspect of my own mother. Her neck would seem to me to snap awry, her mouth turn black, her eyes stare emptily. I'd jerk and twist in turn, only to feel a cool hand on my forehead, and Mrs Marlow would be back again in all her sturdy, full-faced tranquillity.

The nightmares gradually passed, and soon the shadows under my eyes began to vanish. 'Aha!'

Dr Marlow teased one day when he came in to make his morning check on me. 'I see our black-eyed panda has gone back to China at last, leaving young Daniel in his place.'

And then he asked me, 'Would you welcome visits?'

I claimed I would, so Mary and Cecilia were allowed in my room, bringing the trays of soup and milky puddings with which Cook hoped to tempt me.

Sophie was nowhere to be seen. 'Why won't she come?' I asked Cecilia one morning. 'Is she upset with me? Is she unwell?'

'No, no,' laughed Cecilia. 'Mother insists that the last thing you need in your raw state is hearing Sophie rattle on at you.'

It seemed to me that Sophie's merry burblings were just what any invalid would enjoy. But then I realized that Mrs Marlow was trying to protect me from something very different: talk in the town about the death; my mother's body and the cutting down; gossip about the inquest and the verdict from the coroner; descriptions of the tiny, hurried funeral that I had missed.

But I'd been stuck in bed for far too much of my short life to choose to stay. And so next morning I threw off the bedcovers, pulled on my clothes and came downstairs. Sophie was curled in an armchair in the morning room. As I came in, she threw her book aside. 'Daniel! You're back!'

And it did seem as if I'd been a hundred miles away. I pulled up the embroidered stool and sat beside her. 'So,' I said. 'Source of all wisdom, fount of all information in this house, tell me. What have I missed?'

A cloud ran over her face as she remembered all the things that she'd been warned I mustn't hear. But then she started ticking off on her fingers the ones that weren't forbidden. 'Cook's stepdaughter has had a baby girl. She's to be named Kathleen as well. Old Mr Tanner's son has gone back to sea even though, when he came home last year, he vowed he'd never again choose to look out over water. Oh, yes! And Mary is to be allowed to give up the piano, but I am not, even though I am the worse by far out of the two of us.' She scowled and thought some more. 'Papa declares that if we have beetroot one more time this week, he'll pack his bags and leave us all for ever. And—' Now her eyes shone. 'How could I have forgotten? You are one day too late to meet the visitor who has set Cecilia blushing.'

Now that was news indeed. 'A visitor for Cecilia? You mean he came to ask her to walk out with him?'

She flapped her hands. 'No, no. Not quite. He came to paint the doll's house.'

'*Paint* it?'

I spun round. Had someone thought to tamper with the only keepsake from my former life? But there was the doll's house, set in the window bay as before and looking just the same.

Sophie was laughing. 'Not *paint* it. *Paint* it!'

'What, like a portrait?'

'Exactly so! A portrait of your doll's house.'

'But *why*?'

She shrugged. 'I don't know. Papa ordered it. Perhaps he thought that it would cheer you up.' She fell into a fit of mirth. 'I don't suppose it even crossed his mind the painter might cheer Cecilia!'

And on she went, teasing about the artist's yellow curls and pointy beard, speaking louder and louder until her mother, overhearing as she passed, poked her head round the door. 'Now, Sophie! Be kinder to your sister. Not another word!'

Then Mrs Marlow saw that it was me perched on the stool. 'Daniel! You're down with us at last!'

* * *

And so we fell back into the old familiar patterns in which I felt so easy and safe. Gradually my lessons were resumed, but in the afternoons we were all free to wander as far as we chose. Cecilia and Mary preferred to walk in town, where they'd meet friends and stroll round the bandstand. But Sophie was young enough to want to come with me, the other way, into the fields and copses that still so delighted me after my long starvation of all those living creatures that sang or fluttered, or skittered through the undergrowth close to my feet, or even simply stood on hooves and stared out peaceably over country walls.

* * *

One morning Mrs Marlow came into the hall as Sophie stood before the looking glass, fretting at the ribbons on her bonnet. 'You stupid things! Untangle yourselves so I can make a bow!'

She laid a hand on her young daughter's shoulder. I thought for a moment that she was silently reminding Sophie that a well-bred girl tries not to quarrel with her bonnet strings. But she was steering her away from me into the drawing room.

The door closed firmly behind them, but I could still hear Sophie's wail. '*Why* can't I go? If Mary and Cecilia are walking out together, that leaves me with no company—or no walk!'

Clearly her mother, though she was softer-voiced, was adamant. A moment later I heard Sophie complain, 'But if Papa insists on walking with Daniel today, why can't I go as well?'

There must have been another quiet answer. For then I heard, 'Oh! Poor, poor Daniel!'

The door flew open. Sophie stood staring at me as though in horror. Then she tugged off her bonnet, hurled it on the tiles and, eyes streaming tears, ran past me up the stairs without a word.

16

You can imagine that it was with little confidence that, shortly after, I set off with Dr Marlow down one of the narrow winding lanes that led from the town.

'A pleasant afternoon,' he said.

But I was filled with deep enough foreboding to answer sourly, 'Perhaps it is. But I know Sophie fears that there's some shadow over it for me.'

'Ah, Sophie!' He sighed. 'My youngest daughter will never win a prize for her discretion. I'd hoped that we could get a little further before I have to tell you that we are going to see your mother's grave.'

'My mother's grave?' Though I'd imagined it a thousand times, still I was startled. 'Isn't that the other way?'

'The other way? Why should—?' And then he guessed. 'You think she has been buried at the asylum? Oh, my good Lord! If Mrs Marlow and I were forced to think of you sitting in that dank place remembering someone you loved so well, we would do nothing but shudder.'

I couldn't see how it would matter. 'If someone you love is dead, then surely that's the worst of it, not where their grave lies.'

'You think that now because your heart's so young and torn. In time you will know better.'

I had no answer to that, so we walked on in silence. He led me off the road, over a stile and down a narrow path. We picked our way between the straggling rose briars until we reached a fence. Beyond us in the field were cows who watched with interest as we clambered over and walked towards a small stone chapel on the further side.

'Is that the place?' As we came closer I could already see, over the chapel wall, the tops of crosses and the bowed head of a stone angel. 'Is her grave one of those?'

He shook his head. 'Not in the cemetery, Daniel. Closer than that.'

I stared round, mystified. The cows stared back at me. Then Dr Marlow pointed. I hadn't noticed that, a step or two in front of us, there was a patch of grass, shorter and fresher than the rest. And set against it in the graveyard wall, embedded low, there was a headstone.

Liliana Cunningham
A loving mother

Across the bottom was a line I took to be from scripture:

Until the day breaks, and the shadows flee away.

I thought again about the feeling I'd so often had, that something dark pursued my mother through her sad life. Had Dr Marlow sensed the same, to choose such words for her headstone? My tears sprang, and I burst out angrily, 'Why isn't she *inside* the wall with all the others?'

'I wish she were. And when there is more charity in the world, there she will be. But since your mother set her will against the Church's holy laws and took her own life, no one may bury her on hallowed ground.'

'You *asked*, though? Surely you *asked*?'

'Daniel, I didn't simply ask. I begged.'

'And *no one* relented?'

'No one. The rules are clear, and all the churchmen around believe that they must follow them to the letter.' He gave me a wry smile. 'But even the Bible tells us that we mustn't despair. So I'll confess that I went visiting every farmer I know whose land lies by a chapel or a church. And clearly my mission was blessed, because I found one happy to remember a kindness.'

'A kindness?'

He shrugged. 'Only the job that I was trained to do. A visit to his daughter late at night in a hard time.'

'You saved her life?'

74

'Nothing so wonderful. Perhaps her sight. But, still, he let me take this tiny plot of land and fix your mother's headstone to his side of the wall.' The doctor laid a comforting hand on my shoulder. 'And if the chapel truly stands on holy ground, then it is certain that the peace it offers will reach through the stone to touch your mother.'

I looked around. And certainly there was a quietness about the place: the waving elms, the sturdily grazing cattle. I glanced up. Birds were wheeling easily. The clouds were summer high. And I could tell that all year long my mother's grave would catch the morning light. She'd be protected from the worst of winds. Away from footpaths, she'd be left in peace.

I threw my arms round Dr Marlow to thank him. I had been wrong and he was right. It mattered, oh it *mattered* where she lay! He held me close for a moment, then we set off for home. I don't know what was in the doctor's mind. But, for myself, I felt a kind of peace stealing back into my heart. And I knew, one day soon, I would be able once again to think about my mother without tears.

17

Early one evening Cook poked her head round the green baize door and begged me, 'Quick, Daniel. Fetch Doctor Marlow. Tell him that Molly is in one of her faints.'

I ran to the study door. It didn't seem the time to put good manners first, and so I flung it open. 'Well, Sophie, what's the panic now?' he murmured cheerfully, his eyes still on the pages spread in front of him.

Then he looked up. As soon as he realized it was me, his face changed and he swept aside what he was reading. 'Daniel?'

'Kathleen says Molly has fainted!'

Oddly, I thought, he looked relieved. But he said nothing, simply lowered his hand to drop what he'd been reading to the floor on the far side of his chair, then rose to hurry past me across the hall and through the door into the kitchen passage.

I followed him and saw poor Molly slumped on the flagstones. Cook had already raised her lolling head to cradle it against her knees. I don't know what suspicion was in my mind that, rather than take the chance to watch a man pursue the skills I one day hoped to learn, I chose to shut the door and creep away along the passage and across the hall, back to the doctor's study.

I leaned over his chair to lift what he'd been reading off the floor. It was a magazine called *Country Mansions.*

And what had secrecy to do with those? For I was sure his sudden—almost guilty—look had something more about it than simply being caught avoiding work. Curious, I skimmed the pages, flicking through densely written articles on property and fishing rights, and etchings of gatehouse lodges and old manor houses, each illustration finer than the next.

And then I saw it. It was a watercolour painting of my own doll's house. Across the top was printed, *Private Advertisement*, and underneath the picture were the words: *Respectable gentleman would be grateful to receive from any subscriber details of this place of residence, once called High Gates.*

Beside that was a box number to which contributors could write. Now I remembered Sophie's tease about the artist who had charmed her sister. Once I'd assured myself he hadn't used his brushes on my doll's house, I hadn't given him another thought. I suppose, like Sophie, I had just assumed the painting had been ordered in some vain hope of cheering me after my mother's death.

77

Now I knew differently. For it was clear that Dr Marlow had remembered what I'd said about the doll's house being the mirror image of my mother's home.

He had set out to find my history on my behalf.

I know I should have felt nothing but gratitude. I should have felt a flood of warmth for him, and told myself this family's kindness to me would have no end. But I'll be honest, it was fear I felt. Fear and resentment. Hadn't I faced enough upheaval, losing my mother and my home? So what would be so terrible about forgetting my grim past and letting me become a happy member of their family? A brother to his girls. A son to him and Mrs Marlow.

I wished I'd told him nothing more about the doll's house than that it was mine. I wished he hadn't tried so hard to do the right thing by a boy so strangely uprooted. But, most of all, I prayed that nothing would come of his attempt to find whatever might be left of my real family. I hoped that he'd heard nothing from the readers of *Country Mansions*—and that he never would!

Hastily I dropped the magazine back on the floor and left the room—and only just in time. Already I could hear his footsteps in the passage.

'Is she all right?' I asked, trying to look as if the reason I was in the hall was to hear news of Molly.

'She'll do,' he said. 'It happens often enough. She has no iron in her blood.' He laughed. 'And no more inclination to take advice than most of my patients.' He glanced at the clock ticking away in its unhurried fashion. 'But I must get back to my desk.'

Without another word he walked into his study

78

and shut the door. And whether it was seeing the portrait of High Gates that set my feet the other way, I've no idea. But I turned back into the drawing room. Since Sophie first set eyes on the doll's house, I'd rarely had the chance to be alone with it. Now it stood drenched in the sunlight pouring through the windowpanes. The painted roses shone. The ivy coiling up the walls gleamed quite as dark and strongly as if each leaf was freshly grown.

I swung the front open and let my fingers prowl around the rooms, setting a chair straight and putting a tiny bowl of carved fruit back on the polished sideboard where it belonged. I had no wish to start a private game for fear the girls might come back from their dancing class and catch me playing like a child. Still, all these dolls had been so dear to me, and it had been a good few weeks since I had touched them. So out of the box came Topper first, then pouting Rubiana. Hal was the next. A scarlet thread trailed from the beret that my mother had crocheted to hide the scar where I broke off his crown. If she'd still been alive, she would have used her tiny tools to catch it up in an instant.

The sense of loss came as a stabbing pain. I drew my knees up to my chin and clasped them tightly as tears fell so fast that everything blurred. Is that why, suddenly, the doll's house seemed so real? Why Topper seemed to stretch a little in his sleep on the rag rug? Why, when I reached out a hand to pick up Mrs Golightly—that thin peg doll that looked so like my mother—her eyes seemed to hold me in a steady gaze?

I blinked away the tears. I wasn't yet so far from

childhood that I'd forgotten that a doll—however bland its face—can share your every mood. But still Mrs Golightly's bright eyes held mine. No, more than that! They looked at me with fierce need.

I heard my own voice whispering, 'What do you *want*? What must I *do* for you?'

And then the spell was broken. Behind me, I heard the front door sweep across the tiles and cheerful voices in the hall.

The door flew open. 'Daniel!'

What I had feared now came as a relief. Sophie was back, to catch me sitting at the doll's house and demand a part to play in whatever story I could hastily invent. Sophie was here, to throw herself down beside me on the rug, chattering merrily about her visit to the town—and banish shadows.

18

Or so I thought.

But from that day something began to happen in our games. It seemed as if another soul had joined us. The strange two-ended doll took over all our stories. A dozen times a week I'd say to Sophie, 'Let's leave it out of this adventure.' But every time at some point we would need a fresh-faced, mischievous boy to join with Hal, and she would reach for it again. Or, in a tale of pirates, 'Now we need someone who can run the ship. Let it be Captain Severin.'

Curious, I asked her, 'Severin? Why do you call him that?'

She shrugged. 'The name just sprang to mind—perhaps because the poor thing's in two halves.'

I must have looked quite blank because she

added with a laugh, 'A doll that someone chose to "sever in" two!' She tipped the skirts so that the man stood upright. 'Yes! Captain Severin can play the part.'

She handed him to me. I couldn't think of any reason why he shouldn't join the game. He was a doll, no bigger than my hand. But still I felt unease, for every time this doll was in a story, that story changed. We might be halfway through some careless tale of rivers crossed or mountains climbed, but, with the very presence of the new arrival, the nature of the game would shift from innocence and merriment into pure menace.

Or even cruelty. Where, before, Sophie and I would solve a mystery with questions or cunning, once that new doll joined in we'd find ourselves depending on threats and blackmail, even on punishments. I'd find myself locking my precious Hal away in stinking dungeons, or staking his poor body out where ants could torment him. And at my side, the child who'd once insisted on helping her guilty brigands escape from transportation now cheerfully pressed for all of them to be strung up on gibbets without the mercy of a trial.

And there was more. Sometimes I'd hear a voice I didn't recognize, and turn to check that it was truly Sophie making that deep and threatening growl. Had she learned tricks of the voice-thrower's trade? 'You pin him down while I lash him with chains! I'll make the beggar talk!'

I'd steal another glance her way. Her large blue eyes flashed with ferocious greed. Her fists clenched and unclenched as though in frenzy. Even her teeth looked sharper.

'Sophie?'

She'd turn, and there'd be madness in her eyes. 'Sophie!'

She would look baffled, toss her head as if to shake away a dream, then be herself again.

One day I crammed all of the dolls back in the box. 'I won't play any longer.'

'Oh, Daniel!' But it was as if she knew the reason already. 'Suppose we put the Severin doll away?'

'That's what we've said before.'

'This time we'll truly do it.'

'We've claimed a dozen times we'll leave him in the doll box. And, every time, out he has come again.'

'That's true.' Ruefully she inspected the doll that, from the moment we broke off the game, had turned back to a harmless stick of wood, some cloth and paint, patches of glued-on hair. She flipped it over to the man. 'This end's the worst,' she declared. 'The boy has a nature primed for spite and wickedness, but doesn't yet have powers to spoil the game.'

'We are the masters of the dolls,' I tried reminding her.

'Not this one,' she said calmly. 'This doll can make things happen.'

My unease grew. 'Sophie, we are both old enough to know that's nonsense.'

'And we've sat through enough wrecked games to know it's true.'

I couldn't argue. Sophie snatched up the doll and jumped to her feet. She ran to the small woven basket in which her mother kept her sewing silks, and scrabbled in its depths until, in triumph, she fetched up a pin. 'We'll keep the man entombed in skirts and darkness!' She stuck the sharp end of the pin into the folds of stuff. 'Go in! Go through!'

'Sophie . . .'

I prised the doll out of her hand. She'd rammed the pin so hard into the skirts that its sharp point had stuck in the wood beneath. I pulled it out and turned the doll to see what damage she'd done.

The pin had gashed the man's cheek, scraping off the thinnest line of paint. She snatched him back. 'I'll be more careful, I promise.' Then she changed her mind. 'I know! Mary will help us.'

'Mary will laugh at us for making a phantom out of a handful of carved wood.'

'Oh, I won't tell her any of that,' Sophie said cheerfully. 'She'd think we'd lost our minds.'

Sure of the truth in that, I followed her into the dining room where Mary was sitting in the morning light, darning a stocking.

'Put that aside!' ordered Sophie. 'We need your help to sew these skirts up tight.'

Her sister lifted her eyes from her stitching only to say, 'A simple enough task. Why can't you do it yourself?'

But Sophie thrust the doll at her again. 'See? They fall so thickly. We need them sewing up so tight that they can't be unpicked.'

Mary lifted her stocking to inspect her own progress. 'Then sew them up the best you can,' she told her sister mildly. 'And don't unpick them.'

Sophie was adamant. 'No. You must do it, Mary. You can do it tighter and better.'

She didn't add the words aloud, but I knew they were in her mind: 'And then we will be safer, Daniel and I.'

That week, in church, the vicar gave a sermon. 'The devil walks,' he said. 'Make no mistake. And evil is not ugly. You cannot tell, simply from looking at a man, the colour of his soul.'

He raised his arms as if to comfort us.

'But we have one defence, and one alone. The devil can make no headway if he has no help. For him to triumph, we must invite him in.'

On the way out, Sophie dropped back till she was walking beside me. 'Daniel, were you listening? Did you hear?'

'About the devil?'

'Yes.' She patted me as if I were some child who needed comfort. 'So we will keep him in the box. We'll not invite him in. And we'll be safe.'

19

More weeks passed, and I grew in height and strength. Part of me knew I couldn't stay for ever and this must be some sort of holding time. But I'd so little experience of the world I couldn't guess for what we might be waiting.

It turned out to be probate.

One evening Dr Marlow strode across the lawn holding a letter. After a few short pleasantries about the day, he ordered his daughters into the house, and sat beside me on the grass.

'Daniel, your mother's will is finally proved.'

I must have looked quite blank for, though Mrs Marlow claimed I was coming on apace, my education hadn't yet turned into that of a lawyer.

'All her affairs are sorted,' he explained. 'And much as I would have loved to tell you that you're secure, with money of your own, I must confirm my own worst fears. We've found no money tucked away, so now your mother's belongings have been sold to pay her debts, there's nothing left.'

Up until then, I hadn't given my inheritance a thought. But Dr Marlow was clearly sitting waiting for some response, so I said, 'Nothing? Nothing at all?'

'Nothing of value.' He stared uneasily at the grass between his bent knees. 'The poor soul lost so much in life we could not think of taking her wedding ring from her finger, even after death. So there is just your doll's house, and one small token that came with your mother to the hospital. You must have that.' He reached into his pocket. 'It's a pretty thing.'

My heart turned over when he pulled it out. It was the tiny ivory case, no longer than my finger, in which my mother had kept her lace-making tools.

I put out a hand, then, in a thought, recoiled. 'But was this in her pocket when . . . ?'

I couldn't speak the words. But Dr Marlow hastened to assure me, 'No, no. The matron found it tucked in a scallop of your mother's dress when she was first brought to the hospital. Fearing that she might use it to harm herself, or others, she locked it in a desk. And there it lay forgotten for a while. But once it came to light I must admit that I asked Matron to misplace it quietly again, until the bailiffs were done with their grasping.' He pressed it in my hand. 'I thought that, after probate was complete, it might be a comfort for you to have at least one tiny token of your mother.'

One tiny token.

Unscrewing the top, I spilled the set of miniature tools into my hand. They lay like four pretty matchsticks. 'That's all I have of her?'

'For now.' His voice took on the most mysterious tone. 'But we have hopes of finding something linked to you that's more substantial.'

Maybe he thought I'd press to understand his meaning, and wheedle out his secret about the painting of High Gates and its good purpose. But I couldn't trust myself to show even a small pretence of gratitude for efforts to find me some other home. So I just tipped the tools back, screwed on the top and slid the little ivory case deep into my pocket. And then I thanked him for his thoughtfulness and hurried off.

*   *   *

But I kept watch. And finally one morning, from upstairs on the landing, I saw the doctor open one of the envelopes that had been lying on the tray, only to draw out another from inside. Opening that, he read it through and then looked up.

Seeing me watching him, he said uneasily, 'Good day, young fellow.'

I came downstairs and followed him into the room where breakfast waited. The doctor leaned across to murmur something to his wife before she said our grace. It seemed a strangely restless meal, with Sophie casting curious glances, first at my own set face, then at her father. Even the imperturbable Mrs Marlow appeared unsettled. Cecilia and Mary chatted away as usual about their plans for the day; but even they must have guessed something was afoot because they didn't show the least surprise when, as Molly sidled in to clear away the dishes, the doctor turned to me and said, 'Come to my study, Daniel. We must have a talk about your future.'

I hung my head so low I might have been following him onto a tumbrel. 'Now, now,' he scolded me as soon as we were alone. 'I have good news for you, not bad. We've found the model for your doll's house!'

He sounded so proud that I couldn't bear it. 'I wish you hadn't!' I burst out. 'Is it far away? Oh, I am sure it must be! It will be far across the country, or we'd have learned of it before. And I'll be sent away to family who don't know and don't want me, and never see anyone here again!'

He looked appalled. Placing his hands flat on the desk, he stared at me. We sat together in silence. Finally he almost whispered, 'Daniel, I had no choice. We had a moral duty to try to find your own real family.'

'You let the lace-making tools lie hidden!' I accused him. 'And you allowed the doll's house to be carried here before it could be sold to pay the grocer! Why did you have to act on one tiny thing I told you and set all this in train?'

I'd said too much. His eyebrows lifted. 'You knew? You knew of the advertisement I placed in *Country Mansions*?'

'I knew about the painting,' I told him sullenly. 'I saw the magazine and guessed the rest.'

It was, he clearly knew, no time to take me to task for snooping round his study. So, brushing that aside, he tried to comfort me again. 'Daniel, this could be *good* for you.'

'I'm happy here.'

Sighing, he waited. But I had nothing more to say, I just stared at the floor. After a moment Dr Marlow took a more businesslike tone. Waving a letter at me, he said, 'This comes from someone who was once the postmistress in a small place called Illingworth.'

I waited.

'It's on the downs,' he added.

I still kept silent. He pressed on. 'The downs are chalk hills, near the coast.'

'Ten thousand miles away!'

'Two hundred,' he admitted.

'Write to this lady,' I begged. 'Tell her the artist did a careless job and she must be mistaken.'

'Daniel, she says the painting is the very image of a place called High Gates, and when she left for London several years ago the owner was a man called Severn.'

Severn? How could I help but look a little startled?

Dr Marlow leaned across the desk to peer more closely at my face and ask me curiously, 'You *know* the name?'

I shook my head. First Severin and then Severn? But why should I reckon some half echo of a trick of words from Sophie was any more than a coincidence?

'No, sir. I never heard of any person called that.'

Still, I was filled with unease. But whether my disquiet stemmed from not being frank with someone who'd been kind to me, or whether even then I knew the cause lay deeper, it is hard to say.

The doctor shrugged. 'My correspondent says this Captain Severn—'

Again he saw me flinch. After all, hadn't we

90

named our new doll 'Captain' in his very first game?

Dr Marlow broke off to accuse me, 'You do! You know this person!'

'No, sir! I swear!'

Obliged to take my word for it, the doctor shrugged. 'My correspondent says this captain had a sister who would have been your mother's age. Her name was Liliana.' He leaned towards me. 'Do you understand? It seems from this that you have an uncle living. Now think back, Daniel. Did your mother never speak of a brother?'

The memory of my mother on her knees rose in my mind again. *'And keep my precious boy safe, and his Uncle Se—'* Could half a whispered prayer that might have floated from a dream add up to speaking of a brother? I would not have it. No! And I would even brush aside what I had read of all my mother's night-time ravings in the hospital. I didn't *want* an uncle!

So, 'Never,' I answered the doctor firmly.

'Strange, that . . .' he murmured.

His very look of doubt lent force to my next argument. 'And even if this man is anything to do with me, surely the last thing in the world my mother would have wanted is for me to be sent back to somewhere she was so clearly determined to forget!'

I could tell he found this a worrying thought. But still he rallied. 'Daniel, this is your blood family!'

Seeing my chance, I rushed around the desk and, just as Sophie might have done, threw my arms round him. 'Oh, please don't send me away! You know I don't want to go! Why can't you and

91

your family keep me? I'll earn my living—pay you back for every slice of bread and hunk of meat. Haven't I had enough upheavals? Don't send me away!'

He tried to hold me at arm's length. 'Daniel, if for a moment I thought—'

I wouldn't let him finish. 'Oh, please! Losing my mother should be quite enough to make an uncle pity me! Surely this Captain Severn will let me choose for myself if I will come to him, or stay with you!'

It was as if I'd hit upon some compromise he thought might work. 'He may indeed.' The doctor patted me on the shoulder and tried to lift my spirits with a joke. 'Not everyone would welcome into their house such a tornado of emotions as you can offer!' His face turned grave again. 'Still, I must write to him.'

'No, not at once. Let's just delay until I'm old enough to choose for myself.'

But Dr Marlow had turned stern. 'Daniel, he is your *uncle*. And since I'm currently your guardian, now I've been told of his existence I have no choice but to inform the man of yours.'

20

And so, as carelessly as dice are rolled across a table, my future was given to a stranger to decide. Sophie was outraged when I told her the grim news. 'What sort of uncle is this, who never saw you in his life?'

'Perhaps he's been away at sea,' I offered lamely.

'Away at sea? Why should you think that?'

'Because he is a captain.' I watched her face. 'His name is Captain Severn.'

'*Severn?*' Sophie turned pale. 'Oh, Daniel!' Then she, too, tried to arm herself against the strangeness of the coincidence. 'No! I won't think silly nonsense! Perhaps you heard the name in early childhood and called it out while you were in that fever, and I, in one of my own dreams, misheard and—'

I cut her off before her desperation to find an explanation infected me as well. 'Yes! All silly nonsense, Sophie. And we'll not think of it again.' And both of us did try to put all sinister thoughts out of our minds—or, at the very least, not share our fears. But still the next few weeks passed in one flurry of anxiety after another. Perhaps a letter from High Gates would come that day, the next day, the next week. Perhaps it would be a firm reprieve: 'I recognize no nephew.' Perhaps it would be determined: 'A nephew! Then you must send him! He must become my close companion and my heir.'

My mind raced. Was the captain still at sea? And if I went to live there, would it be under his command, or would I simply be a nuisance to his housekeeper and maids, his cook and gardeners? Maybe the captain had fallen on hard times, and High Gates had become a ruin held together only by rampant ivy—some musty dwelling in which we'd shiver constantly and pick our way round rusting buckets set to catch the drips that forced their way through the untended roof?

Each time she heard the postman Sophie would leap to her feet. 'Maybe the letter has come today!'

'Don't wish me closer to my banishment!'

But she'd already have dropped whatever she was holding to race from the room.

One morning she came back faster than usual. 'Daniel, it's come!'

I followed her into the hall. There on the silver tray lay a long envelope. Drawing near, Sophie pointed. 'See. It's from Illingworth.'

But there was nothing we could do but sit and stare at it till Dr Marlow strolled home for his lunch. Seeing the letter, he carried it off to his study. I waited in the hall, and though it can't have been more than a minute or two that I was standing outside, it seemed an age before he called to me, 'Daniel, come in.'

I went in so unwillingly I barely left the shadow of the door.

'In further, boy. It's not that bad. It's not a summons to your *funeral*.'

'But it's a summons?'

He nodded. 'Naturally enough, your uncle says he is most keen to meet the nephew he has never known.'

I tried my hardest once again to argue my way out of my fate. 'How much of a brother could he have been to my mother if she took such good care to keep the secret of my birth away from him?'

The doctor looked uneasy. 'Daniel, you're old enough to know the stern ways of the world. Suppose your mother had no right to wear her wedding ring? Like many other women in her delicate position, she might decide to hide your very existence, not just from friends, but from her family as well.' He frowned. 'And even if she was a lawful widow, you will admit that she had strange ideas, and strenuously avoided company. Keeping you from your uncle is much more likely to be a testament to her flustered mind than to his temperament.'

'But we don't *know* that.'

'We don't know much in life. But we can find a few things out. And here's a start.' Determined to be cheerful, he tossed the letter aside and came round the desk to rest his hands on my shoulders. 'Daniel, you've seen so little of the world. And

95

you've a whole life's journey to undertake. So start off here. Be a brave lad. Go down to Illingworth and meet your uncle. Stay with him for a while. If you get on with one another and find yourself happy, you'll want to stay for longer.'

'And if I don't . . . ?'

He gave me an encouraging pat. 'Well, Daniel! Many boys and girls your age already earn their living in the world. It would be hard to believe that, come your next birthday at the very least, you could not make a success of arguing with your uncle that you should be allowed to leave.'

I think that I was testing Dr Marlow's resolve more than my own. 'By my next birthday?'

He shrugged. 'Why not? The captain seems a thoughtful and a reasonable man.' He waved the letter at me. 'Why, in here he tells me firmly that not only will you be met promptly off the train, but he also plans to send a cart up here to pick up every single one of your mother's and your possessions so you'll feel more at home while you are with him at High Gates.'

At this at least the two of us could share a wry smile. 'All my possessions? I need no cart to carry my mother's little lace-making tools.' I blushed. 'As for the doll's house . . .'

The doctor guessed my thoughts. 'You've lived your life bereft of hoops, and bats and balls, and bows for archery. Still, perhaps you'd not want your uncle from the start to think of you as a boy who plays only with dolls?' He made a kind decision. 'Let us forget the doll's house for a while, and leave it here. I'll tell your uncle everything was sold after your mother's death. That is as close to the truth as we need go for now. Then, if you settle and decide to stay, we'll send the doll's house after you.'

'And if I don't? Then I can come back here?'

He hugged me close. 'How can you doubt it? There'll always be a welcome for you in this house!'

'You *promise* me?'

'I promise you.'

I wiped away my tears. 'All right. I'll go.'

'There's my brave boy. Now let's go out and tell the others we have plans afoot.'

21

From that day on Cecilia and Mary sewed like two furies. 'Here's frogging for your new jacket. Daniel, you'll look as smart as any captain's ensign when we finish this.'

'Come and stand straight while I measure— though Mother says that, since you are growing so fast, I am to cut your trousers longer than you've so far earned.'

The journey was discussed. Clearly the Marlows thought my uncle might demand some say in the arrangements; but from the moment he heard everything was sold and there was no need for his cart to come, no further letters arrived from High Gates. So Dr and Mrs Marlow took it upon themselves to decide on the details of my journey. Up in a storeroom the doctor unearthed some ancient carpet bag he'd used when studying. I watched as Mrs Marlow packed it tight, folding each sleeve back carefully against the sheets of tissue she billowed and let fall between each layer of the clothes that she and her daughters had bought or made for me. I stood by as she stuffed my fine new boots with wadded balls of newsprint, until my left boot firmly declared: *Government Minister Sickens*, while my right cheerfully maintained: *Grand Theatre Opening!*

Then the last evening passed, with everybody under the roof hugging me over and over, and wishing me well for the morning. Two hours before dawn the doctor shook me awake to share a dismal breakfast. We walked together to the railway station and waited in the grim dark until the train appeared round the corner, puffing to a halt. The doctor shook my hand and after squeezing the breath from my body one last time, pushed me aboard. The train door slammed behind me. The stationmaster blew his whistle, loud and long. And finally, like a wrapped parcel that has no notion of where it might be going or why, I, Daniel Thomas Cunningham, was tossed out into the world.

And what a world! I leaned my head against the window of the train and stared as cows and sheep swept past in the dawn light. Pale hills unfolded, slope by slope. Over and over we'd rattle to a halt. Some passengers would leave, more climb aboard.

Under the protection of the guard, I changed trains twice and travelled on to London, where some good friend of Dr Marlow's took me in a cab through that great city. 'Such a shame you can't stop to see the sights. But you're still young. There will be plenty of time.'

Once we were at the railway station at Victoria, he swung my bag up onto the luggage rack and pressed his card into my hand. 'If you should ever be in London again, then look me up. We'll visit all the places we should have seen today. Now, where's your ticket?'

I tapped my jacket pocket.

'And you'll be safely met?'

'Word has been sent ahead about my train.'

'And have you money?'

'Oh, yes. The doctor insisted on giving me enough to see me through.'

'He's not the only one who can insist. Here!'

I tried to push back his gift, but he was firm. 'No, no. You'll be astonished how useful a few loose shillings in your pocket can be to a boy your age.'

'No, truly—'

But he had gone, leaving me no choice but to pocket the money and shout my thanks after him as he strode off through the crowd. Then I was back to staring out of windows, through sooty suburbs, over rattling bridges, and into a countryside of welcoming woods and pretty villages.

And then another station change. At Amford, I waited the half an hour I'd been told, until a shorter train puffed into view. It crept along, stopping at several places—some simply wooden ramps where the track crossed a road or passed close to a clump of cottages. The land around was chalky and plain, and from the wide, wide sky the sun spilled white light on the contours of the hills.

'Are these the downs?' I asked the lady sitting

across from me.

She nodded. So we were almost there. The train astonished me by cutting through one short dark tunnel, then another.

'Tiverley Down and Illingworth!' called out the guard. I reached for my bag and climbed down from the carriage.

Even before my feet were on the station stop, I felt a shaft of unease. The bright, bright world around me darkened as though some huge malevolent bird were flying overhead. I heard my own foreboding—'Now here's a black mistake!'— as shadows rolled across the land. But, glancing up, I saw that this was no natural warning to clamber back on board and leave this place as fast as possible, simply a summer cloud that blotted out the sun.

I jumped down on the rutted path. In spite of my uncle's promise, no one was there to greet me. So I sat on my bag and waited, and it wasn't long before a horse and cart raised chalky dust along the road. I scrambled to my feet, but all the driver did was nod towards me as he clattered past, and in the end I sat back down again, wondering if I'd be there till dark.

I waited a little longer. By now, of course, I feared that Captain Severn, who had so recently heard I was on earth, had already forgotten about my existence. Or mistaken the day. I wasn't used to making efforts for myself and so I sat, steeped in self-pity and anxiety, until it suddenly occurred to me to ask the question: What would young Sophie do?

I knew the answer at once. She wouldn't wait about, fearing the worst and reading trouble in the shadow of each passing cloud. She'd shrug and make shift for herself, and go in search of someone who could point the way.

Did I need Sophie by my side to follow her example? No, I did not. And so, in failing light, I set off into Illingworth, which seemed to me to be no more than a stone church and a few pretty houses set around a green. I saw the post office in which Dr Marlow's earliest informant had once worked, and felt renewed resentment at the officious meddling that had set me off on this unwelcome journey. Because of the late hour its door was shut, like all the others I saw. But coming towards me down the village street were two women so alike in all but age I reckoned that they must be mother and daughter.

When they got close to me I asked the way.

'To High Gates?' Each glanced uneasily at the other. Did they perhaps suspect me of bringing trouble in my wake? But while the daughter stared, the mother took care to direct me, several times over, to follow the road in front of me out of Illingworth, walk up the hill, then take the footpath signposted to Farley Down. 'Be sure to keep to the south side of the woods. Follow the path round. You'll know the house from the stone eagles on the gates.'

I thanked them and set off. But Mrs Marlow had shaken her head at me despairingly so often as she spun the globe that I'd no confidence I could judge south—or west or east or north. I knew the sun was reddening the sky behind me, and that it set in the west. And so I reckoned, if I could only get my bearings now, I might do better with the twists and turns along the way.

So I glanced back.

Sure enough, there was the sun, sinking, huge and blood-red, behind the furthest hill.

But there too were the women, still standing in the place where I had left them, staring after me as if they'd never in their lives seen a boy set off on a walk out of their village.

Part 2

22

The track was well-trodden, the sign to Farley
Down in place and the path round the woods clear
enough to follow, even in gathering darkness. And
when I reached the gates, there, sure enough, two
threatening stone eagles stood on their posts. I felt
a pang. This was my mother's old home. How
often must she have passed between these
weatherworn pillars—even, perhaps, invented
names for these intimidating birds of prey that
loomed above her as they now peered down at me.

But every creature is unnerved by something
different. As I walked up the sorely overgrown
drive, I sent birds flying, squawking fit to burst, out
of the undergrowth between the trees, until I
stepped out of the shadow of woods onto wide
lawns.

The house itself was unmistakable. It was the doll's house full grown, except that now the ivy covered it in so much thicker clusters. It felt so odd to stand in front and stare, as though I'd shrunk to no more than the height of one of my dolls. To strengthen the impression, the moon sailed from behind a cloud, and suddenly it was like being back on all those nights when my imagination let me pretend I was that strong, brave fellow Hal, and fit enough to tackle any adventure.

Was I back in my childhood? Had all the tumultuous events of the past months been nothing but a dream?

As I stood, suddenly unnerved, unsure, the huge front door under the portico swung open. Out strolled a tall and loose-limbed gentleman who stood and looked about as if deciding whether or not to take a stroll in the night air. Though he seemed young enough—and he was certainly no older than Dr Marlow—his shock of hair shone white. In spite of that, he looked familiar somehow. I tried to pin his features onto those of my mother; after all, if this was Captain Severn then maybe there would be some family likeness. But with the square of light behind him it was hard to see.

I stepped out from the shadow.

He noticed me at once. His thoughtful look vanished. For just a moment he looked startled, then his face creased into a welcoming smile. 'Is this my nephew? Daniel, is it, at last?' He strode across the lawn to clasp my hand. 'So, Thomas found you at our apology for a station!' He glanced at my small bag. 'No need to carry that into the house yourself. Thomas will gladly oblige.'

He seemed so affable that it seemed churlish to tell him that any arrangements he might have made for Thomas to meet me had clearly gone awry. So I just held the bag a little tighter and shook my head. 'Truly, it holds so little—'

'Then even a feeble fellow like myself can prise it from your hand,' he broke in triumphantly. And snatching it from me he turned to march back through the carved oak door I recognized so well, into the hugely magnified image of the hall my stubby fingers had padded through so often in my childhood games.

It seemed too soon to claim acquaintance with the house, so I said only, 'This is a splendid place.'

He tipped back his head as though to admire the sheer volume of space around and above us. 'Splendid, indeed! And yet without you I have rattled around it like a dead beetle shaken in a bottle.'

It was a horrid notion. But the captain seemed cheerful enough, opening a door to call an echoing order. 'Martha! Our young man's here and no doubt, like all others of his age, he has a wolf in his belly!' Clapping his hand on my shoulder, he steered me up the curved wide staircase and along the landing to the small arched door set in the alcove. Shooting back the bolt, he went ahead of me up the narrow set of stairs that I already knew led to the attics. His heavy footfalls raised such clouds of dust that it seemed obvious the staircase had been little used for years, and it was hard not to wonder why, if my uncle had felt the need for company so very strongly over his lonely years, he had decided now to put me so far from the house's heart.

He opened the first door along the unlit passage.

'This will do nicely,' he said. Tossing my bag onto the rickety-looking bed, he strode to the window. 'See? You will have the best view in the house—over the woods as far as the rolling downs.' He turned back to assure me, 'You will be happy here. Though I can't find you company of your own age, there'll still be plenty to do. Why, I can teach you how to hunt and fish—indeed, I'm sure the river can be seen from here!'

Sticking his head out of the window, he craned as far as he could, presumably in hopes of seeing river water glint in the moonlight.

I took the chance to glance around. The shade on the only lamp was so mottled with age and damp it threw more shadow than light. The eaves sloped down so low I knew I'd crack my head if I sat up in bed. There were few pictures on the walls. And though the bed was freshly made, the place smelled musty.

Hearing a soft tap on the door, I turned.

There was a drab old woman carrying a tray laden with a tureen so fat and round I couldn't think how she had mustered the strength to carry it up all those stairs. The instant her eyes met mine, what little colour there was in her face drained dead away. Fearing she would let slip what she was carrying, I stepped towards her to prise the tray from her hands and set it down safely as the captain turned. The woman was still trembling, but as his large frame now blocked the moonlight that had fallen on her shocked, lined face, he noticed nothing.

'Ah, Martha! You've brought our young man's

supper.' He lifted the lid of the tureen and raised a corner of the chequered cloth. 'Fine soup! And plenty of rolls, hot from the oven.' He wagged a finger at me jovially. 'You must be on your guard. Martha will feed you so well you'll soon peer in a looking glass and mistake yourself for a barrel.'

The captain stood while Martha bowed her head in recognition of the compliment and left the room. Then he turned back to me and once again clasped both his huge hands round mine. 'There I go, rattling on! Tomorrow will be time enough to hear your story. Tonight you must do nothing more than polish off your supper, then drop your head onto your pillow and *dream*.'

23

Oh, he was right enough there! I never had such dreams as on that night. Welcome as it had been, the soup I'd drunk might have been made by goblins. My hours were wakeful and torn, yet still I couldn't pull myself out of my haunted sleep. The damp stains on the walls became disfigured faces. The people in my dreams opened their mouths to speak and I saw fangs. I ran away from them, only to find myself in overgrown graveyards where stone cherubs wept real tears down marble cheeks, and I could hear their cries of anguish and the wails of the dead.

I forced myself to wake. Had I gone mad, like my poor mother? I made myself get out of bed, and padded to the window in bare feet. Outside lay peace itself. Already it was growing light. A fox was picking its way across the lawn, shaking dew from its paws at every step. Far off, owls hooted.

Gradually my sense of panic stilled. I washed in water from the jug I found outside the door. Then, pulling on my clothes, I crept along the passage and down the narrow stairs, through the small door and out onto the spacious landing.

So here it was—the house in which my mother spent her early life. Familiar—and yet strange. The chests of polished oak were just the same as in the doll's house. And though the colours in the tapestries along the wall had faded to grey, I could make out the stag at bay and splashing waterfall that I remembered so well.

I started down the curving stair and found myself peering in tarnished glass. So something *had* been changed. Back in my doll's house, all the way down these stairs were tiny portraits: a woman cradling a child; a handsome, sturdy boy; a girl in a white gown. Here in their place there hung a positive jumble of country scenes and ill-assorted mirrors, around some of which were stronger patches of colour on the wall showing where differently shaped frames had hung before. Why had the portraits been removed? Perhaps, I thought, my uncle didn't choose to be reminded of what a lonely life he led. Or had he moved the paintings of the ones he'd loved to his own room, so they'd be closer to memory?

Whichever it was, he'd done the job well. I scoured the hall, then each downstairs room in turn, studying everything inside a frame: more mirrors; and paintings of cattle at sunset, and enough fruit and flowers to feed a multitude and deck out a dozen weddings.

But not one portrait.

Hearing the faintest clatter, I pushed at the green baize door that led to the kitchen. And once again I saw there had been changes, because the cheerful passage of my doll's house stood filtered here in greenish gloom; and, at its end, the high bright kitchen in which I'd made my dolls so clumsily handle all their pots and pans looked, in this real world, chilly and cavernous, with blackened water stains stealing down blistered walls towards the cracked meat dishes that were propped awry on the enormous dresser.

Quietly I stepped inside. The room was empty and the back door ajar.

Here was a chance. The kitchen of my doll's house had opened onto nothing but a sea of carpet, or the patch of wall against which it was set. And since my mother never spoke of places she had played, I'd never gathered any sense of what might lie behind the house itself. Curiosity impelled me forward. Outside there was a cobbled yard crisscrossed with washing lines and walled by tumbledown sheds. Not wanting to be caught prying in stores and coal holes, I wandered through an arched gate to the side, thinking to walk around and see again that strange sight of the night before—a house I knew so well standing full-sized against real skies, set on real earth, and—unlike my cheerful doll's house—looking as mouldering and decayed as if its very stones were only held in place by strangling ivy.

And then I saw a shadow move between the trees.

A man. For just a moment it occurred to me that this might be my uncle, up even earlier than myself. But when the figure stopped I saw that he was carrying a hoe across his shoulders, and though his beard was grizzled like the captain's, he was a shorter man—not that much taller than myself.

As I drew nearer, he stepped back, rather as if he hoped that I would let him melt away into the dark between the trees. But I was stubborn, for this man was staring at me in the very same way that Martha had the night before. And something about the mystery of where I was, and who I was, and why things had turned out the way they had, fuelled bluntness in me. Here, I felt, was my first chance to put a shoulder to the door that had been kept so firmly shut against my past.

I came up close and asked the man boldly, 'Tell me, do I look *so* like my mother?'

He kept his eyes on me, but stood in silence.

So I pressed on. 'It's clear from the look on your own face that you recognize mine.'

Still there was no response, just those grey eyes committing him to nothing but the bare civility of waiting wordlessly. Determined to persist, I challenged him, 'And so I think you must have known my mother!'

Now he drew up as if a shock shot through him. But when it came, his answer was steady enough. 'Oh, yes. I knew your mother. I knew her very well.'

Why did my anger rise? Was it because it seemed to me that everyone in the world knew more about my mother than I? This painful thought provoked me into simple insolence. Surprising even myself, I tipped my head to one side like a girl and asked him impudently again, 'Is there *so* much of a likeness?'

115

And now the shock was mine, because I sensed that it took all his strength of will not to reach out and slap me. But he did manage to restrain himself and, curling his lip, admitted only, 'You are as like as it is possible to be, what with her having been a loving, faultless beauty—and you but a callow and unthinking boy!'

Then off he strode while I stood there ashamed, quite as unable to hurry after him with any further questions as if he'd left me mired in mud as thick as his contempt.

24

The misery I felt, standing abandoned by those dark, dark woods! I could have *wept*. I wanted to be back in Mrs Marlow's comforting arms. I wanted to be sitting at the table as Sophie teased her sisters, and the doctor scolded her for her unladylike ways. I wanted to be done with this great house of stone, whose shadows threw a real chill over a real lawn, and hurry back to where I'd come from, so I could sprawl instead in front of my pretend and cosy doll's-house world.

No, I'd not stay! Not in this cold and empty place where I was banished into attics, and people stared at me as though I were some ghost. I'd stay here only as long as it took to prise a little of the truth about my mother out of Martha the cook, or this strange gardener.

Then I'd be gone.

My mind was fogged with childish misery, and I was in no mood to meet more strangers who might seize the chance to show me their disdain. So I set off back to the house, not over open lawns the way I'd come, but by a narrow path I took to run along the edge of the woods, keeping me in shadow. But it was ravelled with so many twists and turns that I soon lost all sense of where I was, and had to wander quite some way till once again I caught the glint of sunlight and, stepping off the path to follow that, pushed my way through thick undergrowth between the trees until I finally stepped out onto open grass.

Now, between me and the house's distant chimney pots, there was a high beech hedge. I skirted it, to find to my surprise it was a curve that led round and round to make a perfect circle, with only one way in: an arch trimmed in the beech, with a small gate.

Was it a *maze*?

With beeches grown so high, surely my mother must have known the place in childhood! Had she run this way and that round the tricky curves and into green dead ends?

Wanting to trace some sense of her young life, I stepped in through the gate, only to find myself again in deepest shadow. The high beech hedges blocked out all sun and warmth. Moss grew so thickly underfoot that I made no sound as I walked along—or rather, round, because the high hedge circle turned out to be, not a maze, but simply an endlessly unfolding spiral. As I walked inward, round and round, the hedges were so high on

118

either side that I began to feel like some poor ant picking his way along a deepening furrow.

Then suddenly the tightening spiral came to an end and I was out in a clearing.

Ahead of me were stones—two or three standing as tall and shapely as grave markers in a churchyard, and more beside them, one short and broken off, one almost flat to the ground. The whole assembly looked so strange, as if this quiet clearing had been some sort of meeting place in which a mix of lives had suddenly been turned to stone and, in the intervening years, damp moss had tightened its soft grip, spreading all over.

What was the terror that suddenly gripped me then? All I know is that in an instant I had turned to run—back, back around the spiral path, breathing more easily as it opened out, but still only feeling halfway to safe as I burst out into the welcome flood of morning sunlight on the open grass.

I found I was still trembling horribly. Knowing the simple presence of another soul, however bent and old, would help me feel more steady, I hurried back across the grass towards the house, and round into the courtyard.

Martha was there, bent over, tugging at a heap of scullery cloths lying entangled in a woven basket.

I'd cried, 'I'll help you!' even before I'd reached her side.

Again she stared, as if the very way I spoke unnerved her utterly. But I was determined not to be ordered off, and bent to scoop up an armful of her damp, rinsed rags.

So that's where the captain found me a few

moments later, pegging the last of the cloths onto a sagging line.

'Ah, *here's* the boy! An early riser! I am glad to see it.' Glancing at my handiwork, he added, 'And a skilled hand around the kitchen and the scullery. Your poor dear mother must have taught you well.'

I tried to gather my wits to tell him it was Dr Marlow's maid who'd shown me how to shake things out and peg them in neat rows. But he'd already turned to Martha.

'Daniel and I will take our breakfast together now. I have a host of questions for the boy.'

He looked my way, and in the morning light I saw for the first time the scars on his face: a narrow livid streak across one cheek, and tiny pitted holes upon the other as if he'd been peppered by shot. I felt ashamed to have had the petty thought that I'd been banished carelessly to my high attic. Here, after all, there stood a man who had been tried in battle. To him, my dusty, faraway room might truly seem the most exhilarating place—a veritable crow's nest!

Surely, in his gruff way, this uncle of mine was doing his very best to make a young boy welcome in his house.

25

In some anxiety—What questions would he ask?
Would I be equal to his curiosity?—I followed him
along the passage to the dining room. Our places
were already laid, so I sat down and fiddled
nervously with my fork until he laid a hand on
mine to stop my tiresome rattling.

'So,' he said, 'you and I must get to know one
another.'

He sat there quietly for a while, studying my
face. When Martha brought in our hot plates he'd
still not said a word, while I sat trying to quieten
my fast-beating heart. He'll ask me first about my
education, I assured myself. He'll ask if I have
friends. He'll question me on where I've travelled,
and what I want to do when I am grown. And I'll
have nothing to say except that I spent the whole

of my early life malingering in a back room, persuaded I was at death's door.

And then it suddenly occurred to me that, just as I knew nothing of my mother's upbringing, so no one here knew anything of mine. Dr Marlow had talked to me of making a fresh start, and told me that he'd been discreet in letters, mentioning to my uncle nothing of my mother's strange fixations, or of her death at her own hand. I was the only witness to my former life. And so, I thought, if I was careful with my answers, I might lead Captain Severn to believe I'd had a boyhood much like any other, with nothing hidden there to make him think I might be tainted by my mother's morbid temperament or strange beliefs.

When the first question came, it took me by surprise. Leaning his elbows hard on the polished table, his sharp green eyes bored into mine. 'So, Daniel,' he demanded. 'Tell me how Liliana fared, once she had fled from all who trusted and loved her.'

Here was a fighting start! I stared down at my plate and, not wanting him to think me a fool for knowing nothing of my mother's early life, I said to him only, 'As far back as I can remember, the two of us lived quietly together at Hawthorn Cottage.'

'Liliana, quiet? Now there's a fine surprise for those of us who knew her as a child!'

And a surprise for me! My mother not thought of as quiet? Already bafflement was taking hold of me.

Meanwhile my uncle kept up his stare and chewed on his fist. 'Quiet, you say? So did your mother not mingle with the townsfolk?'

I still had hopes of hiding her deluded ways, and

122

so it didn't seem much of a lie to answer only, 'No, sir. She mixed very little.'

Staring at me, he said, 'There were no ladies who became her bosom friends and shared her confidences? No handsome men who hoped to win her widow's heart and call you son and heir?'

Again I looked down at my plate and muttered, 'No, sir.'

'What?' he said after a moment. 'Will you not answer me?'

I wondered then if he were a little deaf, so raised my head to say again, more clearly, 'No, sir.'

'No'—here he seemed to chuckle—'*Mr Cunningham*, to offer you his name?'

'My father died before my birth,' I told him somewhat coldly.

Perhaps from kindness, hastily he turned the conversation back. 'You say that Liliana had no friends or suitors.' Narrowing his eyes almost as closely as if he hoped to catch me out in lies, he said, 'Are you so sure?'

I reckoned it need be no secret that my mother's life and mine had been so closely entwined. 'We lived in one another's pockets,' I told him. 'So I am sure.'

His tone turned thoughtful. 'So,' he said, 'a life as quietly lived as if the two of you had been halfway to *entombed*.'

I felt the blood rush to my cheeks. How had he cut so quickly to the heart of things? Bending my head, I made a show of stabbing at my food while he sat drumming his scarred fingers on the table top. Then on he went. How had my mother earned her living? How did she pay her bills? Did she get letters? Did she travel from home? Keep any maids? One after another questions spilled out of him, as if the years he'd spent waiting to know the answer to each one had spawned a dozen more.

I did my best to answer civilly. But the sheer bluntness of his inquisition gradually turned my mood, first to unease, and then resentment. For if this uncle of mine was bothered to try to win my confidence and make me feel welcome, then surely he might have thought to start his fierce inquisition with something more *brotherly*. Perhaps, I thought, he could have asked me, 'Was your mother happy?' Or, 'Did she ever speak about this house?' Or even, 'What did she have to say about *me*?'

But then, as if those eyes of his had truly burned through bone to see inside my brain, he spoke aloud the last words that I'd been imagining: 'So tell me, Daniel. What did your mother say of *me*?'

I needed courage now to meet his eye and still be honest. 'I am afraid she never spoke of you.'

He stared. 'What, *never*? Not a *word*?'

'No, not a word.'

He seemed incredulous, and waved an arm to take in everything around us. 'Nor anything about this house?'

I felt I had no choice but to shake my head. 'No, nothing.'

'Nor the least mention of all the years she lived here?'

'No, not to me.'

Again, his tone turned thoughtful. 'Well, well. Not a single word!'

And so long was the silence that lay between us that I will swear he had forgotten I was there when he said softly to himself, 'Clearly there's more than one way in the world to rid oneself of an unwanted life . . .'

26

It was a different Captain Severn who rose from the table—a man all smiles and affability. He showed me round the house, and once again it seemed more gracious to lean forward and admire the things that I already knew so well in miniature, and let him feel he was surprising me with rooms in which my dear Hal, and Rubiana and Topper, had played out their adventures a thousand times. So I might honestly claim that, at the start, it wasn't just my sense of boyish dignity that stopped me even mentioning the doll's house, but my good manners too.

And after that it seemed too late.

As we came back along the upstairs landing, I pointed to the only door he hadn't opened yet. 'Is this your own room? Do you keep it private?'

'Private!' he scoffed. 'Lord, no! It is a veritable Piccadilly Circus. Here I do everything. I sleep. I study. I sort through tiresome papers. But I do have a view almost as fine as the one from your lofty eyrie. Come, let me show you.'

He moved towards the door, then suddenly turned to point back over my shoulder. 'But before that, young Daniel, admire the chandelier!'

Obediently I leaned over the ebony banister. But the first thing to catch my eye was not the chandelier but a thin bar of bilious green light across the flagstones below, which startled me by rolling back upon itself and disappearing. As I turned, someone had promptly shut the door to the kitchen passage.

Had Martha, like that strange gardener, been watching me from the shadows? Now that whoever it was had gone, I dutifully peered at the drops of dusty glass hanging in airy circles and festoons some way away from me. And as I stared I heard behind my back a soft grunt, then the faintest tinkling sound, as if my uncle had seized the moment of my back being turned to reach for some metallic thing in one of the little Chinese porcelain jars that sat high on a shelf above the door to his room.

Did he not hear the sounds he made, just as he hadn't heard my soft reply at table? Clearly my uncle's hearing was nowhere near as sharp as mine. But if he chose to hide the key to his room, that was no business of mine, and so I leaned across the banister and spoke of the beauty of the chandelier until I heard the lock click.

Then I turned back. Already he was opening his door. But then, as if he'd spotted something in the room that gave him pause for thought, he pulled it shut again.

'No. It's too glorious a morning for grimy studies and old sailing maps. Another time!'

He ordered me ahead of him down the stairs to the hall. 'One moment!' Then, with the key dropped with a soft chink into the little porcelain pot, he hurried after me and took my arm. 'You must see everything!'

And so we went outside. The sun shone on pale wisps of weed that sprouted through the cracks in the stone steps. He drew in breath. 'See? I was right! It's far too marvellous a morning to waste inside the house.'

He set off at a fearsome pace across the lawns towards the spreading cedar, and on towards the river he had pointed out the night before. Catching a flash of copper on the far side of the shrubbery through which we walked, I pointed. 'Over there, was it planned first as a maze?'

My uncle looked puzzled. 'Over there? A maze?'

'The beech hedge circle,' I explained.

He stopped dead in his tracks. 'Ah,' he said, peering down at me without a smile. 'I see you've lost no time in prowling around the grounds.'

Prowling? My heart began to thump. 'If it's a place you would prefer me not to go—?'

'No, no!' Suddenly he smiled, as if at some delicious joke. 'A place I would prefer you not to go? The very opposite! I tell you honestly, I cannot *wait* to see you in the Devil Walks.'

27

'The Devil Walks?'

He roared with laughter now, then told me, 'It's where the gentlemen of the house strode off to curse and swear.' He took three steps, then smashed one fist into the other, startling me horribly until I realized that, far from his mood changing, he was only making a pretence of being in a fury. 'The devil take him!' he shouted. 'Blast that man into hell! A curse on him and every last one of his family!' Dropping back smoothly into his earlier tone, he added cheerfully, 'That sort of thing. I fear it doesn't take a lot to make the ladies blush.'

I was astonished. 'Someone grew those high beech hedges just to walk behind when they were in a temper?'

'That's right. So that we untamed creatures—
men not abroad at arms—can safely storm from
the house and round its hidden paths, churning the
gravel underneath our boots, and spitting and
cursing fit to burst till we are calm enough to
return to our more mannerly wives.'

He was so merry that I thought to share the
joke. Tipping my head, I spread my hands and said
in high-pitched wifely tones, 'Do you feel better
now, my dove?'

He took up the jest at once, and growled, 'I'm
quite myself again, thank you, my angel.'

We laughed together. And truly, from that
moment, I felt that he set out to make his company
a pleasure. He walked me all the way along a track
to show me a badger's sett. 'We'll come together
one night to watch them frolic, Daniel. You will be
amazed.' He pointed out where mushrooms would
be growing when the summer came to an end. He
made the effort to explain how hares behaved in
moonlight.

And yet he seemed to have no sense of the
effect that some of the things he said might have
on me. 'That's where your mother cut her knee
and bled like a stuck pig.' 'Look over there. Do
you see all those brambles? Well, Liliana claimed
their fruit was always the juiciest. The times I saw
her reaching up at them to fill her basket.' 'See,
Daniel! There's the hollow oak in which your
mother spent whole days playing at being a
squirrel. Lord, how I scoffed at her! I look back
now and am ashamed of my young self-
importance.'

What did he *think*? That all the feelings in my
heart were buried with my mother? I stared

towards the oak. Here's where my mother had spent her hours kicking up leaf mould, catching her pinafore against tree bark, and jumping out of hollows. Why, I could almost see her there, her hand aloft, smiling at—

Who?

Well, not me, ever again. So my eyes filled and then the image blurred, just as the captain became impatient with my stolid gaze into the woods. 'What are you staring at? What can you see?'

I turned away to hide my tears, only to hear a stir of leaves and catch a glimpse of yet another barely moving shadow. It was that same grizzled gardener as before. At any other time I might have taken the chance to ask my uncle about these strange servants of his who seemed to be forever peering out at me from behind doors or trees. But I knew that my voice would still be trembling from thoughts of how my mother had amused herself each summer in this place. So I just shook my head and, though my once weak legs were tiring more with every step, I let the captain lead me on and on, further towards the river.

On the way over a wide field he pointed to a blackened streak on a huge fallen cedar. 'That's where the lightning struck. It must have been a flash to wonder at, to fetch down such a beast.'

'You didn't see it happen?'

'No, no. You take the air beside a sturdy Old Salt. By then, in hopes of making a great fortune, Jack Severn here had turned himself into Jack Tar.'

'You'd gone to sea?'

'I had.'

And instantly his face turned dark and

brooding. My earlier unease swept back in force, for I too felt on no firm ground with this tempestuous man—so affable one moment, so brusque the next. Perhaps, I thought, even from childhood his moods had swung this way and that, and the rough life on board ship had no doubt sharpened any tendency to gruff impatience.

Now, clearly irritated at my slowing pace, the captain strode ahead deliberately fast.

'And do you miss the life?' I asked, trying to slow him.

'No, no! Seafaring is a fine and useful past!' he called back over his shoulder so firmly that I felt he was attempting to persuade himself, not me. Then his voice dropped to a mutter, and it was only because I'd hurried to catch up with him that I caught his last words, meant for his own ears only, not for mine. 'But me? I'm set on quite a different future.'

Hastily I fell back, leaving him to what he clearly believed to be a moment of privacy. But when he turned, his face was still the grimmest mask. What did he mean—a different future? If he still cherished all his childhood dreams, what was he doing, as he said himself, 'rattling around the house like a dead beetle shaken in a bottle'?

Why wasn't he out in the wider world, minting whichever fortune he had in mind?

What was he waiting for? What kept him here?

28

So once again I tried to coax my uncle out of his dark mood. To that end, I kept prattling as we walked on, asking a host of questions about the places he had sailed and dangers he'd seen. And he seemed happy enough, as we turned back towards the house, to talk of steamy islands he had visited, strange cargoes they had carried, and all the curious people he had met.

I couldn't help but be thrilled. 'One long adventure! And you were still a boy when it began!'

'No older than yourself when I set off on my first voyage.'

'Did you see natives like the ones in story books? Men with bones through their noses? Tribesmen with bows and arrows?'

'All those—and more. You haven't run till you've outraced a poisoned blow dart.' He grinned at me. 'Why, I've dodged assegais, and fallen into traps, and once I even found myself whipped up into a tree and spinning from an ankle noose woven from creepers.'

I told him frankly, 'I would be dead from fear alone.'

He shrugged. 'It's foolishness to let the things of this world frighten you. Better to save your anxieties for stranger terrors.' And he went on to talk of pounding drums and eerie singing, of squawking chickens killed for sacrifice and altars sticky with blood. He spoke of men in fearsome masks, and tiny figures crudely carved from roots or fashioned out of clay, and naked priests who called up ancestors and chanted spells.

'What sort of spells?'

'Spells of all kinds. Spells to bring love, or end it. Spells to make people sicken or die. Spells of revenge.'

'But Mrs Marlow told me such things are primitive nonsense, and there's no power in them.'

'Then she's mistaken,' came the sharp retort. Hastily he tempered his tone. 'Why, even your own mother recognized that there was more around us than we understood. I can remember Liliana saying things your Mrs Marlow would have found very strange fancies.'

Perhaps it finally occurred to him, when I fell silent, that it was his mention of my mother that stilled my tongue. And that was partly true. Into my head had come a memory of her sweeping through my bedroom door with one of the musty books from those dark shelves below. *Tales of the*

Caribbean Islands, it was called. For hours I'd thrilled over its graven plates of twisted trees in darkest mangrove swamps, and lush green forests set between mountain ranges. I'd read of moist trade winds and furious hurricanes, ground sloths and crocodiles. I'd been entranced with colourful accounts of priests performing rites of sorcery, witchcraft and magic. The book had been a favourite for many weeks. But, in the end, like all the others, it went back on the shelf and I moved on to something else, with only a few last images of what I'd seen, and traces of the things I'd read, becoming foggier in my mind.

But I soon threw off the grey cloak of memory to ask more questions. How could I help it? I'd led a life so dull I had to pester him about the battles he had seen, the ships on which he'd sailed.

And so the morning passed.

At noon, with my poor legs feeling as brittle as glass rods, and just as likely to snap, he walked me back into the house and told me he'd eat alone. 'Martha will bring a tray to my room. I'll join you again when the gong sounds for supper.' He sighed. 'Till then I face my usual struggle with the household accounts. And you must surely have at least one letter to write to those whose kindness has so miraculously brought us together.'

Letter to write? Still, in my mind, was the conviction I'd be back with my beloved Marlows sooner than any letter I might send. And yet my uncle had done his best to be a good companion and show me round my new home, so it seemed courteous to nod agreement and ask for pen and paper.

The captain took the stairs at a pace. I followed

much more slowly, and once again heard that metallic rattle before he opened his door. Had he not realized that his slight deafness masked, not just soft answers and approaching footsteps, but this clear hint to where he kept the key to his room?

Courteously I hung back, pretending to admire a tapestry while he went in and shut the door firmly behind him. When he came out, he handed me a little pot of ink, a fat gold pen and generous amounts of paper.

'There!' he declared. 'Now, like your mother, you may write your memoirs!'

'My mother?'

'Did no one tell you? Whenever she wasn't tumbling round the grounds, playing at squirrels, Liliana would be found hunched in a corner, scribbling secrets.'

Smiling, he shut the door.

And I too probably kept a smile on my face till I was safely through the alcove door. I forced my tired legs up the stairs and into to my attic room, then slumped against the panels of the door and wept.

No! Wept is too weak a word. I fell into a very storm of tears. The rage I felt! She was *my* mother. *Mine!* Yet everything about her life and character came as fresh news to me. To me! Her *son*. I howled and howled, stemming my sobs of fury and resentment only on hearing footsteps trudging up the stairs, and then an old cracked voice outside the door.

'Daniel?'

Martha. She tapped once, then again, but I said nothing, only pushed my spine back harder on the

136

panels of the door to keep her out. I heard the scrape of the tin tray she left for me, and I ignored it. How long I sat there I don't know, but only when it seemed I'd no more tears to fall did I climb to my feet.

Only to face another insult. Someone had searched my bag! Was it my uncle, while I was out of the house alone, early that morning? Or Martha, who had looked at me as if I were a ghost, and peered from doorways? Perhaps even that sturdy gardener, who'd seemed to track our journey through the woods? Who was to say which of the three had lifted out those layers of clothing with such care, then put them back in such good order, with even sleeves so neatly folded back?

And yet the secret of this visit to my room was out. For how could any snooper have imagined a boy might glance with swollen, reddened eyes at crumpled wads of newspaper and see the words *Carriage in Ruins* where *Grand Theatre Opening!* had been before, and *Voters Frustrated* where once had been the news that *Government Minister Sickens*, and know at once that someone in this house had searched the things he'd brought with him so thoroughly they'd felt down to the very toes of his new boots?

Once again, rage and frustration fought to take the upper hand. Why should I stay another single night in such a house? Wasn't my bag already packed—twice over! The shillings in my pocket would get me as far as London. I had the calling card of the doctor's friend. He'd lend me money for the onward journey. And, if he wouldn't, I could beg food, and walk. Why not abandon all these mysteries and hurry back to my old life?

137

But then the next thought sprang: what life is that? For till the day that Dr Marlow took me into his house, my life had been as much a blank as if I'd never lived. What had the captain said as he gave me the pen? 'Now you may write your memoirs!'

A sour joke! For I'd deliberately been raised so I'd go nowhere, never meet a soul and waste my days in bed. Here was my only opportunity to find out why my mother kept me so hidden from the world that no one knew of me almost until her death.

Was I too scared to snatch the chance to make even my own past half-life real to me?

No. I'd be brave. Then I'd be gone—back to the family I'd grown to love.

29

So I picked up the pen and pulled my rickety little table across to the window to catch the light. I fetched my tray and ate my good fresh hunk of bread, and drank my frothing milk so I would seem to be a simple boy who noticed nothing and settled down obediently to do an uncle's bidding.

And since I knew he might reach out—even in jest—to read what I had written, I picked my words with care. I wrote about the journey and the rolling downs. I tried to describe High Gates without a mention of the spiders and the dust. I told about the captain's shock of white hair on his youthful frame, but not a word about the way he'd startled me with all his savage questions about my mother's life. I told of the badger sett and the burned oak, then sucked the end of my pen and, fearing that Mrs Marlow would worry that there was no one in this house to care for me as she had done, I wrote of Martha and how I'd helped her peg out the kitchen cloths, and how I planned to fix her washing lines more firmly to the wall.

And then, at last, I wrote the only thing I truly wanted to tell them: how much I missed the happy hours in their company. I sent my love to all, then I laid down my pen, thinking so warmly of this family who truly loved me and had made the effort to introduce me to the world and make me smile and treat me plainly and honestly, without recourse to secrets and silence.

Folding the letter, I wrote the direction carefully, then put it in my pocket, where it sat while I unpacked my carpet bag and laid things out with sour thoughts of making life a little easier for those who spied on me.

Then I sat twiddling my thumbs until a surge of restlessness drove me down to the empty drawing room. To my unhappy eyes the book shelves seemed filled with nothing but the leaden histories of pompous men. Boredom and the sheer mustiness of the room combined to make me lift the latch of the French doors and walk out on the terrace to kick at weeds and peer in cracked and empty urns.

And see that selfsame gardener watching again.

Now irritation spurred me into action. Drawing the letter from my pocket, I strolled across the lawn towards a wooden bench, as if all my attention was on the paper in my hand and he'd no need to play his usual game of sloping away into the shadows. But, just as I went past him, I swung round, demanding, 'When will your curiosity be satisfied? Am I so strange? Have I two heads, or five arms, that you should be forever gawping at me?'

To my surprise, the gardener broke into a broad smile.

That irritated me even more. 'Now I *amuse* you?'

'No, no!' He tried to set his face more soberly. 'It was a memory that made me smile.'

'A memory?' I dropped my peevish tone. After all, wasn't this why I'd stayed—to find out more? 'What, of my mother?'

He nodded. 'The thought sprang up at me that you're not just the image of your mother in looks, but you're alike in temperament as well.'

I was amazed. 'My mother had a temper?'

'Temper?' The gardener grinned. 'At times she was a *spitfire*.' Mistaking my astonishment, he hastened to assure me, 'But though I didn't guess it at the start, and offered you sharp words, I think you probably take after her in other ways as well.' Again he smiled. 'She too would have saved a servant from a roasting by saying nothing to give him away.'

'Because he failed to meet me from the train?'

'Meet you?' He looked disquieted. 'That's what you understood?'

'It's what my uncle assured my guardian would happen.'

The man's expression darkened. 'Perhaps if the captain had cared a little more about your welcoming, he would have thought to mention it to those he hoped would undertake the task.' He shrugged his irritation off. 'No, I meant earlier today, when I was in the woods.'

I wasn't going to confess I'd been discreet back there only to hide my tears, and so I said, 'My thoughts were elsewhere. Captain Severn was showing me my mother's childhood haunts.'

He laughed. 'An easy enough task, since there's no place for miles around that wasn't one of them!'

Again I had that strange, unsettling feeling that my old world had been some weird delusion—nothing real. In Hawthorn Cottage had lived my shuttered, silent mother. Yet here she'd been the Liliana of whom the captain and this gardener spoke: some talkative and merry Liliana, who had a fiery temper and jumped from trees, and wandered far and wide among the brambles.

How could these two so very different creatures have been one and the same? I stood confused, watching the gardener raise his eyes to the windows of the house as if he feared that we'd been talking too long.

Then he reached for the letter in my hand. 'Better to leave that with me than trouble the captain with it. I will make sure that it gets sent.'

Was it a *warning*? Some bland suggestion that Captain Severn was not to be trusted with any confidence that might be on the page? So was it, then, my uncle who had searched my bag with such great care?

And yet—to have the gardener offer to take charge of my letter! Even, perhaps, pay for its carriage onwards from his own small funds. Now that was surely out of the usual way of things. I stood in indecision. Who, in this strange house, was I right to trust?

Needing a moment more to think, I tried distracting him. 'This is our second meeting. I

142

should know your name.'

'Thomas.'

So *this* was Thomas. And he was a man who knew my mother well. I stared. For what was *my* name? Daniel Thomas Cunningham. And why would a mother choose a name for her own son, except from her past loyalties and old affections?

The choice was made. I put the letter in his hand. Then, since the man seemed generous-spirited enough, I burst out, 'Thomas, please! Tell me about my mother!'

It was a reasonable request. After all, wasn't I now some kind of orphan? Who could begrudge me the comfort of knowing more about my family?

He answered carefully, 'I'm sure the mother who raised you was the same soul who left this house.'

Now we were both uneasy. How could I say, 'Impossible! The Liliana who raised me was secretive and silent. And she was frightened all the time. And she went mad enough to rip her clothes and hurl her food away from her, and hang herself from a rusting window bar!'

I couldn't say it—no, not yet. Still, something about his face and gentle manner made me determined to confide in him. 'I thought I knew her well enough.' I felt tears gathering. 'But since her death she has become a stranger, even to me. She told me nothing of her childhood. Nothing! And though I've looked, I've yet to find a single painting in this house that might show her as a child.'

'Oh, there you'll be wasting your time!' he burst out bitterly. 'There are no portraits any more. No, not of her, nor any of her brothers.'

143

Brothers?

Not just the one? How many secrets had my mother kept from me?

He'd seen my shock. 'You didn't know? She didn't even tell you about her brothers?' I watched him hesitate before he added softly—perhaps for fear he had raised hopes in me: 'And their sad deaths.'

'She told me nothing!' I burst out again. Then the tears truly sprang. 'She's left me stumbling here alone and—'

Already his hand was on my shoulder, and he was chiding me, 'You're not alone!'

I made a scornful face. 'Oh yes! Forgive me! I have an uncle who forgets to send a man to meet me at the station, then taunts me with the details of my dead mother's life.'

'No, no,' he soothed. 'You've better friends that that.'

I grabbed his sleeve. 'Then tell me more about my family. How did these brothers of my mother die? Why did she run away? And if my uncle thinks she fled from all who loved and trusted her, why has he sent for me?'

Once again Thomas glanced towards the house. I turned to see what he was looking at, but now the sunlight gleamed so hard against the windows it was impossible to tell who stood and watched.

But Thomas must have seen something, for, 'Not now!' he warned.

'Thomas—'

But he'd already turned to stride back into the woods.

I stood a while, distraught, then tried to follow, but he'd been too quick for me. Soon I no longer even heard the rustle of his footsteps, or saw more of the shadows that led me to believe he might have gone this way or that.

So, still in tears of misery and abandonment, I turned back slowly to the house.

30

Dusk had crept into the air by the time Martha rang the gong for supper. I joined my uncle in the dining room. Now, as at breakfast, he was grave in mood and narrow-eyed with concentration.

And full of questions still. 'You say your mother never spoke of her past?'

'No, sir.'

He waited while Martha heaped potatoes on his plate. 'And if you questioned her?'

'Questioned her?'

Already he was impatient. 'Yes, Daniel. Asked her a simple question like, "Where were you born?" or, "Was your childhood happy?" Even'— and here he nodded up at Martha carelessly— '"Who was the patient soul who sat for hours teaching you how to make such pretty lace?"'

146

Behind him Martha stiffened, as if to arm herself against the casual cruelty of this reminder of a happier time. Then she came round the table and made a trouble out of filling up my plate, giving me time to search for any answer that might prove honest enough.

I spread my hands. 'I know that we had very little money, and so our lives were narrow. If I'd had company, I might have thought a little more about my own childhood—even asked my mother more about hers.' I shrugged. 'But, as things were . . .'

'It seems to me,' he said incredulously, 'you asked your mother *nothing*.'

I tried to defend myself. 'You claim she was a lively soul. And yet, with me, my mother was always steady and quiet. And I accepted how things were, and was content.' I thought some more, then added frankly, 'Indeed, I think I must have been a very incurious child.'

He narrowed his eyes at me. 'Incurious? Perhaps we should go one step further and call you *stupid*.'

Oh, he was in the worst of moods. He shovelled food into his mouth, then set about his questions again as if his only aim was to torment me. 'So here you are, your feet under my table. Yet you have nothing to tell about your mother and your upbringing. Why, you could be no more than some false interloper who has wormed his way into this house!'

If he was trying to browbeat me, he'd chosen the wrong tack. I barely needed to remind myself that I'd begged to be left where I was happy, and it was this man glowering at me across the table who had

147

insisted that I come. Interloper, indeed! Since at that moment I'd have sold my soul to have him order me back to Dr Marlow's house, I summoned up the courage to say to him coldly, 'Yes, I suppose I could.'

We ate in silence for a while. And then, as if he had more toads to spit from his mouth, he asked, 'So what did your mother think most precious in this little house of yours?'

I stared. Here was a hint indeed as to who might take trouble to root in secret through a visitor's bag! And Martha, bringing in a jug of water, seemed to freeze at his words as if even to let him know that she was in the doorway behind might lead to trouble.

Impatiently he rapped the table top. Hot drips of wax fell on the backs of his fingers but he ignored them. In flickering candlelight his eyes were slits. 'You heard the question! Before she died, which of her few possessions did Liliana value most?'

I had no reason to help him in his greedy quest. I answered stonily, 'We had so few things of our own by then, I wouldn't trouble you with a list of them.'

My uncle leaned closer across the table and asked me fiercely, 'Was there a doll's house?'

I saw the start of anguish on Martha's face. Begging me with her eyes not to betray her, she stepped back into the shadows of the hall. My blood ran cold. Was this some old vendetta from the nursery? Or the first clue as to why I'd been fetched to this house? I slid my hand into my pocket to touch the little ivory case that held my mother's lace-making tools, and hoped the

148

memory of her unhappy life and pitiful death would give me courage not to answer him directly.

'After she died, all that she owned was sold to pay her debts.'

Our poverty meant nothing to him. 'Yes, yes! But did you never see a model of this house, set up with dolls?'

I would not lose this battle easily, so I played dumb. 'Dolls?'

I was frustrating him with my stupidity. 'Yes, dolls! Dolls that your mother stole from this house.'

The hateful look upon his face! This desperate grilling! Was he like this in childhood? Was this why my mother fled? I kept my fingers round the little ivory case and told myself I would not have her bullied by her brother in this way, even in death.

Taking a breath for courage, I raised my head and told him coldly, 'I'm sure my mother only ever took away from any house things that she thought her own.'

Still he was watching me with those cat's eyes. 'So you have seen no doll's house and no dolls?'

I knew he didn't believe me, but I stared him out. 'I had no sisters, sir.'

He gave a thin-lipped smile. 'No more you did. Nor any brothers, either!'

And I will swear, as Martha dared to bustle back to us with heavier tread, still carrying the jug, I heard him adding softly to himself: 'Thin pickings from our dearest Liliana—and yet, to pit against that, quicker work.'

31

Cunning grows fast. Instead of going up to bed when I was ordered, I walked no further than the hall, then slid from sight behind a tattered screen. I waited till I was sure that Martha had made her last shuffling journey back and forth along that dank and gloomy passage carrying her plates and crocks, and then I hurried after her into the kitchen, determined to trick her into spilling some of the secrets of my mother's life.

She was already in the scullery, washing the pots. I pulled a drying cloth from its hook and set to work beside her, wondering if I should confess I'd lied to my uncle, or whether it would be wiser not to mention to someone I was not yet sure that I could trust that this old doll's house was now mine.

In the end I hedged and, after a few words about the meal she'd offered us, I asked her only, 'Why is my uncle so determined to track down a nursery toy?'

She kept her head down, playing as dumb as I had earlier. 'A nursery toy?'

'The doll's house,' I insisted. 'You heard him say that it went missing when my mother left.'

'As well it might,' I heard her mutter, 'since it was hers to take!' Lifting a dish from the water, she turned to me and said more openly, 'You should have seen it, for it was a marvel. You wouldn't have believed how like it was to this house, down to the last coil of ivy.' Her old face softened at the memory. 'Inside, the rooms were perfect—even the patterns on the wallpaper. And every stick of furniture was like for like.'

'Who ordered it to be made?'

'Ordered?' She shook her head. 'Nobody *ordered* it. It was a labour of love.'

They were the very words that Dr Marlow used when he first saw it, I recalled. And I repeated them. 'Labour of love?'

Her withered lips creased in a smile, as if some thought from long ago had warmed her heart. But all she said was, 'Ah, to know more of that, you would do better to ask the gardener.'

'Thomas? Why? Did *he* make it?'

She was amused by my astonishment. 'Indeed he did. It took him four long years, and it was done only to please your mother.'

I stared. 'They were so close?'

She nodded. 'Yes. Back then, Thomas's father was head gardener, so Thomas spent a good part

151

of his own life joining the children in their games.'

'The *children*,' I repeated to myself. These were the brothers I had never known my mother had. How strange the idea still seemed!

But Martha was explaining about the doll's house. 'By then, of course, Thomas was grown enough himself to have a host of jobs around the house and grounds. Yet we all knew he had a gift for working with wood, and Liliana stood in front of him day after day, teasing and begging, "Please make me a doll's house, Thomas!"'

Again it came, that unnerving feeling that the child they'd known was not the woman who'd raised me. I stood, quite baffled. How could the intervening years have turned a frank and cheery-sounding child into the stiff, unbending soul who kept me so immured she'd even imprisoned herself?

Forcing my thoughts to settle, I pressed Martha to keep on with her tale. 'So Thomas agreed?'

'No, not at first.' She laid more dishes to drain. 'He claimed he'd no time for a task like that. But she kept on at him till he gave in.' She shook her head, remembering. 'And after that I was forever coming across Liliana struggling with a hoe, or clumsily trailing nets over the raspberries. I'd ask her, "Now what are you about, you naughty imp?" and she'd insist that she was doing Thomas's work for him so he'd keep whittling some tiny table for the doll's house, or one more trail of ivy up its walls.'

I reached for another dish. 'So was it Thomas's idea to make it look exactly like this house?'

'No, no. Thomas, I'm sure, would have preferred to make something far, far simpler. But

152

Liliana was a strange little soul, and she was adamant: "It must be perfect, down to the last small roof hatch." And when I teased, and asked her why she'd set poor Thomas a task as long and hard as any in a fairy tale, she'd only shake her head and say that one day I would understand, because the doll's house, made just so, would save a precious life.'

'Save a life? How would she know that? Nobody can foretell the future.'

Martha laid the last pot to drain. 'Your mother had a way of sensing trouble even before it came. Often, I think, she knew the secrets of the future that was coming to her. She told me once, "Martha, I know I shall be loved. But I shall not be happy. And misery and worry will follow me for my whole life."'

She broke off. Down the passage, coming towards us, were the ringing steps that we both recognized.

'Quick!' Martha urged. 'The captain's on his nightly rounds. He won't be pleased to find you still about.' Snatching the cloth from me, she pushed me hastily through the door to the servants' back stairs. 'To bed—and quietly!'

Easily enough said. For those who'd trodden up and down those steps for years, no doubt there was no problem with a creaking here, a sudden turn in the dark there. But for a boy who knew this cramped and unlit staircase only from the games his dolls had played, it was a trickier matter. In the end one step too many gave out a noisy groan as I crept up, and I thought it was safer to hold still till my uncle left the kitchen.

I heard his voice below. My heart thumped. Had

153

he realized that I was missing from my room, and come in search of me? Or was he just embarking on some discussion with Martha about the meals to come? I sank down on my heels to wait, and in my nervousness my fingers wrapped around the step's wooden rim.

To feel a tiny coil of rusty metal underneath. Was it a hook?

Was there some hiding place under the step?

It was too dark to see, so I was careful not to move a muscle till I heard my uncle's cheery tones. 'Well, then! Fruit pies it shall be! And plenty of cream, remember, Martha, now that we have a growing boy about the house!'

A door slammed. Then another. I waited to see if Martha came to check that I was safely gone. But she'd no doubt assumed I'd had the sense to scurry up as fast as possible, not sit in terror lest a creak of stair gave me away.

So I bent down to lift the hook I'd found beneath the rim. And when I gave the gentlest of pushes, part of the facing of the stair tipped back, as if on a hinge. I slid down a couple of steps and, on my knees, reached into the little hidden space I'd found.

Did I touch spiders? I've no doubt! I'm almost sure I felt them scuttling over my hand as I reached round in all that dust of years. What did I feel? Soft leather. Was it a wallet? How long had it been abandoned there? Perhaps, I thought, no one in this whole house knew of its presence except me.

And so I drew it out, and since I could not see what I was holding, tucked it away in even deeper dark—under my jerkin—and crept on up the stairs and through the door that led out onto the landing, then past my uncle's room and across to my attic staircase door.

To find it bolted shut.

32

Here was a brand-new terror! Had my uncle taken to locking me in at night? I could go through the door, but how, then, could I slide the bolt back into place behind me? Should I find a place to hide till he shot it back at dawn, thinking he'd freed me? Or should I sleep in my own bed, and face his wrath in the morning: 'What? Were you out prowling yet *again*?'

The very thought was enough to bring me to my senses. Let him believe he'd had me safely caged the whole night long! I crept back down the stairs, and past the dining table at which he had enjoyed tormenting me such a short time before, into the little room beyond, flooded with moonlight.

I settled in the largest chair and pulled the small leather package that I'd found out of my jerkin.

Now I would look for secrets! I picked off stray strands of cobweb and blew away dust, and wiped my fingers down my jerkin till they were clean enough to pull the wallet open.

No, it was not a wallet but a book. Even in moonlight I could see that someone had covered the first page with swirling patterns. And, on the next, penned in a childish form of a familiar hand, I saw the first words:

Liliana: her private diary

Was this what my uncle had in mind when he described my mother as forever scribbling secrets? I took the book to where the moonlight fell more strongly over the page. And there I sat on dusty floorboards for an hour or so, turning the pages to read her childhood worries about the squirrel with an injured leg, the way her governess scolded her careless stitching, accounts of her dreams—even her cunning plan to coax Thomas into guessing that a better, bigger rabbit pen would be the best gift for her coming birthday.

I turned the page to find another worry:

Why does Jack act so meanly? It seems to me that he lives on a seesaw. He can be cheery and open, then, in an instant, full of spite. Sometimes I watch him as a choice is made, and it's as if he ponders gentleness, then invites devilry only because it seems to him to be more interesting—perhaps more fun. But Mother says that habits begin as cobwebs, then turn into cables that will hold you fast. And when we were in church the minister spoke warmly of how we must train ourselves to step away from the dark path or it will draw us ever closer to the pit. And I believe that, as he said those words, he looked particularly at Jack. So now I hope with all my heart that Jack will change his naughty ways, for only today we came across him on the steps tormenting poor little Jolyon, and Edmund had to rebuke him for holding back the ball till Jolyon cried.

I turned the page. But she'd moved on to write of stumbling as she climbed the river bank and scraping her knees. I laid the journal down, remembering what the Marlows' vicar had said in church as I sat there with Sophie. 'The devil can make no headway if he has no help.'

Had he been right? Is that what had gone wrong with young Jack Severn? Had he invited some sort of devil in? I pushed the diary safely away, deep in a pocket; but somehow the very thought of someone playing games with wickedness turned it into the worst of nights. I tossed about in that huge, musty chair, dreaming of horrors and waking at every creak or whisper of the old house. Still, even that was better than returning to my room, alerting the captain to my midnight wanderings and tipping his mood into the same fierce irritation that I had faced the day before.

And yet at breakfast he was a different man. 'Daniel!' he greeted me. 'Look at the morning! Such bright sun! Such crisp air! Today I must teach you how to be a countryman. Which shall we try our luck at first? Shooting or fishing?'

I had no wish to learn to kill any poor creature. But he was in such a cheery mood that only a braver boy than I would have dared cross him. The thought of some fine, sunlit bird caught short in flight and falling to the earth with bloodied feathers sickened me so much that, when he pressed me, 'Come, boy! Choose your sport!' I plumped for fishing.

'To the river, then! Martha will find you something warm to wear. I'll fetch the rods. We'll meet down at the bridge.'

He went off one way, I went off the other, to find Martha dealing cutlery into a drawer. 'Good morning, Martha. I come to ask you for something warmer than this jerkin to see me through a morning by the river.'

She pointed to the door on which hung two drab jackets. 'You can take Thomas's and, in return, carry down something to warm him while he clears the Devil Walks.'

I shivered at the memory. 'It's a cold place.'

'Yes. Cold and sad.'

She handed me a basket in which she'd put a jar of soup and a hunk of bread, and I set off across the lawns towards the Devil Walks. As soon as I was through the gate I felt the chill, even through all the wool of Thomas's jacket. Round and round I walked, deeper and deeper in shadow, until at last I stepped out into the clearing.

The circle of grass smelled freshly cut, and in the middle Thomas stood beside one of the slabs of stone.

Seeing me swamped in gardener's tweed, he chuckled. 'Off for a morning's sport?'

I made a rueful face as I put down the basket. 'I fear my uncle is determined to make a proper man of me.'

He laughed. 'Then I'm the lucky one, here with

159

the good things Martha's sent.' He leaned his rake against the hedge behind and reached for the jar of soup.

Seeing the rake begin to slip, I stepped across to catch it by the handle and, turning back, noticed a pattern carved on the nearest stone.

I looked more closely. Under the moss I thought that I could make out faded letters:

oſyo

Into my mind sprang the name I'd seen in my mother's diary. 'Does that say Jolyon?'

Thomas nodded.

'Is it a *grave*?' I waved a hand towards the other stones. 'Are they *all* graves? All family graves?' Turning round to peer more carefully at each in turn, I made out enough lettering to read aloud: '*A deeply loving mother . . . The kindest father . . . Dearly beloved Samuel . . . In memory of Edmund . . .* All dead?'

I knew the world was filled with horrors. Still, for one family this seemed the grimmest litany of grief. Was this, I wondered, part of the reason why my mother fled from home—because the place seemed cursed?

Again, Thomas was nodding. 'Yes. All dead.'

'But how?'

He shrugged. 'What does it matter now? Death's all one story. Jolyon died young in his bed. Samuel was killed in the woods. And Edmund— Liliana's precious Edmund—was lost at sea.'

'It is the saddest story! Three brothers out of four!'

'Four?' For just a moment Thomas looked confused. Then his face cleared. 'Ah, yes. Count in her stepbrother, and there were four.'

Here was another surprise! So Captain Severn was not my mother's brother from birth. And I'll confess that as I walked away, back round the spiral of the Devil Walks, I felt as if a load rolled off my shoulders. If he was no real brother of my mother's, then surely the world had far less of a right to blame my mother for hiding him from me—and me from him.

He was not part of my blood family. No proper uncle at all! My obligation to stay was, in an instant, gone. And at the very thought my heart lifted and my spirits soared. I think that I was even singing softly to myself as I strolled down the short cut through the shrubbery and on to the river where the captain stood, flicking his rod back and forth over the water.

'Ah! There you are at last! Our lesson begins! Now, seize the rod, Daniel. Wrap your fingers round—like so! And so!'

He was a tireless taskmaster. It seemed an age before he would declare my clumsy casting 'good enough not to disgrace a novice'. Then we stood side by side, trailing our lines. Fearing that if I left him to brood in silence his mood would change and he might start to question me as fiercely as he had the night before, I begged him, 'Tell me some more about your life at sea. Were you adventuring? Or were you busy in trade?'

'Hard to do one without the other in most of the places we anchored.' And out the stories of his old life poured as I relentlessly kept steering my questions down one track after another. 'So,

161

Uncle, did you never want to marry?'

He roared with laughter. 'Me? *Marry?* And be forced to keep a roof over some lady's head while she talks nonsense to the babies she dandles on her knee?'

I was confused. 'But you already have a house that's more than fit to shelter any family.'

'This place?' He gave a small, contemptuous smile. 'Lord, boy! I have a finer destiny mapped out for me than mouldering in this backwater. I'll soon be gone.'

'Gone?'

He chuckled quietly to himself. 'Yes,' he said. 'Gone in as little time as it can take for one thing to be found'— he looked at me the same way foxes in my nursery tales looked at the chickens, and added quietly—'and yet another *lost.*'

The mischief in his look disquieted me so much I let my rod drop almost to the water. He leaned across. 'Don't jerk your line that way! Your catch will barely have been hooked before you lose it!'

And so began another lesson. But I can't claim I pleased my tutor, because my freshly rising fears had turned me stupid and clumsy. The rod lay heavy in my hand. My arms were tired.

Finally the captain noticed that, as time passed, I shifted the rod's weight ever more frequently from one hand to the other.

'You've had enough for the moment,' he declared. 'And it was fair enough, for a first try. But I shall stay—and possibly do better for an hour or two without you stirring up the water at my side.' He took my rod. 'Leave that on the bank with me. And, in the meantime, do me the favour of asking Martha to send Thomas along with

162

something to keep me in spirits.'

I looked down at my red raw palms, and his dismissal felt like the happiest reprieve. 'I'll tell her. I'll go now.'

And gratefully I slipped away from him, into the woods.

33

I took the basket Martha filled to Thomas, who had left the Devil Walks and was now dragging dead wood from the shrubbery. He smiled. 'So you've become the kitchen boy.' Seeing me wince as a stray strand of wicker from the handle of the basket scraped at my skin, he took my hands in his and turned them over.

'Aha!' he said. 'Now I see why it's me who has to take the basket down to your uncle. You have already tired of manly sports.'

'I have,' I said. 'And of his grisly tales of warring tribes who feast on their enemies' brains, and kill small squealing children for a sacrifice.'

'And carve their horrid little wooden dolls to look like living people!'

He spoke with such contempt he made me

curious. After all, Mrs Golightly must have been carved to look at least a little like my grandmother for her to end up making Sophie think she was the mirror image of my mother. But I had kept the secret of my one inheritance well enough not to want to mention it now. So all I said was, 'But Martha told me you yourself made Liliana a doll's house.'

He shuddered. 'Not for the sort of doll the captain talks of—fiendish things with strange and ancient powers.'

'Ancient powers?'

He grinned. 'Oh, not by rising to life and growing large and strangling you in your sleep. No, much more cunningly. It is a sort of magic. Voodoo, the captain calls it. You cast your spell. And after that the doll, and whoever it was you made it for, are intertwined till death. If you torment the doll, your enemy writhes in misery. Shower favours on it and your friend will thrive.'

I saw again the grey engravings of the Caribbean mangrove swamps, and memories of things that haunted me so long ago rose in my mind. If I'd been left to brood I surely would have hit upon my uncle's secret even then. But Thomas had had more than enough of tales of savages. And of my worries. 'No need to fear the captain will come back to order you down to the river for yet another lesson. Once his rod's over the water he's lost for hours.'

But I was not convinced. And so, my errand done, I went back to the kitchen where Martha was at work on her pies. I watched her as she spooned out flour, then, sliding onto a chair, I took a couple of apples from the pile in front of me.

165

'Shall I peel these for you?'

She handed me the paring knife then moved along the table, back to her pastry bowl. Knowing she'd be more free with what she said if she believed that I already knew my mother's story, I framed the first of my questions with great care.

'You knew my mother's brothers too, of course. Tell me about them.'

'Her brothers?' A shadow crossed her face. 'Oh, how you would have loved them! This house was such a happy place when they were all alive.'

I took a chance with weasel words—half guess and half invention. 'I'm sure my mother wept so when she thought of them that only a brute could have forced her to tell the story of her family more clearly.'

She shrugged. 'Happiness leaves no mark, so there was little story to tell until the children's father fell from his horse a week after Jolyon's birth.' She sighed. 'The house was bleak with grief, and it was two long years before Liliana's mother dried her tears enough to travel off to London to sign some last few papers. And it was there she met George Severn, whose own poor wife had died some years before. They fell in love and married, and since her new husband could boast no house or fortune of his own, he joined her here, bringing his only son.'

'The captain.'

'He was young Jack back then.'

'What was he like?'

Inside the mixing bowl, her fingers stilled. I had the feeling she was determined to be fair about her first impression of this half-grown boy who'd joined her precious family.

She forced a smile. 'Oh, just another cheerful, impudent lad with locks of jet-black hair falling across his face.'

'Jet-black?'

She chuckled at my surprise. 'Oh, yes. Look at him now, and you'd not recognize him as the same Jack Severn who prowled around this house so restlessly, counting the days till he was old enough to go to sea. Some say his hair was bleached by tropic sun, and others whisper that he had a fright so horrid that it turned white overnight.'

'Which does *he* say?'

Her mouth pursed, and it took a moment or two for her to answer guardedly, 'You'll find that what the captain says does not always settle a story.'

Hastily I led my questioning back, away from her discomfort. 'But when he first came to this house?'

'Why, it was mostly all smiles. The children's mother found herself happy again, and certainly she'd lit upon an excellent union because the captain's father was a gentle man, easy with all. Samuel and Edmund and Liliana tried hard to offer friendship to their new stepbrother. They did their best to ignore his shifting moods and his occasional spite.'

Here was the selfsame word my mother used of Jack in her diary. So, 'Spite?' I repeated softly.

'Oh, yes. He could be harsh, and though but a child himself, still he would say cruel things about the merry games the others played together. Often there was contempt about his manner, as if Jack felt himself destined for greater things than anyone round him. "When I am grown," he told us constantly, "I will make such a fortune that even a

167

fine house like this will be beneath my notice."'

'Then he aimed high!'

'So we all thought. Indeed, George Severn would laugh and shake a finger at his son. "Take care, Jack! Better to praise your dear stepmother for the fine home she's given you than talk it down in favour of some dream." Then, in an instant, Jack's mood would change. He'd turn and, grinning to show that he'd meant no offence, he'd beg the children's mother for pardon, praising the very flagstones on which he stood.'

'And was he always forgiven?'

'Oh, every time. I think we all knew Jack was born with an unsettled nature. One minute up, next minute down. One moment merry and the next cantankerous. It was as if the devil and an angel were wrestling constantly for his soul. Sometimes the one stood behind him, sometimes the other. Indeed, I remember one of the stable lads saying to Edmund once, "Give your stepbrother Jack a stick, and it's a wager whether he'll choose to use it to beat down weeds or kill his own best friend."'

34

We sat in silence for a while. Where Martha cast her mind, I could not tell. But I was thinking of the troubling ways in which my step-uncle had blown, first hot, then cold with me since I arrived.

At last I dared to ask, 'This stable lad—did he say this of Jack before or after the first of the brothers' deaths?'

She shot me a strange look, as if the very fact I had to ask the question puzzled her. But then, perhaps reminding herself that it was no strange thing for someone as young as I to learn a family story back to front, and know some parts of it and not the others, she replied, 'It was before.' Her face set. 'The first death was young Jolyon's. He was no more than five years old. A chubby, happy fellow—the last child in the world you'd think to come across in bed one morning, black and blue around the face, with all life fled.'

'My mother never brought herself to speak of it,' I said quite truthfully.

'*Nobody* did,' she told me fiercely. '*Nobody* understood how such a thing could happen! Grief stopped our tongues. Sometimes I'd look up at the portrait of him on the stair and think the artist must have imagined him, and he had never been on earth. Nobody even spoke of him—no, not till a few months later when that cursed shot rang out deep in the woods.'

I thought back to the toll of deaths Thomas had listed in the Devil Walks. 'Samuel?'

'Yes, Samuel.' Brushing the flour from her fingertips, she pulled her shawl closer around her shoulders as if her body had run cold. 'And your mother *knew*. She sat where you sit now, playing at puddings with the scraps of pastry I had trimmed from pies. We heard the shot, and it was far and faint. Still, I will swear that Liliana went white, and bundled up her pinafore to crush it to her face. And through its folds I heard her crying softly to herself, "Oh, not again! No, please! No, not another!"'

Gathering her pastry, Martha began to knead as if she thought that she might knuckle all the pain out of her story. 'I thought her fanciful, of course—to make a fuss like that about some bird that had been shot in flight. But she was right and I was wrong. For there had been'—she spat the words—'some sort of *accident* in the woods. And this time it was Samuel who lay oblivious to the loving tears that fell on his poor face.'

I asked her outright: 'Who was it fired the shot?'

Her tone was bitter. 'Nobody who'd confess to having done so. Though, of course, everyone knew who had been in the house—and who had not.'

She didn't need to say his name for me to know the one whom she suspected. And I was mystified. After all, here I was, new to this house. For all she knew, my tongue could run as loose as hers. And since her suspicion of her employer was plain as paint, I couldn't understand what she was doing cooking pies for him—unless she had some special plan to blight the man with hideous stomach pains until the very day he died.

Still, I'd not throw away the chance to learn more of the family's story, and so I asked, 'And *was* Jack in the house?'

She gave me a level look. 'No. He was gone—down fishing in the river. Or so he said. And nothing could be certain, since there'd been gardeners about as well.' She threw the last of the pastry on the board. 'That's when most of the other servants left—some for fear there would be another accident, and others because they thought a villain who had proved himself so cunning might next time throw the blame on someone else.' She scowled. 'Who'd want to hang to do a devil a favour?'

But I was still astonished. 'Did no one in the family suspect him? I understand why no one might dare to say a word to Jack's father. But why did no one try to warn the children's *mother*?'

By now Martha had rolled the crust so thin that, when she peeled it from the board, I saw her shadow through it. 'I tried. Lord knows, I tried. So did the housekeeper and the maid. But the poor soul was sick already. Indeed, she was so weak she barely understood that her dear Samuel was gone. It was a terrible time. She had such cramps. She could hold nothing down. The doctors shook their heads, and even sent some bumbling limb of the law to rattle around my pots and pans in search of poison.'

'Poison?' I was aghast. 'So was it Jack again?'

'Who knows? Lord, we were careful! But it is hard to keep a growing boy who claims his belly's empty from prowling around the kitchen of his own home.' She scowled. 'The nurse the captain's father hired was nothing but a fool, and Jack could charm ducks off water. It was no effort for him to wheedle his way into the sick room over and over "to say a few sweet words to his dear stepmother".' Now Martha shivered. 'By the end, Liliana's mother's pains were so bad that some of us were glad to see the poor tormented soul at rest.'

I sat without a word, imagining how grim things must have been. And finally, I asked, 'What of Jack's father?'

'George Severn?' Martha shook her head. 'Robbed of both wives by death, he was a broken man. He lived just long enough to see Jack off on his first voyage, then drank his way into oblivion.'

'So you could say that Jack did for him as well.'

'Indeed you could.' She nodded over my head towards the passage. 'That's why there are no longer any portraits in this house. My proud employer keeps one in his room—the one he ordered painted of himself in his fine uniform when he was first made captain. But as for the portraits of all those who are gone, they were torn down during one long crazed night.'

172

Her lips set tight as purse strings and she added bitterly, 'After all, even a painted eye can look reproachful.'

We sat in silence. It was the strangest feeling. I'd come into this kitchen, a crafty boy fuelled with a plan to use whatever trickery I could to learn about the past. And out it had all spilled as if this woman had been waiting years to tell her tale.

Yet nothing made sense. If one small half of what she said was true, then why were she and Thomas still living here, chopping the wood and rolling out the pastry for someone they believed to be a murdering monster? And, if he was so dangerous a man, why hadn't one or both of them warned me to run for safety the moment I arrived?

Gently I nudged her back towards her tale. 'But you stayed in the house?'

'What else was to be done, except to try to keep the last two children safe, and trust to fortune?'

'Still, always to live in terror that what had happened before would happen again!'

'And did . . .'

But, looking up, I caught the same strained look I had so often seen on my own mother's face, and something in me shrivelled at the thought of pressing Martha on the fate of the last brother. All I could do was shudder. 'So many deaths! Small wonder, when I asked the way, the village women stared at me as if I'd told them I was setting out for hell.'

'They think the devil walks round here. That's why the captain's had no other servants to this day.'

Then out my accusation fell. 'But you and Thomas have stayed here all these years!'

She looked at me as if I were a fool. Her voice was tight. 'Of course we stayed. Who else would be here, ready to watch over Liliana, should she come back again?'

'But when you learned about my mother's death from Doctor Marlow's letter?'

Again she stared at me as if she found it hard to believe a boy my age could be so slow in wits. 'Why, then we knew for certain we had to stay— because we knew you would be coming in her place.'

35

Then out the terror spilled. 'But, Martha! I'm next in his sights! He'll want to kill me too! Indeed, he already does. I've seen the way he looks at me. I've heard the jokes he's made! Why, only yesterday he told me that he couldn't wait to see me in the Devil Walks!'

She laid her fingers on mine. 'No, no. You're safe enough.'

I snatched my hand away. 'Safe? How can you call me safe when there's a string of graves behind me, with no good reason mine won't be the next?'

'There *is* a reason. It's why he sent for you, and why you needn't fear he'll try to harm you yet.'

Yet? I was still panicking. 'But what? What reason?'

She came around the table to lay a hand on my

arm. 'Listen,' she whispered in my ear. 'You hold the key to finding something that the captain wants. We don't know what it is. But it is clearly something from long ago: something he lost and thinks your mother took away with her. Late at night, passing his room, we hear him mutter in his dreams; and sometimes, when he fails to hear our footfalls coming close, we hear him raging. But till he's sure there's nothing more that he can learn from you that might bring what he prizes back to him, you can be sure that he won't harm you.'

It was cold comfort. To be sure, I'd kept my secret well, showing the blankest of faces when my uncle persecuted me about the doll's house. And lucky that I had! For that same stubbornness the night before had probably saved my life. Once he knew where it was, it would take nothing for the man to order me to send for it. And after that there was no reason why I shouldn't suffer as convenient an accident as all the others in the family. Why, he could take me for another fishing lesson. I could slip off a rock and crack my head, or tumble into the river.

I could just vanish.

And no doubt would. For even in this nest he so despised, the captain was a cuckoo. Hal, Rubiana, Topper and I had run through more than enough high-flown tales of hidden wills and lost inheritances to know that I was one last egg that he might need to smash to keep whatever prize it was that clearly lay somewhere inside the doll's house.

But where, exactly? Was it some buried treasure map from days at sea, spread out of sight under the patterned paper? Perhaps it was a handful of smuggled diamonds, each one painstakingly

176

embedded in its small globule of paint and masquerading as a rose over the portico—or, still more likely, packed inside the Severin doll that had itself been carefully entombed under the window seat?

I couldn't guess—except to know that hidden in the doll's house somewhere was a prize set fair to drive a grasping and tempestuous man as far as one more murder.

Mine.

*   *   *

And so I sat, brooding unhappily as I worked on with my knife. Martha turned back to her pie. The minutes passed, till suddenly both of us heard footsteps ringing down the kitchen passage.

The door flew open and it was my step-uncle. To add to my confusion, the man was cheeriness itself, in far too lively spirits to notice any pallor about my face, or my hands trembling.

'Martha! A fine day's sport indeed! Here, take them!'

He threw the fish he'd caught down on the table and picked up a handful of my peelings. 'Neat coils. You're handy with a knife, I see! Then you must gut these mullet!'

Hastily I slid off my chair. 'I wouldn't know where to begin.'

He grinned. 'Martha must teach you. But perhaps not now, because I have a host of other things to show you.'

And off we went, into the drawing room, where he tugged open a door. 'See! Last night I had a sudden memory of happier times, when my dear stepbrothers were alive and we played games for hours.' One by one he was tugging things out of the cluttered cupboard: an old roulette wheel and an archery set, a wooden bagatelle game with steel balls rattling inside a small net bag. A cricket bat and stumps. A set of croquet mallets.

'See! Here you have whole summers of amusement waiting to greet you!' He put his arm round my shoulders and squeezed. 'I saw your tight little face down at the river and I told myself, "Jack, you have been too harsh! Here is a boy who has been raised by his mother. He's not yet strong enough to withstand hours of river sports. You must be gentle with him! Give the lad time to build his forces slowly!"'

I lifted the quiver and the bow. 'They're to be *mine*?'

He waved his hand over the piles he'd tumbled out onto the floor. 'All of it! All yours, to treat as you choose. The only thing I want is for you to be happy.'

And off he strode, leaving me standing in the middle of all these splendid amusements.

Unhooking the net bag slung from the bagatelle board, I spilled out all the silver balls. They rolled across the floor in as disordered a fashion as my own thoughts. So, yes! My uncle was mercurial by nature. One minute up, next down. On one occasion fierce, thoughtful the next.

Did that make him a real, live *murderer*? Maybe the deaths were truly accidents, and from the very start Martha had wronged the boy she couldn't help but see as an intruder with her suspicions that he'd played a part. Clearly her judgement was not always sound. After all, if she believed the things she said, then she must realize that at any time I might, by accident, let slip the knowledge that my uncle sought and put my life in danger. She would have known the safest thing to do was turn me round and send me straight out of High Gates, back to the people who had cared for me.

A clearer mind would have had Thomas harnessing the cart to take all three of us away the moment I arrived.

No, she was old. Old, with a mind still horribly befuddled by one sad loss coming so soon after another. Such a grim run of deaths would take its toll on anyone, and turn the sanest person mad with grief.

Even, perhaps, my mother. For hadn't Martha called her fanciful? Who was to say that, bolstered by her nurse's frenzied suspicions, Liliana hadn't lost her judgement too, when she ran off for fear of young Jack Severn?

And so I sat upon the floor and sorted out the bats and stumps and balls I knew about only from books, and vowed to ask some questions of my own next time my step-uncle and I sat down for supper.

36

And he was in fine mood when we began, making me laugh by imitating his shipmates, and teasing me about the arrows he expected to find stuck in his fundament once I had chosen archery as my sport.

I waited till the apple pies were set in front of us and Martha had shuffled back to the kitchen. And then I said, as idly as I could, 'You'd think that everyone around would want to work in such a house as this. And yet you seem to manage with one bent old lady and a single gardener.'

'And keep those only out of charity!'

I stared.

'You are surprised? Think, Daniel! Why should I want a doddering woman who can barely lift a bucket, and one stubborn gardener who lets the place turn happily into a jungle while he cares only for the Devil Walks? I don't! I'd trade the two of them tomorrow for two strong people from the village who'd do my bidding more than their own.' He spread his hands. 'But Thomas and Martha have both lived at High Gates since they were no age at all. This is their home. It would be cruel to uproot them.' He chuckled. 'And so I bite my tongue and learn to live without complaint amongst the dust and spiders, leaving the two of them happy in their cloud-cuckoo-land.'

'Cloud-cuckoo-land?'

He dropped his voice. 'Have you not noticed that Martha has a host of strange notions? Listen for half an hour and you would think this house was set about by goblins. And as for Thomas . . .' The captain sighed. 'Why, sometimes I believe he has as many weird beliefs as she does.' He gave me a broad smile. 'But your dear mother was so fond of both of them.' He chased a lump of apple round his plate. 'And Martha makes the finest pies!'

We laughed together. And I confess that when the body is determined to show itself at ease, it's hard for a suspicious mind to stay on guard; so though from time to time unease crept back, still I admit that I enjoyed my uncle's company. Twice he leaped up from the table—once to fetch me oil for the cricket bat ('No, no! If I don't find it now, I never will!') and once to pull out a map and show me the straits through which, on one of his many voyages, he and his shipmates chased pirates. 'Ah, that was back when I was young and free. Now I've responsibilities that spill out of my ears. Why, even tomorrow I must be off to London to see to some tiresome affair that hangs forever around my neck.'

He leaned across the table to pat my hand. 'It

181

may be a few days. You won't be lonely?'

I shook my head. 'I'm used to quiet, and my own company.'

'There's a good lad!' With one last smile, he threw down his napkin and pushed away his plate. 'I leave at first light. I'll miss our friendly suppers. But I'll be back as soon as I can.'

He rose. 'Wish me good fortune in my quest, and in return I'll wish you a goodnight.'

Obediently I wished him both, then climbed the great curved staircase, and up to my room. The fishing must have tired me out because I fell asleep at once. But when, later in the night, the moon had scudded across to wake me with its light, I felt uneasy suddenly, and rising from my bed, I crept down the narrow attic staircase to see if, yet again, the bolt was shot across to keep me in.

The door swung open. If my step-uncle planned to rise at dawn, there was no need for him to miss the chance to lock me in overnight.

So was it Martha who had pushed the bolt across? Or even Thomas?

Whoever it might be, I was no prisoner now. Or had I somehow been mistaken the evening before? Whatever the explanation, the feeling of disquiet that had drawn me down the stairs now drained away.

Yawning, I scurried back to bed, quite ready now to sleep as soundly as a hibernating squirrel the rest of the night through.

37

What was it made the next few days such a delight? I'd found the captain's turbulent changes of mood so terrifying that, once he was gone, it felt as if the very air was settling quietly around me. But, if I'm honest, part of the pleasure sprang from being free to test my new-grown strength. Each day I'd prowl around the grounds in search of Thomas. We'd exchange a few friendly words about some frog that hopped across the path in front of us, or last night's rain, and then I'd take myself off anywhere that I'd be out of his and Martha's sight.

And there, with no one leaning on a hoe to watch me fail, I threw balls, tucked my arrows in my bow to let them fly, and swung the croquet mallet. Each time it rained I summoned an imaginary companion, and sat with him on the veranda, where I played both our turns in games of bagatelle until I'd finally mastered the skill of letting the spring uncoil with just enough force to spin the silver balls into the circles with the highest score.

My days seemed filled with pleasures—all pleasures new to me, and each one adding to the earlier delights that still felt fresh: the feel of wind against my skin, strong sunlight in my eyes, the drone of insects buzzing around me.

But maggots are born to chew and chew and chew. How could I help but start to wonder, in those halcyon days, just how my mother could have remembered—as she surely must—all her own days in this garden, running and jumping and feeling her own growing strength, and yet denied these joys to me, her only son. I couldn't stop the bitter feelings rising. She had been selfish! Selfish!

True, she believed she had good reason to keep me close.

But to have kept me in my bed! No, that was *cruel*.

And once her long deception had been discovered, why did she hide from me? What would have been so wrong with sending for me from the hospital, then opening her heart to tell me plainly why she'd tricked me into the belief I was an invalid? Didn't she realize I'd have forgiven her gladly? Didn't she even know that much about me and my love for her?

She was a mystery indeed! So I kept at my plan to find out everything I could before I left. In between swinging the cricket bat with growing vigour and sending the croquet balls more often through the hoops, I haunted Martha and Thomas, pestering them with what I hoped they'd think were idle questions.

And so I found myself one day seeking out Thomas as he shifted last year's leaves into a barrow.

'I'll help you, shall I?'

He pushed the hair back from his eyes. 'Tiring of play?'

I nodded and went off to fetch another fork. After we'd worked a while, I asked him casually, 'Tell me what games my mother played in this garden.'

He chuckled. 'Tell me what games she didn't! Why, she and Edmund were forever hurling balls about and climbing trees and teasing the chickens.'

'Chickens?'

'Edmund kept chickens from the first day he was strong enough to pick one up and fall in love with it.'

'There are no chickens now.'

'No.' Thomas's face set. 'And there'll be no more till Martha's six feet underground. One single cluck from a henhouse can set her weeping to this very day.'

'Because of Edmund?'

'Yes, because of Edmund.'

We both fell silent. Then I said, 'You told me that he died at sea.'

'He did.' He thrust his fork tines deeper in the mulch. 'And I will not forgive myself for that.'

I stared. 'How can his death be any fault of yours?'

He searched my face, as if deciding whether or not to share his story. But then the need to speak overtook reticence. He threw the fork aside. 'Oh, I'm to blame! You see, it was my chattering. All of

185

my life I'd dreamed of seeing high seas, and all those wonders of the deep that sailors talk about. I was forever telling tales of dolphins frolicking in the wake of ships, and whales as big as houses that rose from the waves. And I infected Edmund with my dreams. So when Jack tempted him—"One voyage, Edmund! Just to see the world!"—he couldn't resist.'

'But he knew Jack. He must have known the risk he would be taking.'

'Oh, he'd more sense than to go to sea with such a stepbrother. And Jack was cunning enough to know it. So when Jack came back one summer to hear that Edmund had a plan to join the *Brave Redoubt*, Jack filled our ears with talk of his own new commission on a ship he called the *Pride of Passage*, sailing from Portsmouth. He even packed his bag and left again within a week. So, till the ship that Edmund joined was safely out of harbour, nobody knew that Jack was also on board.'

I watched as Thomas kicked a clod of moss and made it spin before he added angrily, 'And after that even a child would have been able to guess the end of the story. Just some brief mystery an ocean away, and one more good and loving soul was lost to us for ever.'

'And so my mother was the only one left. Is that the reason she fled?'

'That's why we made her go—that very night, though she was weak with weeping. Martha packed up her few possessions before the captain could get home from his dark work.'

I thought of Martha's claim that Liliana had sensed Samuel's death. 'But if the boys were on the very same ship, how did my mother know about her brother's death before Jack came back home?'

'Ah, now, for that,' said Thomas, cheering suddenly, 'we have to thank your father.'

'My *father*?'

He smiled. 'You surely can't be such an innocent you didn't think you had one.'

I felt the blood rush to my cheeks. There was no way to explain to someone who had known a different Liliana just how impossible it was to ask my mother anything about her past.

Now he was curious. 'You never guessed who it might be?'

'Guessed?' Into my mind there sprang an echo of my step-uncle's chuckle of amusement at the idea of any Mr Cunningham who might have wooed my mother and offered me his name.

'I had no reason to believe I lived under the shelter of any name that wasn't mine,' I told Thomas shortly. Then, in a sudden burst of words that took my own self by surprise, I raised my eyes to his and added frankly, 'Though, if I had spent time guessing about some other hidden father, then from the first few days I was in this house I might have thought that it was you.'

38

You'd think I'd told him that I thought he might be King of Spain. 'Me? *Me?* Your *father?*'

I tried to defend myself. 'Why not? I knew you spent your waking hours making a doll's house for my mother. And Martha has quite openly declared that it was a labour of love.'

He laughed, then laid his arm around my shoulders. 'Daniel, I would be *honoured* to stand in his place. But no, your father was a man called Harry Hetherington.' He peered at me in gathering astonishment. 'You've never heard the name?'

I shook my head.

'Truly? Your mother never once spoke of your father?'

'Except to tell me he was dead. And make it clear it was a matter on which she had no more to say.'

He shook his head in wonder. 'Poor soul! Her heart can never have healed.' He took a breath, as if even to tell the story would cost some courage. 'He was a friend of Edmund's—a fine-looking lad. As soon as Edmund told him he was off to sea, he wouldn't be satisfied till he'd arranged to go along. And on the day the two of them left on that fatal voyage I watched Liliana standing on the dockside waving her handkerchief until the ship was no more than a speck on the horizon. And though not a word was spoken, we all knew that Harry was as much in her mind as her beloved brother.'

'He couldn't save him, though.'

'Nobody could have saved him, for what went on there was the devil's business. There was a fire on deck, and much confusion. Still, Harry said, it was a mystery how someone as sure-footed as Edmund could vanish overboard in such a way.'

'He thought it was no accident?'

'He was *convinced* it was no accident. He'd heard the whispers about the other deaths. And here was Jack, one further stepping stone towards the family's fortune. Harry was wise and kept his counsel till the end of the voyage. But when they berthed, he gave your step-uncle the slip and rode home in a blaze of speed. I can remember seeing him pull Liliana after him out onto the veranda. "You won't be safe," he warned. "No, not till you're out of this house and hidden away. That Jack's the very devil and won't rest till you have joined the rest of your benighted family—in death!"'

Thomas was shuddering at the memory. 'Poor Liliana didn't say a word. She was unfit from weeping. But we all knew that she loved Harry. And he said he loved her. So it seemed safest by far for him to rush her away and marry her next day, and keep her safe in some far town.' He pushed his hair back from his forehead as if still panicked at the memory of that grim night. 'You see, we hoped that if the captain thought that it was passion that had made her leave the house, not terror of his wiles, he was less likely to chase after her.'

'And so you tried to make it look as if, even before Harry sailed, the two of them had planned to run away together afterwards! And that's why he'd rushed off the ship!'

'Smart boy. So Martha tumbled Liliana's few possessions into bags and threw them on the cart. And Harry and I fetched down the doll's house because the captain knew she cared so much for it that, if she'd left in anything less than some great storm of hurry, it would have gone with her.' His face turned dark. 'But one of the things that Liliana took away with her that night must have been precious to your uncle—so precious he won't rest until it's back. He chased poor Liliana and Harry until your father was tired to the bone of moving towns at dead of night, and changing names to leave false trails, and never being able to hold to a profession or a friend. And, in the end . . .'

Rather than say the words, Thomas fell silent.

But I was not prepared to let the matter drop. 'So this fine-looking father of mine deserted my mother.'

He tried to soothe me. 'Harry was not a saint.'

'He said he loved her!' I burst out.

'And I am sure he did. But you'll soon learn that when trouble flies in the window, love often chooses to creep out.'

'Then it's not love!'

'Perhaps.' His face changed. Over it spread a puzzled look. 'But there was something else as well. Over the years he had sent word that Liliana was changing. She was becoming cold with him, he said. She had turned stiff and unfeeling.'

'He should have tried a little harder and a little longer!'

'Perhaps he did. But we don't know because his letters stopped.'

'So he had gone! Leaving my mother—and me.'

'Perhaps he didn't realize you were on your way. Certainly we knew nothing of the matter.' Thomas brushed the last leaves off his sleeve. 'But clearly your mother soon did. And looking back, we now believe that it was Liliana's fear for your safety that stopped her sending her beloved Martha any more messages.'

'What, not a word?'

'No. Not a word. And though we waited, always trying to live in hope, we could learn nothing of her whereabouts—or whether she was alive or dead—until, walking behind the captain one day, I heard him muttering about the letter he'd received from Doctor Marlow.'

My head was spinning from the tale. 'What of my father?'

Thomas shrugged. 'A man who leaves his wife is not much prized among his friends and family. We think he started off another life.'

Another life! I felt a stab of bitterness. So Harry Hetherington—my father—had carved out two full

191

lives where I had only had the shade of one.

Yes, only the shade. Because although we'd spent the years cooped up together, it seemed I had not truly known my very own mother. She had not shared a single moment of her past with me. *Everyone* knew more about her than I! To me, she might as well have been some wooden-headed doll, quite empty of the sort of love that will share memories and hopes and fears. She'd cheated me of any knowledge of my own place in the world, down to my own real name. She had preferred bland silence to the truth of who I was, and, for her own convenience, had forced me into living one long debilitating and bedridden lie.

And then, to cap all, she had deserted me! Nobody *murdered* her. She didn't die of fever, like the doctor's unhappy patients. No. She had put an end to her own life simply because she couldn't keep things in the way that suited her.

She'd put her own desires before her duty to her child.

I felt a hand on my shoulder. 'In time you'll come to understand.'

I shook him off. 'I won't! Not ever, no! Both of them made the coward's choice. I won't forgive my father for deserting her, or her for abandoning me. No. Never! Never!'

Breaking free, I ran away from him, down to the river, to follow the track along to the hollow tree in which my mother spent so many of her childhood hours. The smell of leaf mould rose around me like a cloud as I squeezed in. I sat exactly where she must have sat so often all those years ago, on a small rounded lump that formed a kind of seat. And here I pulled out her diary and, in between spasms of tears, I read it through again from first to last, in desperate search of some small proof that this young Liliana had always been a spoiled, selfish person who cared not a jot for anyone around her.

What was I trying to do? Convince myself that she had never merited a single ounce of my love? If so, it was a hopeless task. The diary was studded with things that proved the opposite:

Yesterday Mother decided that Edmund was careless with his letters, and so today she kept him in the house all morning, scraping away with his pen. Jolyon wanted to jump on the veranda steps. But it seemed cruel for Edmund to have to hear us playing happily outside. So I led Jolyon into the raspberry canes, where we spent the rest of the morning playing at tigers in the jungle.

I turned a page or two, only to find:

I found a rabbit with a mangled leg. Thomas said it would be kinder to snap its neck and be done. But I let fly at him, saying I wouldn't trust a single mouthful offered to me under this roof from that day on. So Thomas sighed and laid it carefully in a cage. I hate to watch the poor thing shivering. It longs all day to be free. If only it could understand that its imprisonment won't last for ever!

Then, on the next page, yet another tale of someone else's woe:

Poor Jolly! The tiny fellow woke covered in angry spots, and Martha is insisting he rests in his crib.

He roars and roars, though whether from the irritation of the pox or from the horrid business of being cooped up, no one can tell.

I snapped the diary shut. No, it was hopeless. This was no tiresome, heartless girl going her own way with no thought for others. This was a loving, caring child. So in the end I sighed and slid the little leather-bound book back in my jerkin, ready to leave my mother as the mystery she had become to me and pack my bag.

If I could not make sense of my own past, still I could do my best to build a future.

And I would.

Filled with determination, I went back to the house.

39

There in the open doorway lay my uncle's travelling bag. I hoped to slip past, but he must have seen my shadow on the steps, for out he came. 'There you are, boy!' He pulled me into the house. 'So, Daniel, have you kept this place in order while I was away?' Without waiting for an answer, he drew me closer. 'Why, I believe you've grown another inch since I've been gone.'

'It has been only days, sir.'

'Enough for a bean to sprout!' He thrust me to arms' length and studied my face. 'Your eyes are raw. Have you been *weeping*?' He roared with merriment. 'Did you miss me so much?'

'No,' I said stubbornly. 'Something stung my eye.'

His tone changed. Thrusting his face at mine, he

told me threateningly, 'You'd best take care. More than one thing can sting under this roof.'

And then again he roared with laughter, reeling around under the chandelier almost as though he were dancing with an invisible wife. Where had he been? What had he been about, that he should come back home in such a mix of anger and elation?

Suddenly spinning to a halt, he pointed a finger at me and declared, 'We shall have supper together. Yes! And we shall have it now.'

He reached down for his bag. 'Tell Martha she must root up something to serve at once. I'm as starved as a bear in spring.' As he went up the stairs, he added in a mutter I'm sure he thought that only he could hear, 'And I'm as sick of playing the gentleman as any man can be.'

*   *   *

By the time Martha had laid the food on the table, his mood had changed. He barely raised his eyes as I came in to take my place. I wished him a good evening and picked up my napkin.

Still he said nothing.

As I sat wondering if I dared ask if I'd somehow displeased him, down came his giant hand to make the silver rattle and the plates jump.

'So! Now we play the frightened rabbit, do we?'

'Sir?'

'Staring down at your plate like some waif in a poorhouse. Come, you're a guest under this roof. Sing for your supper!'

So I obeyed. Although my heart was thumping at his rage, I stammered out some tale about my growing skills at archery and bagatelle. I told him how I had been helping Martha in the kitchen, and wandering around the grounds. The whole time I was spilling out my childish news he kept his eyes on me, but still I had the feeling he barely listened to a word. Was he just satisfying himself that nothing had changed and I was still the stupid and unthinking boy he'd left behind some days before?

Or was there something else that chewed away at him?

I couldn't tell. Still, maybe he found the mere sound of my voice soothing, for soon I saw that he'd begun to nod along with things I said. Then he began to prompt me. 'So you've enjoyed the books that you've been picking off the shelves. Then we shall find you more.' 'You took to archery? Then you must let me show you how to sharpen arrow points.' The minutes passed, and gradually I saw that he had slid back into that elated mood I'd seen before, grinning away at me as if each word I said pleased and amused him.

Feeling a little safer, I dared ask, 'And your own business? Did it go well?'

'Go well?' Again the fist came down on the table. 'Why, it could not have gone better if I'd found a pot of gold at one end of a rainbow!' He chuckled. 'Oh, it was well worth the journey.'

Now he was eyeing me with such great mischief that I felt shudders of terror. I couldn't help but think again of that strange face that haunted me through childhood—that illustration in my book of fairy tales which, looked at one way up, was just a smiling girl but, turned the other, showed the wicked stepmother.

Narrowing his eyes, he leaned across the table and added in a dangerous tone, 'And I have spied out a *secret.*'

Martha had said there was an angel on one side of him, a devil on another. I almost saw them as I stammered out, 'A secret?'

He leaned even closer. 'Oh, yes! A secret that someone else would no doubt have preferred to keep.'

My hands were slick with sweat as I laid down my knife. His eyes looked devilish-green as he kept on, 'And, why, I ask myself, would anyone try to keep a secret if he did not hope to cheat another?'

I trembled. 'I'm sure I don't know.'

'Oh, but I'm sure you *do.*'

The clock ticked grimly on. I was as surely gripped by those strange, cat-like eyes as if he mesmerized me in the candlelight. Suddenly I felt the urge to tell him everything. I couldn't bear the weight of secrets any more. I would explain about the doll's house—throw myself upon his mercy, hope against hope that—

The door swept open. There stood Martha, and I shook myself back into sense. How could I even think of helping the captain in his quest to make my life no longer worth a bean? And so we sat in silence as Martha gathered up the dishes that had been pushed aside and left the room. *Tick, tock. Tick, tock.* Pretending my attention was on the apple pie she'd slid in front of me, still every few seconds I stole odd glances at my step-uncle, only to see him spooning up his food in great haste, glowering horribly.

Then, with one last quick grimace of contempt, he threw down his napkin. 'This meal is done. So off to bed with you!'

There was no chance of that, for I was terrified and didn't plan to stay a single moment longer under his roof. The moment I was sure he wasn't following, I hurried to the kitchen where Martha stood as usual, bent over her stained sink, rinsing the crocks.

I came up behind her. 'Martha!' I whispered hastily. 'Wherever the captain's been, whatever he's done or heard, it's changed things. I'm not safe to stay.' I tugged her arm. 'Promise me now that you'll come after me. I swear the Marlows are the kindest people. I know that they won't rest till they've found you and Thomas work and shelter.'

She kept her face turned. 'No point in running, Daniel.'

My panic turned to irritation at her stubbornness. 'You saw his mood at supper! I'll be safer gone.'

She turned to face me. 'Safer? And just how safe is *that*? This is no fairy story, Daniel. Think! Your mother was pursued into the *grave*. This is no petty wickedness you can escape by running off.'

A chill fell over me. 'What are you *saying*, Martha?'

'Daniel, this is some deep, deep evil we are dealing with—an evil that has done for one fine boy after another. And for the sweetest lady who ever lived, and her one gentle daughter. Surely you understand that if you are to live the rest of your life in any sort of peace or safety, you must be rid of what hangs over you.'

I looked into her face, and it was lined with age and anguish. I tried to comfort her. 'You've done your best for me, I know. And I am grateful. But

the man is in some strange and twisted frenzy. I'd
be safer gone—this very night! No! Now!'

40

So off I stumbled in the gathering dark, across the courtyard into the shadow of trees. I didn't dare go down the drive to the main gate. Suppose the captain were watching! So I set off directly for the nearest stretch of garden wall, planning to find a tree that I could climb to drop myself over.

I stumbled down one path after another that seemed to snake the way I wanted through the thickening woods, only to turn on a whim to lead me in some other. But finally, in luck at last, I followed a well-trodden path that ended at the wall.

Or so I thought, until I saw that, hidden beneath a clump of overhanging ivy, there was a door.

I pushed it open. On the other side the path led

on, first through more trees, then past a host of fruit bushes and into a rose walk so old the trellis arches leaned awry. But though the paving underfoot was soft with moss, the roses had been tended carefully, for none of the heady blooms slapped in my face and no thorns snagged as I walked through.

I stepped out onto a narrow path that led to a cottage. Outside on a bench there sat a man, hunched over, whittling wood in the shaft of light that fell from the lamp in his window.

Hearing the rustle of my footsteps, he looked up. 'Daniel? Is it you?'

'Thomas!' I burst out in astonishment, and stopped to stare at the dwelling, so low and squat it looked as if it might have sprouted from the ground. 'Is this where you spend your nights?'

He grinned. 'Why? Does it look to you as if the roof is too much rotted to keep the weather off?' His look turned curious. 'Here's a late visit! I would have thought your uncle would have packed you off to bed well before now.'

'He has.' And, for the first time since I'd seen the captain's bag lying there on the step, I felt a little safer. My heart stopped thumping.

Thomas raised an eyebrow. 'So was it Martha sent you here?'

I shook my head. 'I found the door in the wall by accident.'

'In the dark? After the captain ordered you up to your attic?' Plainly bewildered, he rose to lead me into his little house. And while he pushed a few untidy pots of herbs along the table to make room for his lamp, I peered around at his cosy bed against the wall, his tools hung up in rows, the jug and ewer, and his heap of clothes piled on an old armchair.

I kept as close to him as a duckling would to its mother as he set out his supper. My offers followed one another as fast as raindrops running down a windowpane. 'I'll slice that loaf for you.' 'I'll stir that soup.' 'Let me bank up that fire.'

He found my clinging manner tiresome. 'Sit down,' he ordered me at last. Then he asked outright, 'Were you running away?'

The pitiful attempt at explanation tumbled out. 'I didn't dare to stay—not even to pack my bag or wait to say goodbye! The captain's come back in the strangest mood. His eyes shine, and he wheels about, punching the air in triumph about some wonder that has come his way, some secret he's unearthed. He says harsh things and thumps the table top to make spoons dance, then smiles as if he were the cat and I the mouse, and—'

Thomas put out a hand to quieten me. 'Now, now. No need to take fright at the captain's moods. That's just his way. Whenever his business affairs go right the man is giddy for days.' He made a wry face. 'And when they don't, Lord, how we pay for it!'

'His business affairs?' At once I felt a little calmer. For truly, what had stocks and shares and London banks to do with me? Up till that moment it had never occurred to me the captain could not live only on air, or some small naval pension. Of course his financial gambles and investments would matter to him and, if they went well, he'd be triumphant.

Thomas was grinning now. 'And things must be going well. For years the captain's barely left this house. But, in the last few weeks, we've seen his restlessness growing again, until, this week, he took us by surprise and hurried to the city.' Still he was grinning. 'Whatever business affairs he was about, things certainly must have fallen in his favour, because the moment he was home he called to Martha to warn her that a cart arrives tomorrow. And couldn't we do with that! Martha claims she is almost out of flour and meal, and if I have to crawl much further into the cellar to find a bottle of wine, I shall be nibbled by toads.'

I tried to smile, but Thomas could see the effort fail. He raised the lamp to my face. 'Pale as a grub!' he declared. 'The captain all too easily forgets you're just a boy.' He pulled back the bedcovers. 'You can stay here tonight. You'll be quite safe.'

'Quite safe?' I wailed. 'I fear I won't be safe till he has shaken me to a limp rag to check no secrets fall out of my pockets. But Martha says that if I leave, he'll only follow me.' My tears were flowing now. 'I'm like a rabbit in a cage.'

Thomas said cheerily, 'We have had those before, and set them free.'

He handed me a rag to wipe my face, and sat beside me till my spirits rose and I felt braver. Then he insisted that I take the bed, and pulled the covers over me. 'There's time enough to talk about your future in the morning.'

I knew the only future I could countenance, and thought with longing of the family to whom I was determined to return. Thomas, I knew, could easily be persuaded to leave his morning tasks and walk me safely into Illingworth to catch the earliest train. And so I lay with eyes obediently closed, willing the clock to tick faster through the hours till, soothed by the soft clatter as my tranquil, confident companion moved around the room and damped the fire, I finally fell into a deep sleep.

*　　　*　　　*

I was the first to wake. Thomas still lay, wrapped thickly in a counterpane in the armchair, dead to the world.

In the dawn light, I looked around the cottage.

Over there—in that dark corner! Did I see tiny staring eyes?

I threw the covers off to cross the room and look more closely. Along the top of the oak chest there sat a row of dolls: fat baby dolls in knickerbockers and flounces; tall, stately dolls, and pretty childlike dolls; dolls who were made to be cuddled, and dolls so stiff and stern they looked as if they could be left in any school room and, though made only out of wood, keep perfect order.

When Thomas woke I asked him, 'Did you make all of these?'

He stretched and yawned and nodded. 'I make the dolls and Martha dresses them, and they're sold in the village shop. Sometimes I make them to order. And sometimes I just make the doll I choose to make.' He waved a hand towards the tumble of wooden people on the chest. 'If no one buys it in a matter of months, then back it comes to join my little family.'

Pushing his body stiffly out of the chair, he went towards the range to throw more sticks onto the fire.

As he reached for the bellows I asked, 'Do you

make houses for them too?'

He shook his head. 'The one I made for Liliana was the first and last. Since it could never be matched, I never tried.'

My brain felt as if the jumbled pieces of a puzzle inside were shifting suddenly. Picking my words with care, I asked, 'So was it *you* who made the dolls my mother always said were in her doll's house?'

He looked up, startled. 'She talked to you of those?'

I thought of telling him the truth: not only had she spoken of the dolls, but they were mine. Yet I had kept my secret so well in this house. And if I planned to leave, then it was surely better not to burden this good man with confidences that he'd have to hide.

So once again I spoke warily. 'I know that, when she was a girl, my mother had a peg-thin lady doll . . .'

'The image of your grandmother—though it was wrong of me to carve her as such a starveling, for though we did not know it at the time, she was already halfway to death's door.'

'There was a rosy-cheeked girl.'

'Liliana herself.'

'And a young man with a crown.'

Now Thomas stared in true astonishment. 'How the past vanishes!' he said. 'I had forgotten that she made me carve the Edmund doll a crown.' Now he was smiling at the memory. 'Indeed, the order came so late in the whittling that in the end his glorious crown could be no more than a thin coronet—and that a fragile affair.'

Again I felt the pieces of the puzzle twist, to

take a newer, more disturbing shape. 'What of my step-uncle?' I asked.

Thomas reached for the kettle whispering on the hob. 'What of him?'

'Did he ask you to make a doll for him?'

'Jack? Ask for a doll? He had no mind for games like that!' He poured the steaming water on his bran and mine, adding, 'Though I remember once that Liliana made me whittle a doll to her stepbrother's likeness. It was to be a special gift for the day he was made captain. "A kindred spirit," Liliana joked, "to share his cabin." But then she couldn't for the life of her decide if she wanted me to show him as he'd been when he was younger, or how he was now he'd grown to a man.'

The last of the pieces fell in place. 'And so you whittled both!'

Chuckling, Thomas passed me my bowl of bran. 'Indeed I did. A head at each end, thinking to trim whichever Jack she finally dismissed down to his long thin legs!' He shook his head. 'I spent whole hours on it, week by week. It was a masterpiece.'

Now everything was clear to me. 'And even then my mother couldn't choose!'

'She told you that? Yes, right to the very day Jack left, Liliana was dithering. "Shall I give him the man? Oh, but the boy's so like! Oh, Thomas, I can't choose!" So in the end she gave the doll as it was.' Again he laughed. 'All those hours whittling! All Liliana's fretting! Simply for Jack to lay it by with barely a word of thanks.'

'But,' I said, sure of the whole story now, 'he took it with him, didn't he?'

'In the end, yes.' Thomas scowled at the memory. 'But only to tease Edmund. Just as Jack left the house he snatched it up again and said, "See, Edmund? Even this little man of wood dares come a-seafaring! Next time it must be you!" And then he thrust the little doll into his canvas bag and hurried down the steps.' I watched as Thomas spooned the last scraps from his bowl, then added, 'And yet, for all I know, the first thing Jack did once he was on board the ship was toss it overboard, for neither Liliana nor I ever saw it again.'

41

So I felt braver, now I knew for certain that the Severin doll was what my step-uncle craved. I'd seen the passion in his eyes. I'd seen the way he lost control each time he spoke of the doll's house. I'd been a fool, guessing at hidden wills behind its wallpaper and diamonds in the roses. The captain had no interest in anything except the doll Thomas had carved of him and he'd despised—until the day his ship sailed somewhere effigies were prized, and sorcerers clung to ancient powers.

He would have heard his shipmates' outlandish claims: 'Stick pins in such a doll and you will make its mirror image writhe in agony!'

'Pour treasures on it, and its living twin will thrive and thrive!'

Who wouldn't long for such an easy path to

fortune? On which of his many voyages had he dared carry the little figure ashore and barter with the witch doctor to cast a spell? How much blood had been spilled? How much gold paid? Small wonder it was precious to the captain!

And on the day he sailed away on one last murderous voyage, to tip the last son of the family into a watery grave, what better place to hide the little figure than in a doll's house?

I shivered, chilled to the bone at the mere thought of Captain Severn's fury when he came home to find that Liliana had fled—and taken with her, unawares, the small demonic effigy that had been primed to work its master's will.

My mother couldn't possibly have guessed at its dark powers. But now I realized for the very first time why I had lain in bed for all those years. Because the doll was locked away! Sophie was young enough to look at things without the prejudice of reason. What had she said? 'This doll can make things happen.'

People might say to her, 'Oh, nonsense, child! A doll is just a doll. It has no strength of purpose.' But Sophie had seen things clearly.

Only my mother hadn't understood. Blindly she'd fought to protect me from evil that she sensed was growing around her. Now, at last, things fell into place.

That night I saw her on her knees, whispering a prayer to 'keep safe my precious boy Daniel, and his Uncle Se—' I had misheard. She had been begging for her son to be kept safe *from* his uncle.

And now I realized that all the time this doll lay locked away as though inside a coffin, its poisonous spirit had been quietly seeping into our lives—turning my mother's mind, making her change from the warm, open Liliana everyone remembered into some pale, weak mockery of that malignant little manikin, and causing her to clamp down on my life as if I too had been shut in a box.

But nothing more. For what had the vicar said in church that Sunday? 'Without our help, the devil can make no headway. For him to triumph, we must invite him in.'

And she'd not done that. No. Indeed, her faithfulness and love had somehow managed to weaken the hateful manikin's powers to make another's sufferings mirror its own.

But these were strong. I thought again about the scar across the captain's cheek, remembering Sophie's careless scratching of the doll's face when she attacked the skirts so hastily with a pin. Then, too, hadn't the captain told me how much he longed to leave High Gates—how he despised the place! But the imprisoned doll he so resembled had clearly, over the long years that they'd been apart, held him almost as fast as he'd held me—the victim closest to his hiding place.

And suddenly I felt a very flood of all my former love for my poor mother. All these long months since Dr Marlow made it clear that there was nothing wrong with my health, the image of her face had come to me, over and over, and each time I had had to stifle—

What? Loss, certainly. Misery, too. But something else as well—something as hard and hateful as that small double-headed doll. Resentment. Anger, even. Why, I had wondered constantly, had someone who should have cherished and cared for me—my very own mother!—offered me nothing but a shuttered life, and kept me locked away for no good reason?

The answer was now clear. And I could also understand what had been in mind that day when I held up the thin peg doll that so resembled her and looked into those anguished eyes and whispered, 'What must I do for you?'

At last—at long last—came the answer to that too.

I must forgive her.

And I could.

42

Along with the relief I felt, courage poured into my heart. Oh, I was still determined to leave High Gates. But now it was for quite another reason. I had begun to wonder what mischief the doll was pursuing alone with Sophie. Was she again speaking in horrid voices? Or being forced into her bed?

'Thomas!' I grabbed his arm. 'I must get back to the Marlows. See me safe to the station stop!'

'Come, come!' he soothed. 'What will the family think of a boy who hurries back to them without the shirts they took such care to stitch, and boots that cost so much?'

And so I hurried after him down the path into the old rose walk, telling myself that though my uncle might be puffed with city secrets, he'd not discovered mine. I must be safe. We fell in step, through the door in the wall and then along the path in the woods.

I looked across the lawn. My step-uncle was pacing up and down beneath the portico.

'See?' Thomas said. 'His mind's on more important matters than where you are. He's waiting for the cart. I know his moods, and he won't rest till it's arrived. If you're determined to go, there's time enough for you to cram your few possessions in your bag.'

Again I looked across to my step-uncle as he strode up and down, and it was hard to believe that anyone in such a frenzy of waiting might be distracted.

'Go through the courtyard,' said Thomas.

So I did, and once in the kitchen did indeed feel myself secure enough to make my way along the passage. Now I could see the shadow of my uncle as he paced to and fro outside the open door. I hurried up the stairs and thrust my few belongings into Dr Marlow's bag in such short order that I knew that I'd be out of the house in half the time it would take any cart to spin up the long drive.

I hurried down the attic stairs and along the landing till I reached the door to my step-uncle's room.

Why did I stop? Had I lost all sense? Or was it just that, with the gradual unravelling of this great mystery that had consumed my life, I felt impelled to snatch this one brief chance to see the only portrait in the house—the one I knew would mirror perfectly the most feared half of my step-uncle's doll?

I leaned over the banister, and from the hall I

could hear nothing but the sound of pacing.

So I took my chance. Dragging a chair from the alcove, I climbed on it to dip my hand into the porcelain jug. Yes! There was the key he hadn't realized others with sharper ears might guess he kept in there.

The key turned in the lock and I crept in. Drapes made the room so dark that it was difficult to pick my way across to tug one back. The narrow ribbon of daylight I let in lit up a tide of papers lying carelessly across the floor, a strip of faded wallpaper and there, above, caught in the tail end of the shaft of light, the portrait.

There the captain stood in full dress uniform, the Severin doll, with that familiar face smirking contemptuously as if to say, 'Who would have thought you would be such an innocent as to be fooled by a little white hair?' I knew at once why Martha had spoken of the painting with such bitterness. How well I knew that haughty, taunting and malevolent smile that had tormented me so often over my supper. Indeed, the very sight of it was enough to bring me to my senses and send me flying, first to tug the drapes back into place, then to the door.

The room was now again so dark that I was feeling for the handle like a blind mole. My fingers brushed the coat he had left hanging on the door and touched thin papers tucked inside a pocket.

Each nerve in me insisted: *Go! Get out of here at once!* But still I stayed, to feel around the folded edges.

Opening the door a crack, I listened out again and heard the same impatient footsteps—up,

down, up, down—as I unfolded the pages.
   They were in Sophie's hand.

43

My dearest Daniel,

   What joy to get your letter, and oh, how we've missed you! Since you've been gone the house has seemed so empty and dull. Even games with the dolls have turned into a miserable matter. I swear that hateful Severin doll gets stronger. I leave him out of all my adventures, yet still his horrid nature seeps into the stories. I cram him back in the box and move it further away; but over and again I get the creeping sense his little wooden limbs are twitching there in the dark. And when I lift the lid to check I'm being fanciful, I find him insolently staring up at me as if to say, 'Yes, Sophie. You have every reason to imagine that I am gathering my powers.'

Now terror rose. Not only was the doll at his uncanny tricks again, but I was plunged into the deepest danger. My only hope was that the captain had stuffed this letter into his pocket without the bother of unfolding it and casting his eye over the outpourings which would so quickly have led him to the proof of my deception.

I turned the page.

And things get worse. Yesterday I burst into tears at his foul meddling in my imaginings for Hal and Topper. I raised the box lid, only to find him smirking at me with so much spite that I ran to Cecilia to beg her for pins. And then I hammered him back under the window seat where we first found him. But, Daniel, would you believe it, that very hour he took revenge by making Mother lose her temper over some small tease so that, instead of sending me as usual to shell peas or string the beans, she locked me in my room for the whole day!

So things are horrid and I am miserable. If that mischievous doll is free he poisons all my games. And if he finds himself locked up, then so must I be—out of sheer malice—as if he has the power to punish me with some small shade of what is done to him.

I held the letter away from me and tried to still my thumping heart. Why did she call the doll *mischievous*? The doll was evil. Oh, this was fearful stuff, confirming all my worst fears. I forced myself to read on, skimming the next few lines about some book Sophie had tossed aside, some walk that came to grief, and gossip from the kitchen, to reach the bottom of the page where suddenly the writing broke off.

I turned the letter over. There, in a far more hasty hand, was added:

Oh, Daniel! Such a surprise! A rapping on the door, and Kathleen opened it to find the cheeriest man you ever saw who said he was on business in our town. And only guess! It was your uncle!

My heart stopped. The captain? Truly? So far from London?

So Father invited him to dine. And he has spent the last hour telling us how settled you are, and that you have become an expert angler, and chatter merrily all day, and that the two of you already have become such good friends and companions that you've decided to stay. And though our faces around the table must have shown disappointment, Father frowned warnings at us all to rally and assure the captain that we are glad you're happy. So we have made the effort to persuade him—though I for one have to admit I cannot yet feel anything except my own dismay.

And then the captain said you'd begged him, as he left High Gates, to make the fastest possible arrangement to fetch your precious doll's house.

I had to read the words a second time. But they were clear as paint! So it no longer mattered a jot whether the captain had read this letter of Sophie's through, or thrust it idly into his pocket. The secret he'd so triumphantly unearthed was indeed mine!

219

In deepening shock I read on further through the pages Sophie had added in such haste.

But I accused your uncle, 'That's not the truth you're telling!'

'Sophie!' cried everyone. But I was firm, and told them all how, only a moment before, when Mother sent me to the Kitchen to ask for more redcurrant jam, I'd overheard George the carrier gossiping with Kathleen and Molly. And he was saying that a man with ash-white hair had spent three days striding about the town, seeking out carriers to ask about the clearance of Hawthorn Cottage all those months ago. And George said when he told this man about the doll's house coming here, the stranger's eyes had flashed and he had smashed his fist into his palm in triumph, as if this came as splendid news.

So I knew I was right. How, I asked everyone around the table, could Captain Severn be so astonished and delighted to hear from a carrier that the doll's house was here if, even before he left his own house, he had been begged to fetch it?

Now I was trembling as I read on.

At that my mother and father glanced at one another across the table, both deeply puzzled. But almost instantly your uncle chuckled and said, 'Sophie's a sharp young miss, and I admit she's fairly trapped me in a small deception. Daniel begged no such thing.' He turned to Father and added, 'But I could not help but recall you told me in a letter that all my sister's goods were sold.' (How Father blushed at that.) 'And knowing that

220

she would have kept her doll's house to the very end, I hoped that I could track it down in secret and buy it back to give to Daniel as a grand surprise.'

And so, of course, Mother assured him that the doll's house was yours to keep, and therefore his to take. Then he astonished everyone by saying briskly that the carriers he'd hired to take it with him to High Gates were already waiting outside.

How we all stared. But just then Kathleen hurried in to say that Molly had fallen into one of her faints, burning her hand as she fell. So Father rose, saying, 'Forgive us, Captain Severn. Now we will be in turmoil. Please ask your men to come again in the morning.'

Your uncle wasn't pleased. 'But I've a berth on the night train and would be glad to see this matter settled, and the cart safely on its way.' But Father insisted burns need fast treatment, and ushered Captain Severn from the house, with Mother following, assuring him that she herself would pack the doll box and the furniture safe on the cart along with the doll's house first thing tomorrow morning.

And, Daniel, I can't say that I am sorry. I'll be so glad to be rid of the nasty Severin doll that I won't mind losing Rubiana, Hal and Mrs Golightly—even beloved Topper. It's good to think that within a day or so they will be with you again, if only to remind you of happy hours we spent together. And now I must close because kind Kathleen has promised that if I finish this before she leaves the house, she'll give it to the station master who can press it in the captain's hand before he steps on the train. And here she comes!

The letter ended in a scrawl of signature. But even if she had kept on, I wouldn't have been able to read another word. Terror had frozen my brain. I thrust the letter back into the pocket of the coat and hurried out. I locked the door behind me and dropped the key in the jug, half sick with fear at realizing that, since the moment that the captain spoke to George the carrier, he'd known that I'd been lying.

Worse! My step-uncle now knew that what he prized so much was on its way! Clearly until his heart's desire was in his hand, he'd thought it best to play along with my evasions and deceit. But, once the cart arrived, bearing the doll's house, he would prise up the window seat he had once thought such a safe hiding place—

And I'd be cat's meat! I had no secrets now!

I pushed the chair back into the alcove and leaned over the banister.

The sound of pacing had stopped. *Quick, quick!* I urged myself. *Get out of here at once!*

I took off down the servants' stairs. Reaching the kitchen safely, I pushed at the back door to sneak into the courtyard. At the gate I looked in every direction.

There was no one in sight.

Desperate to find Thomas, I moved into the shadow of the trees and worked my way around the grounds, not daring to call out, just stopping now and then to catch my breath, or listen for the thud of a spade or scrape of a hoe against gravel.

Just as I reached the high beech hedge I saw a shadow move around the curve and turned in time to see the sunlight flash on Thomas's spade as it was carried through the arch into the Devil Walks.

I'd found him!

But where was my step-uncle? Had he lost patience and hurried off to meet the cart at the gates? Or was he spying out on me from some dark place? Determined not to be seen in this, the last few moments before I ran for safety, I took my time to creep around the outside of the hedge.

Then I was through the arch. I raced along the spiralling path, round and round, further and further in, until at last I heard the thud of a spade digging in earth.

So nearly there! On I ran, on and on, until I skidded round the very last tight curve and almost fell out in the clearing's sunlight.

The spade's blade cut into the ground even as I reached out. 'Thomas! Leave that and help me! I'm in the deepest trouble! The secret that the captain has unearthed has turned out to be mine! And I know his! I am no longer safe!'

44

The hand that fell on mine was round my wrist in an instant, as strong as steel. 'Smart boy!' he baited me. 'I do believe that, like your mother, you must have some way to tell your future!'

How could I have been so stupid! I pulled back hard, but Captain Severn held me tight. I looked across the clearing to where the cluster of memorial stones stood in the sun. Then I looked down and saw the first few spadefuls of turned earth.

Into my mind sprang something he had said on our first walk. 'I cannot *wait* to see you in the Devil Walks.'

My blood ran cold. Was the man digging my *grave*? I wriggled fiercely. 'Let me go!'

He chortled. 'Forgive me. But can you truly

believe that I will lay aside my aims, forget my purpose, just because a worthless little sprout like you demands it?'

'*What* aims? *What* purpose?' Still I was struggling, and still his grip was tightening around my wrist.

'Come, now. Back to the house. I have a plan for you.'

'What plan?'

'It's time for you to write a note for me to send off to your precious Marlows.' His grin was merciless. 'The farewell note you kindly wrote to me blessing me for my kindness and telling me that, fired by my fine example, you're off to sea.' Again he chuckled. 'Never to be seen again.'

'I will do no such thing!'

The chuckling stopped. His voice was razor sharp. 'I think you will!'

He gave me a sharp tug. My feet scuffed the moss as he dragged me as easily as he might drag a log back through the Devil Walks. I tried to shout for Thomas, but Captain Severn clapped his free hand over my mouth before the cry was out. Now he was treading backwards round the widening spiral, pulling me after him between the cold dark hedges. Strips of sky spun above as I tried to dig my heels down into the gravel underneath the moss to slow our progress through the Devil Walks.

I fought the whole way to the house. As he manhandled me towards the stairs I kicked out, sending chairs flying and grasping at everything in our path in hopes the clatter would bring Martha to the passage door.

But he was strong enough to lift me bodily. I

might have been a child of five for all the good my struggles did me. Within a minute we were on the landing, and he was pushing me through the attic door onto the stairs.

The bolt rasped as it slid across.

His voice came, barely muffled, through the door. 'There! Kick your heels until I finish my work.'

Digging my grave? His *work*? With one last effort of will I doused the fears that sickened me enough to shout the warning, 'Thomas and Martha already know you for a murderer!'

'What's that to me?' he called back carelessly. 'I'll chain the Walks so well the devil himself won't get inside to see my handiwork, then send those old fools packing. As with the other accidents in this house, they can prove nothing!'

I heard the thud of footsteps down the stairs and hurled myself against the attic door. Small as it was, it held fast. Surely there would be something I could find to beat a way through it? Some heavy lamp stand or some rusty tool?

I rushed into one dusty and neglected attic room after another. But there was nothing but a few old chairs whose worm-ridden legs would serve no useful purpose. I would be trapped up here until he'd finished the black task he'd set himself, then doubled back to force me into writing the letter he would need to cover his tracks.

Then I'd be mincemeat.

What could I do to save my life?

And it was in that self-same thought that my deliverance came. The very words triggered a memory. What had my mother said to Martha once? That if the doll's house was made perfect down to the last trap door, then one day it would save a precious life?

Sophie had made the trap door slide! She'd stuffed our brigand doll out on the roof and made him climb the ancient coils of ivy, down to the ground. The thought of looking down from such a height made my head swirl. But this was not a moment for squeamishness or lack of courage. I had the shortest time to get myself out of my step-uncle's clutches, and if this was the only way it could be done, then I would do it.

Hauling the rickety desk out of my room, I set it under the trap door and climbed on top to see what could be done.

There was no catch. No hook. No bolt. Nothing that I could see to push or tug or lift to slide the hatch across.

Was I on a fool's errand? Desperate, I peered more closely, running my fingers around the edge. Surely if there were any way at all to shift this heavy wooden mass, there would be something to see, something to feel.

And then I noticed it. A hole as tiny as a woodworm's passage. Was there some cunning sort of spring inside? But how to reach it? My little finger was a hundred times more stubby than this hole, no bigger than a stitch in lace.

A stitch in lace!

I dug my hand deep in my pocket. And there it was—my mother's last, most precious gift: the dainty ivory case.

I spilled the tools into my palm. That one? No! This! It could have been made for the task! Balancing myself with care, I raised it over my head and slid it in the tiny hole.

I heard a click. The hatch sprang to the side a finger's width. The job was done! I slid in both my thumbs and pushed.

As if it had been oiled yesterday, the hatch slid back, and I was blinded by a shaft of light that fell through a cracked roof tile.

Now it was just a matter of a leap. The desk beneath me toppled as I kicked out to scramble up. It clattered down the stairs, leaving no clue as to the route I'd taken to get away. I slid the hatch back over carefully, knowing that if nothing over his head looked odd or different, my uncle would be bound to waste at least a few precious minutes going through all the attic rooms in search of me—his vanished prey.

Then I was off, crawling along the splintery joists that lay beneath the rafters until I found that second heavy trap door that led out onto the wide roof.

45

That parapet! It seemed a whole mile high! I could
see all the way across to Illingworth—a better,
braver prospect than looking down.

But I'd no time to hang about, gathering
courage. At any moment my uncle might glance at
the house and see me standing clear against the
sky. So, dropping to my knees, I crawled along to
where I knew the ivy might be strong enough to
bear my weight: right at the end where, all those
years ago, Thomas had carved the thickest of his
pear-wood coils.

The ivy that was sturdy then would surely be as
strong as iron now.

I sat astride the parapet. *Come now!* I urged
myself. *If Simple Jack can clamber down a
beanstalk, then so can you!*

The first few footholds were the hardest to find. My heart banged in my chest. The merest rustle of leaves drowned me in terror. But I kept at it, foot beneath foot, hand under hand. I didn't dare look down—not for a moment! No, I buried my face against the whiskery stems and forced myself to think I was a child from one of my old story books who climbed down trees as easily as he ran over bridges or paddled in streams.

Down, down. I could see casement windows now on either side. They were too far away to reach, but still they cheered me with a sense of making progress. If I kept going, then each minute that passed I would be safer.

So down again. Another foot and handhold. Down, down and down, till I was almost to the ground.

I turned my head to check no one was near, and then I slithered down a little further, till my feet hit earth.

*   *   *

And so I left High Gates through the door in the wall that led to Thomas's cottage. I scribbled a farewell then, rather than cut back round the outside of the wall and risk the captain and his hovering eagles peering out to see me, set off directly across the downs, planning to meet the track to Illingworth beyond the woods, further along the way.

What was I feeling? Terror, certainly. And yet in spite of that, springing inside me was a shoot of happiness. For I was going back! I'd jump the train and buy a ticket from the guard, and sit in perfect safety and content, counting the minutes and hours as I retraced the long, long journey I had never sought to make.

Finally I'd arrive where, from the day I left, I'd longed to be again. I saw it all in my mind's eye as I strode over the downs, setting my path by Illingworth's church spire. I'd hurry up the Marlows' garden path and rap at the door. It would swing open. Here would be a surprise to send poor Molly into one of her faints! I'd watch her mouth fall open in astonishment as I stepped past her into the cool hall. She'd say my name with quite as much amazement as if she'd seen a ghost, and then from every room would run the members of the family. 'Daniel?' 'Can it be you?' 'What joy!'

I would be home at last.

I faltered in my stride. Had I said *home*? How much must have wheeled about if, after these short months, the word no longer conjured up a picture of my mother sitting by my bed in that small room in which I'd languished so long, but a large airy house cluttered with bonnets and ribbons, bursting with merriment and laughter.

Now I walked slower, and absorbed in thought. So much had changed since I first shuffled on the doctor's arm out of my mother's house. I was a different boy. So the old saying's true, I told myself. The way we live will make us what we are.

And that in turn led me to think about my step-uncle. Perhaps the wickedness in him had in itself been born of doing evil—as if it were some sort of muscle he had exercised by all the choices made along his way—until it was his own true self, and he'd become a man who would bring back from all his marvellous travels, not gorgeous silks and

231

spices along with wonderful tales of leaping dolphins and shining minarets, but some stick creature which had been shot through with poisonous magic.

Perhaps . . .

Something drew my attention back. What was that I could see ahead of me? A tiny cloud of dust coming this way from Illingworth—and very fast.

It was a wagon rumbling along the chalky track.

Still thinking it much safer not to be seen, I threw myself behind a slope and watched as it rolled by. And it was by the purest chance that, as I looked back, a gust of wind lifted the heavy cloth to show against the silvered sky that silhouette I'd known for ever and will see in dreams until the day I die.

The doll's house. On the final leg of its long journey.

And even now I can't explain what happened next. It seems to me I must have lost my senses. But I was damned if that vile doll was going to end up in my uncle's hands. It had, I knew, twisted my mother's mind till she kept me entombed. Its black, black shadow fell on everything around it. It made my harmless wooden Mrs Golightly hang awry to presage my own mother's death. It had turned patient, loving Mrs Marlow into a mother who could banish Sophie to her bedroom for almost nothing. For heaven's sake! This vicious, haunted puppet had managed to turn even sweet Sophie's games into monstrosities of cruelty and spite.

Once in my uncle's hands—once evil had joined hands with stronger evil—what might not happen?

I could not bear the thought.

Already I was running after the cart and, with a flying leap, I hurled myself aboard. I threw back the tarpaulin, revealing the doll's house's dusty front. I felt around for the hook and tugged it open, thrusting my hand towards the cushioned window seat in which the foul manikin lay.

Sophie had pinned it down well, so I dug in my pocket for my mother's ivory case. Surely, I thought, two of the tools held together would be strong enough to prise the seat open again.

The wagon bucked and rocked. Twice I was thrown aside, and twice I stabbed my fingers with the tools till the blood sprang. But I would not be thwarted. I stuck the sharp little hooks under the seat top and pressed down hard.

There! It was done. There lay the Severin doll. And I will swear that though its eyes were painted, they fixed on mine with living hatred. Tugging the stiff thing out, I felt a scorching burn shoot down my arm. Then everything around me seemed to chill and darken as if some monstrous cloud had swept across to cut out light and warmth.

The doll was hard to hold. I grasped it tighter and tighter but still the devilish thing seemed to be trying to whip itself out of my grip.

The cart kept rattling on. I tried to hold the doll down on the boards. Was it just stones on the path that seemed to send us flying from side to side, hurling me this way and that? I felt true anger. Yes! This doll could pass its feelings on to anyone around. It was a coiled spring of nastiness. A powerhouse of fury.

But, holding it so tightly, so was I. Its power fed me and I felt my teeth grinding together as I bared my lips and snarled at the strange thing that

233

seethed in my hand, 'Oh, no! You won't defeat me now! I'll stop you struggling! I'll keep you still!'

I thrust it back on the boards with all my strength. But in my haste and fury I'd slammed it down just where my dear mother's lace-making tools lay spilled.

A delicate steel hook spiked through the manikin's heart.

My vision clouded and a bolt of pain ran up my arm and through my body, leaving me breathless. Everything around me shook. I heard a sullen roar, as if some giant soul were bellowing in agony. Under the rocking of the cart it felt as the world itself were heaving angrily; and in an instant I'd been hurled, empty-handed, backwards onto the chalky track.

Sensing a shift in weight, the driver turned in his seat. Seeing me sitting in the dirt, he shook his head as if to say, 'Rude boy, to steal a ride and not give so much as a word of thanks!'

And then, presumably without another thought, he whipped the pony on towards High Gates.

46

I scrambled to my feet. There was no chance of catching up with the cart again before it rumbled through the gates between the hovering eagles. In any case, I longed to run for the train. I stood in indecision. Should I turn this way, or that? To set my footsteps on to Illingworth would be the coward's choice—and in that moment no one in the world felt more faint-hearted than I. But even as I stood there wavering, I seemed to hear the echo of my own harsh judgement on my father and mother: 'Both of them made the coward's choice!'

I had forgiven my mother. But now I realized Thomas had been right about my father too. He'd said one day I'd come to understand how a man could be tired to the bone with hiding from the devil. My father had been faithful and strong for years. Yet here was I, planning to run for safety after the shortest time.

Had I no courage either?

But then another memory sprang to mind, of Dr Marlow in the garden warning me that I'd a whole life's journey to undertake, and must be brave.

And Martha and Thomas had been good to me—and to my mother! How could I sit in a warm railway carriage and watch the downs rolling away behind me without assuring myself that they were safe?

Brave I would have to be.

So back I trudged, scratched, bruised and terrified, along the track until I reached High Gates. I slipped beneath the eagles' outspread wings and into the trees, making my way down all the winding paths that I now knew so well. There was no sign of the cart and, guessing that the captain had ordered it round to the courtyard, I set off that way.

But as I followed the path round towards the arch I saw the front door opening.

Was it my step-uncle? Had I been spotted in the shadows?

No, it was Thomas, staggering out onto the steps and gazing around as if in deepest shock.

What? Was he wounded? Did he have a knife stuck in his back, to make him so unsteady on his feet? His chest heaved and he slumped against a pillar.

Not even thinking that the captain might come after him and stab me too, I raced to his side. 'Thomas! You're hurt! What has he done to you?'

He couldn't speak for panting but he shook his

head.

'Quick, let me look!'

While Thomas fought to cram more air into his lungs, I pushed him forward to run my hands over his jacket, front and back. But I could find no blood-stained tear, no small stiletto hole, and finally I let him fall back once again against the pillar with his legs splayed out.

'Thomas?'

What was that on his face? A grimace of pain?

No, he was *smiling*.

'Thomas?' I begged again.

And finally, his breath back in his lungs at last, Thomas began his tale. 'The captain ordered me away, down to the river to cut logs. But then a wheel on the barrow went awry, so I crept back to make a wedge, and by the purest chance I saw him stride out from the Devil Walks, tossing a spade aside.'

'And you knew why!'

'Only a fool would think the man had spent his time clearing the leaves. Fearing the worst, I followed him towards the house.'

'Where he was after my blood!'

'I had no doubt—indeed, so keen was he to get his black work done, he took the stairs three at a time. I was hard pressed to stay close, and truly you would have thought the thunder of my footsteps up behind would have reached even his stopped ears.' He shook his head. 'But, no! Your uncle was too taken up with thoughts of murder to look behind him and, shooting back the bolt, he disappeared up the last stairs in search of you. I heard his war cry: "Here I come, boy! Your grave's already dug! So! A few lines written in your best hand for my convenience. And then—a sad farewell!"'

Shuddering at the memory, Thomas pressed on. 'I waited, thinking to creep up and spring on him while he was standing over you and forcing you to write. But all I heard was doors slamming, chairs and tables being hurled about and venomous shouts. "What? Have you become a rat, to slip away behind walls? Show yourself, boy!"'

I could not help but say it in some triumph. 'For I was gone!'

Now Thomas shook his head at me in wonder. 'I'd barely dared to hope you knew the secret of the hatch—or had the wits to take advantage of it.'

There would be time enough, I thought, to tell him how my mother's childhood stubbornness—'It must be perfect, down to the last small roof hatch'—had saved my life. So all I murmured was, 'Yes, I was gone.'

Thomas picked up his tale. 'To cause confusion! For when I reached the top of the stairs and crept along to peer through a crack in the door, I saw your uncle standing in bewilderment, muttering, "The cunning brat! He's slipped away. But where? And how?" I watched him smash his fist into his palm and hurry to the window to scour the grounds for any sign of you.'

'You should have pushed him out!'

'If I was tempted, I was soon distracted! For as the captain suddenly leaned out further, over his shoulder I saw a tiny cloud of dust coming along the track over Farley Down.'

'The pony cart!'

'Yes, getting closer. And as it came towards High Gates his sharp eyes must have seen a shape he recognized, because he suddenly cried out, "The doll's house! On its way!"'

'He must have been delighted,' I said bitterly. 'His heart's desire come back at last.'

'More than delighted. He was in a rapture. He threw himself upon his knees as if he prayed in church. "Oh, hurry! Hurry!" he cried. I tell you, Daniel, he might have been a mother calling to the son she had waved off to war a dozen years before. "Hurry!" he kept on whispering. "Come back to me! Oh, hurry!"'

Again I saw myself sitting by Sophie that day in church, hearing the vicar's warning: 'Make no mistake. The devil walks. But he can make no headway unless he has our help. For him to triumph, we must invite him in.'

I stared at Thomas. 'You heard him calling someone—something—to come to him?'

'Daniel, I heard him *begging*.'

My heart began to thump. 'What then?'

'Over his bent back I could see the cart jolt closer down the track. Then suddenly it seemed to sway and, as I watched, a further cloud of dust flew up behind as if some small part of its load were lost. Your uncle let out a fearsome, anguished cry that chilled my blood, threw out his arms and fell with as much force as if a knife had stabbed him.'

I thought again of that sharp little lace-making hook. 'What, in the back?'

'Just so.' Thomas spread his hands. 'Though there was nothing to see. Nothing! And then he started screaming. "No, no! Not me! Not me!"'

I watched as Thomas shuddered. 'There was one last, long, awful, awful writhing. Then he lay still.'

My heart leaped. 'So, is he *dead*?'

'I am no doctor, Daniel. To me he looks like a felled log. I called for help, but with the noise of the cart as it rattled up towards the house, Martha could not have heard. So I have loosed his collar and turned his body over.' Thomas grasped at my hands and whispered, 'Daniel, his eyes stare out as if he sees into the very pit of hell.'

We sat in silence for a moment or two, and then this good man took a grip upon himself and scrambled to his feet. Making as if to shake off some grim memory he knew would haunt him all his life, he slid his arm around my shoulders and told me gravely, 'And I am glad.'

47

The cart was in the yard. Thomas walked up and raised the cloth that hid its load.

As I watched, his expression softened. Pulling a rag from his pocket, he rubbed it over the small portico and round a coil of ivy. 'So,' he said softly. 'Almost as fresh and gleaming under the dust as if I'd made it only yesterday.' Since there was no sign of the carrier, he turned to me. 'It's home at last. Come, help me pull it off.'

Unwilling, I stepped back.

Thomas rebuked me. 'Daniel, the carrier must fetch a doctor to the captain's body. He'll travel faster with no other load.'

So up I reached with Thomas, and together we slid the doll's house to the back of the cart, then, with an intake of breath to aid the effort, lifted it off and lowered it to the ground.

Thomas went off in search of Martha; but the two of them were like two Swiss men in a cuckoo clock for, as he vanished through the kitchen door, Martha came out of one of the courtyard sheds, bearing a bottle of cordial to refresh the carrier.

'The doll's house!'

Thrusting the cordial away on the nearest ledge, she hurried forward, then drew back her skirts as if she'd almost stepped on something precious lying on the cobbles.

I watched her reaching down. She was within a moment of picking up the Severin doll before I gathered wits to shout, 'Martha! Don't touch it!'

'But, Daniel—'

'No! Martha, it's not just one of the old dolls you remember so well. It's *changed*.'

'Changed? How can a doll—?'

But I'd pushed her aside and, reaching out a foot, I tipped it over.

Sticking out from its back, Martha saw something else she recognized.

'What's *that*? Can it be Liliana's lacing hook?'

Her old griefs quickened by the sight of something that had once been so familiar, the blood drained from her face. A bitter sob rang around the courtyard and her shoulders heaved. Her knees gave under her, and though I tried my hardest to hold her upright, down she sank.

Thomas came running. Once at her side, he took one look at me then, clearly reckoning my strength not great enough for the purpose, called to the carrier who, hearing him, peered round the kitchen door and, seeing Martha on the cobbles in a faint, hastily hurried over.

Together the two men lifted her onto the cart.

'Drive her round to the front,' said Thomas. 'The hall is cool. She can recover there. I'll find some bedding she can rest on, and meet you on the steps.'

He vanished through the kitchen door. The carrier whipped the water bucket away from his resentful beast and led it from the courtyard.

I was left alone, staring down at the monstrous thing my uncle had had bewitched and planned to use for all those grasping purposes he'd had in mind when first he brought it home from that strange voyage all those years ago. He and the doll were supposed to work as one. But, with their parting, something had gone wrong. Perhaps because its master was so far away, the little voodoo spirit had grown its own patterns of spite. Its poisonous dreams had worked on my poor mother to drive her mad, then send her to an early grave. It worked on Sophie till her mouth spat horrid voices that were never hers. It worked on all our games, to darken them and spread its shadows of cruelty. Its powers had whipped around in futile wrath, bringing down everyone they touched, and yet achieving nothing.

Small wonder that my step-uncle had banged the table top and gnawed his fists and longed to have it back. Once in his grasp, the evil no doubt would have swung round like a compass, to face his own true north: not just damage and hate, but deep corruption; theft; embezzlement and crooked influence. To what heights might he have risen in the wider world with the doll's help? What awful powers might he have gained? How much destruction might he have unleashed?

243

But mercifully he had died before he'd ever had the time to harness properly the forces he'd let loose and steer them back from scattered devilry into the grander orbit he'd so yearned to command.

He was the snake, felled with his own black venom.

48

Leaving this devilish little thing.

And what to do with that? While I was wondering, I reached down for the doll and tugged at my mother's pretty hook, to free it. But something about the very feel of that vile thing under my fingers struck to the core of me, and I went wild. I shook the doll as if it were some weasel a miser had caught stealing eggs. 'All of this trouble!' I hissed at it. 'All of this pain and misery! These ruined lives! All of it springs from you!'

Then I was given a mortal fright. The monstrous thing had heard me and it understood! I felt it squirm, and knew that, though it was carved in wood, it was alive!

Still, fury spurred me on from simple terror. Surely, I told myself, *some* of the rules of God must stand! And wood will burn!

And so, for all its writhing in my hand, I held it tight and carried it into the kitchen. There I tugged open the range door and thrust the doll into the flames. I slammed the door shut. 'There!' I hissed. 'I know that you came out of hell! So get back there again!'

From inside I could hear the frantic hiss of scorching sap. And then the oven door flew open. I could see the doll inside, writhing so horribly that you would think it was real flesh that burned. I'll swear a wooden stick on fire could never jump and twist like that.

And then the monstrous sprite sprang out. Even before my eyes it sprang out onto the floor!

And there it danced as if in agony, throwing out frenzied sparks, and seeming to screech and whistle in its pain. I look back now and am amazed that I dared stay to watch. That vile thing was as filled with spirit as anything alive. But I was so determined to see the back of it for ever that I think I'd have waited at the gates of hell to watch them swing apart to take it.

However small it was, however scorched and charred, it fought and fought. I snatched a broom, and each time the devilish little fiend tried to escape, I pushed it back into the middle of the flagstone floor.

And there it burned and burned, flinging itself about over and over until the charred bits dropped and burned to ash on the stone. And then the stem of it flared up, first high, then lower, lower. The smell was foul, as if a score of midden heaps were smouldering. Acrid smoke fouled the air till it was hard to see through the cloud of it enough to poke the last few shards of glowing wood back in a pile to burn to the very last.

Then it was gone, and all that lay on the stone floor was one small ashen circle, white as the captain's hair, as if a tiny version of my step-uncle were sinking through the flagstone down to hell.

I turned away, desperate to get outside and ease my burning lungs with good clean air. But then I saw, between myself and the door, a spreading ripple of flame. In its death throes the frantic thing had thrown out enough sparks to set light to the mess of twig and bark beside the log pile.

Even as I watched, the fire spread to rags that drooped from Martha's washing basket, and then, lithe as a snake, blazed up to snatch a sheet that she'd left hanging. Hearing a crackling behind, I spun round again, to see that one of the logs spilled from the range when that foul thing jumped out had set alight a heap of papers on a woven stool, and flames from those already licked at Thomas's jacket.

Racing into the scullery, I wrenched the tap. Only the usual turgid trickle ran from that and so I turned about and jumped the spreading flames to reach the door.

Outside stood the rainwater tub. Beside it lay the bucket the carrier's horse kicked over as he was so hastily dragged away. Snatching it up, I filled it from the tub and ran to the door. Already flames were billowing out. Oh, I tried hard, hurling in water by the bucketful, shouting for Thomas and the carrier all the while, until the water in the tub was gone, and smoke and fumes drove me back. And then, despairing of my own lone efforts, I dropped the bucket and left my post to run and fetch the two men back.

Seeing the sooty state of me, they came at once, and hurried to the courtyard gate. Thomas took one look at the leaping flames, then turned away. 'If we're to lose a battle to save your kitchen or your cook, I know which I choose.'

I stared at his departing back. '*My* kitchen? And *my* cook?'

He called back over his shoulder, 'Whose else?'

Whose else indeed?

I stood a moment while the idea lodged itself inside my brain. Then, while the carrier dragged the doll's house over the cobbles, further from the fire's reach, I raced after Thomas, and between the two of us we guided Martha down the steps and onto the safety of the lawn.

49

The carrier took word to Illingworth. Within an hour the village folk were gathering. Some had come quickly on carts to form a chain with buckets carried from the pump. And others who had made the journey out of curiosity, on foot, were still arriving, fanning out across the lawns to watch the virulent splutters and sparks that greeted them, and talking in high excitement.

I swung my buckets with the best till Thomas came to take my place. 'You're at the end of your strength. Go comfort Martha.'

I worked my way across to where he pointed. On every side, the air was live with gossip. Oh, the things I heard! For Captain Severn had had the blackest reputation for miles around; and had the villagers not known that Thomas and Martha too had spent their lives behind that high stone wall and those forbidding eagles, I do believe they might have travelled to High Gates only to cheer the flames.

And such flames! Orange flares that raged up at the skies. I heard the talk around me:

'See how the fire rises! Such a sight!'

'The chandelier! Hear how each crystal drop explodes like gunshot!'

'Stand clear! There goes another beam!'

'Who would have thought live ivy could burn so fast?'

Part of the roof caved in with an enormous, lasting roar. The crowd around fell silent. What their thoughts were, I can't say. All I know is that, to me, it was as if each pane of glass that blew out, each beam that cracked and dropped, each burning shutter falling on the urns beneath felt like one more snapped bar of the unyielding cage in which I'd lived my fettered life.

Martha was sitting on an upturned barrow, far back from the watching crowd, where Thomas had clearly led her for safety. One shock might well have rushed to take the place of the last over and over in that hour, but still there was a flush of colour in her cheeks, and she looked stronger.

I stood beside her. Neither of us spoke—just watched the fire burn until, hearing men shout, we looked across to see that Thomas and another man had broken from the bucket chain. Along with others he was calling down the line, 'This effort's wasted. Time to step back. There can be nothing of the place worth saving now.'

Lifting his sleeve to rub at the mix of soot and sweat across his face, he walked across to stand on

Martha's other side and squeeze her hand for comfort as, with a deafening crack, more of the roof collapsed into the con- flagration.

Hastily, the crowd surged back, then, as the rain of sparks gradually thinned, crept forward once again.

I think that Martha seized the chance of their distraction to ask the two of us quietly, 'Where is the captain?'

I watched as Thomas pointed up to where the last of the attics blazed.

Again her face turned pale. 'So all the whispers around are true? He's dead?'

'Stone dead.'

Her face showed horror. 'Trapped and *burned*?'

'No, no,' said Thomas. 'It was from apoplexy, some would say.' He glanced across at me. 'Though others might believe that he was felled by his own black wrath.'

Still she was baffled. 'Way up there?'

He scowled. 'Up there. And not just up there. Up to no good there! And by the time there was no more to do to try to save the house, it was too late to get back up the stairs and drag his body out.'

It was a moment before Martha spoke again, and when she did I saw that she was pointing to the flames whose licks of light danced over all our faces. 'And this—this fire? How did it come about?'

Thomas grinned. 'Ah, now,' he said, 'for that you must ask after Daniel's fresh idea for kindling.'

Martha turned my way in astonishment. 'So it was *you* who set the house on fire?'

I answered ruefully, 'With a little devilish help.'

251

And then, in fits and starts, in between showers of sparks, I told the story, first of my struggle with the Severin doll up on the cart, then of its frantic fight with me down in the kitchen. It took time in the telling, for I'd so much to explain about the secrets I had kept and things I'd known; and when I'd done, all that the two of them could do was stare at me and shake their heads in wonder.

Martha looked back into the roaring flames. 'And so the pattern lasted to the bitter end. The captain's body shared the foul doll's fate.'

We all fell silent as we watched the great house burn. And, in my heart, I could feel nothing but relief.

50

By morning there was nothing left of High Gates but a spread of orange embers licking round the last few blackened timbers.

Thomas kicked one of the smouldering piles apart. 'I sometimes think,' he said, 'that it is only fire that knows how to leave behind the past and face the future cleanly.' He turned to ask, 'Will you rebuild?'

'With what?' I asked him ruefully. 'The few coins in my pocket I aim to use to buy my ticket home?' I seized his arm. 'Will you come with me? Will you bring Martha with you?'

He shook his head and chuckled. 'Martha and I are not like you. We're far too old to start our lives again.' He ground his heel into the soft earth we were standing on. 'But, with your permission, she and I can make a living on this land.'

With my permission? Another strange reminder that all these pretty ripples of flame that he and I had stood, as if bewitched, watching all night, belonged to me. So did the spluttering ashes, the heaps of blackened stone and all the woods behind.

Could I live here in peace and happiness?

Perhaps some day. Far in the future, maybe, when I had earned enough at the doctor's trade to pay for laying one stone on another till I had built a house fit for the wife I hoped to find, the children we would have. Children who'd tumble around these gardens as happily as Liliana and her brothers had before Jack Severn came. Children who'd scramble in and out of hollow oaks, and fire their arrows in the air, and tangle the nets over the raspberry canes, playing at tigers.

With Thomas at my side, I wandered one last time around the grounds. Was it an accident that led us to the Devil Walks? Together we walked round the spiral until we reached the clearing.

There stood my grave, fresh dug.

'A lifetime early,' Thomas said dryly, and took to kicking heaps of soil back in the hole while I strolled between the stone reminders of my lost family and my past, running my fingers over the mossy stones. Perhaps, I thought, I will lie here one day. But right now I'm in need of a bright future more than any past.

I turned to Thomas. 'Do what you want,' I told him. 'Do what seems best to you.'

He laid a hand flat upon Edmund's stone. 'If I did that,' he said, 'I'd raze the Devil Walks down to the ground.'

I had a thought. 'And grow a maze in its place?'

'A fine idea!' he told me. 'And by the time it's tall enough to please a child, you may be back with some.'

We stood in silence. Perhaps he thought of Liliana and Edmund, and all the others in his past. But I could think only of days to come. I could think only of the family I longed to see, the family who took me in as keenly and as warmly as if I were their son and brother. The family to whom I would return, whose name I'd ask to take to start my brand-new life. The family with whom I'd learn my trade, and grow into a man.

The family I'd love as dearly as if they were my own.

I felt his hand on my back. 'Come. Let me walk you to the morning train.'

Together we strolled back between the hedges and out onto the sadly trodden lawn, half black with smuts. I said goodbye to Martha with a long hug, then turned to take one last look at the smouldering embers.

'We'll send the doll's house after,' said Thomas.

Without a thought for Sophie, 'No!' I begged. 'It holds too many memories for me now.'

I watched him turn and stare at it, still lying where the carrier had pulled it safe from the gathering fire.

'And for me too,' he said at last, and hurried over to it, as if to think too long about the task would make it harder.

I went after him. Together we dragged the doll's house into the receding tide of burning embers. It sat there longer than I thought would have been possible before a single tiny wooden rose beside the portico exploded into flame.

And then another.

And another, till it was fully alight.

Did I regret destroying the very last token of my mother's childhood? The last link with the past?

No. For I suddenly remembered the morning I'd stood at my mother's grave and read on her memorial stone the words Dr Marlow chose for her—almost as if they were a promise:

Until the day breaks, and the shadows flee away.

Well, if it was a promise, I'd kept it for her. Now her son was safe, with people who would love and care for him. And he had learned enough about his mother's nature to know she must have done her very best to love him. That wooden and unbending heart had not been hers, and she could be forgiven for my strange, joyless childhood.

Everything had changed. And she could rest in peace.

Thomas stood close, his arm round my shoulder for comfort as, together, we watched the delicate carved ivy shrivel and the tiny roof tiles flare.

Gone. Gone.

As I myself would be, on the next train, back to the happy and useful future I could now foresee.

*This book is dedicated to the memory of
David Brazil, colleague, friend and
fellow-traveller.*

Thanks

Many people contribute to the final shape of a published book, but particular thanks must go to the following:

The several years of undergraduate and MA students at the University of Nottingham who have helped us collect the data, worked with it and given us invaluable feedback on the transcripts, especially Freya Williams, Jodie Looker and Helen Herbert. Several MA groups at the University of Valencia in Spain who have tried out the units in this book with us and offered unfailingly constructive criticism. The long-suffering teachers of the annual ICC seminars at Chorley, Lancashire, who have been the guinea-pigs for more than one of our books, and who have also always given invaluable feedback. Jean Hudson and Julia Harrison, who have worked with us in the corpus team at Nottingham and provided outstanding technical as well as intellectual support. Ann Collins and Gill Collett, who have helped with editing the manuscript. Colleagues past and present and other scholars who have contributed their opinions and advice, especially Keith Mitchell, the late David Brazil, John Sinclair, Antonia Sánchez Macarro, Tony Fitzpatrick, Geoff Tranter, Rebecca Hughes, Mike Mackosch, Roger Smith, Martha Jones, Michael Lewis, Almut Köster, Bethan Benwell, Nurdan Özbek, Mario Rinvolucri, Luke Prodromou, Michael Goethals. Jeanne McCarten and Colin Hayes of Cambridge University Press for their continuing support of the CANCODE project and the research, the books and other products which emanate from it. Geraldine Mark for being the most efficient and pleasant editor we have worked with. Anne Colwell and Linda Matthews of the design and production teams at Cambridge University Press who manage to transform dull paper into a real book, Nóirín Burke, Cambridge University Press editor, who has liaised with us throughout in a patient and friendly manner. Jane Carter for providing moral support in the book's darkest moments. Finally all the many relatives, friends, neighbours, students and complete stangers (to us) across Britain whose willingness to be recorded and have their words reproduced has contributed to making the CANCODE corpus and this book a reality.

Ronald Carter
Michael McCarthy

29 February 1996

Ronald Carter is Professor of Modern English Language, and Michael McCarthy is Professor of Applied Linguistics, both at the Department of English Studies, at the University of Nottingham.

Acknowledgements

Book design by Anne Colwell
Illustrations by Sarah McMenemy
Cover illustration by Sarah McMenemy

Contents

Section F   Debate and argument

Extracts in which people take up positions, pursue arguments, expound on their opinions on a range of matters.

Section G   Language, learning and interaction

Language in an institutional sense and in the context of learning.

Section H   Decision-making / negotiating outcomes

Extracts in which people work towards decisions/consensus or negotiate their way through problems towards solutions.

Introduction

This book explores authentic examples of contemporary spoken English. Its main aim is to provide learners and students of English with the opportunity to see, hear and understand conversational English in a range of different contexts of use. During the past ten to fifteen years there has been an explosion of interest in the analysis of extended stretches of spoken and written language, and increasing reference to and use of real language in English language teaching materials. To the best of our knowledge this book is the only publication since Crystal and Davy's *Advanced Conversational English* (1975) · to collect such extensive samples of naturalistic conversational data and to describe and comment on that data in ways which will be of maximum value to teachers and students of English. And in several important respects *Exploring Spoken English* breaks new ground.

Spoken English Data

There is spoken English and there is spoken English. During the 1990s there have been a number of projects designed to collect large quantities of spoken data. Such projects (see, for example, Crowdy 1993; Rundell 1995a & 1995b) have involved sophisticated computational technologies and methodologies and will continue significantly to inform pedagogic projects, particularly in the field of learners' dictionaries of English and related lexicographic materials development.

However, it is one of the paradoxes of spoken data collection that the more interesting and valuable the data, the more difficult they are to obtain. It is important therefore that too much data are not obtained from a single category of talk; for example, large quantities of broadcast talk can be collected relatively easily by recording TV and radio output and it is similarly relatively unproblematic to record lectures, discussions, meetings in formal settings or speakers narrating or reporting straight into a microphone. Such data is unlikely to be representative of typical conversational interaction if speakers always know that they are being recorded or have too many opportunities to plan or to rehearse in advance what they are going to say and how they are going to say it.

The data in this book are drawn almost exclusively from a research project based in the Department of English Studies, at the University of Nottingham, Great Britain, and funded with the support of Cambridge University Press, the publishers of this book. The project has been named the CANCODE project (Cambridge-Nottingham Corpus of Discourse in English). The data-base for the CANCODE project consists of five million words (as of 1996) constructed mainly from spontaneous, everyday English speech in a variety of social contexts and interaction environments. The speakers reflect a full social, cultural and geographical range (within the British Isles) with samples which are also representative of age and gender differences. The corpus is designed to enable the study of spoken discourse in general, and spoken grammar in particular in relation to different genres of speech. Although it is the most difficult to obtain, the emphasis is on informal speech genres rather than on more formal varieties. This is a dimension which has not always been prominent in previous projects. For example the data collected in Crystal and Davy's *Advanced Conversational English* are largely personal anecdote and monologue in form; in this book we have collected data which are monologue and dialogue in form (though mainly dialogic) and which contain examples in which participants engage in both symmetrical and asymmetrical conversations. That is, in some units speakers are equals and in other units they have encounters in classrooms, restaurants or shops in which different social relations obtain.

Speech genres

This is not the place to articulate a fully formed theory of speech genres and, indeed, a more detailed illustration can be found in McCarthy and Carter (1994: ch 1). However, it is important to recognise that different types of talk produce different types of language and that the broad distinction between formal and informal or between public and private conversational discourse is not the only categorial distinction. In this book we have assembled CANCODE data from a variety of sources and we demonstrate, for example, that a key grammatical structure such as situational ELLIPSIS, which is particularly associated with informal English, occurs in most genres but not very commonly in **narrative** genres; we demonstrate that in **service encounters**, stretches of conversation often rely very heavily on DISCOURSE MARKERS; we demonstrate that in **language-in-action** genres there can be extensive interaction without reference to the main objects in front of the participant and with a constant reliance on DEIXIS such as *this* and *that* and *here* and *there*.

Genres are episodes of speech of which participants (if interaction is successful) have a shared view of their nature as social encounter. Hence, after a conversation, we can usually say, with confidence, things such as 'Jo told me an amazing story', or 'Oh, we just chatted about this and that', or else 'We had a bit of an argument'. Equally, we reflect our frustration at unsuccessful engagement in genres with remarks such as 'It was more like an interrogation than an interview', 'I didn't realise it was just a joke ... I thought it was a true story', or 'It was a very one-sided conversation'. Genres vary in the surface grammatical manifestations such as ELLIPSIS and DISCOURSE MARKERS, but these merely mark the socially-determined differences of purpose, degree of shared knowledge, institutionalised 'rules of speaking' (e.g. in classrooms, debates, etc.), roles and relationships between the participants, and so on. Finally, we bring to every genre our previous experiences in that same genre; every genre carries its own history with it, and there is a constant historical tension between the repetition of experience in encounter after encounter, and the freshness and uniqueness of each new conversational encounter.

The CANCODE project has from the beginning attempted to obtain data in a range of different genres so that a wide range of contextual features can be seen to influence the talk, and research can therefore pinpoint differences between different forms of language and the types of conversation conducted. Such a principal design feature is felt to be of especial value and benefit to learners of English who above all need to appreciate the kinds of choices of language available in different contexts. If there is an insufficiently sharp differentiation between different varieties of talk then learners are unable to develop any real sensitivity to which forms of language create which meanings (and, crucially, which sorts of social relationships) for which purposes and in which situations.

Most importantly, too, such a project design allows insights to be developed concerning differences and distinctions between spoken and written language use, with particular reference to grammar. The major contemporary grammars of the English language are largely based on written examples; the new data are exemplifying common, 'standard' patterns of use alongside patterns more familiar from written-language-based grammar. For example, new data, illustrated in this book, reveal key interpersonal functions in the use of tense, modality, ellipsis, deixis and clause structure; the crucial role of spoken discourse markers, acting as a kind of conversational punctuation, is also illustrated. Additionally, variations in canonical (written) word order can be shown to be common across a wide range of genres of speech.

Note on language and gender

The CANCODE project has tried to keep a good balance of the genders (as it has done of social classes, geographical distribution and age-groups). We have tried to do the same in this book, with 32 adult female speakers and 28 adult males, though it has been impossible to match the numbers exactly. Much debate has taken place as to whether there are differing styles of discourse between males and females, and whether males, for instance, unfairly dominate talk, interrupting more than females. The transcripts in this book present no firm evidence of differences of these kinds. For example, features such as HEDGES and TAGS (sometimes thought to be 'female' characteristics) are used by both genders (see for example the table of TAGS in Unit 4). However, users are invited to approach these transcripts with a view to observing gender-distinguishing features if they are present, and to analyse the texts in a way that is beyond the scope of this book. The authors certainly do not view themselves as experts in the field.

The design of the book

There are twenty units in this book and there is a balanced distribution across a range of speech genres. There are eight main genres as follows:

Narrative: A series of everyday anecdotes told with active listener participation.

Identifying: Extracts in which people talk about themselves, their biography, where they live, their jobs (or job aspirations), their likes and dislikes.

Language-in-action: Data recorded while people were doing things such as cooking, packing, moving furniture, etc., where the language is generated directly by the actions being carried out.

Comment-elaboration: People giving casual opinions and commenting on things, other people, events, etc. around them and in their daily lives, without any set conversational agenda.

Service encounters: Extracts in settings involving the buying and selling of goods and services.

Debate and argument: Data in which people take up positions, pursue arguments and expound on their opinions on a range of matters, with or without some sort of lead-figure or chairperson.

Language, learning and interaction: Language in use in the context of institutionalised and informal learning.

Decision-making/negotiating outcomes: Data illustrating ways in which people work towards decisions/consensus or negotiate their way through problems towards solutions.

There is no claim to comprehensiveness here and other speech genres could have been included. It is further recognised that no speech genre can be entirely discrete; for example, **narrative** is such a core genre that narratives can be embedded within other main generic categories, and overlap occurs between and across other genres. The genres represented in the book are, however, important genres for speaking in use in educational and pedagogic contexts and towards conversations involving students in ways with which it is hoped language learners will be able to identify.

Using the book

The book is designed as a practical guide to the study of spoken English and can be used in the classroom or for self-study purposes. Each unit begins with a task which normally involves students in an activity-based exploration of some aspect of language; however, completion of the task is by no means essential. Each unit provides a brief description of the social setting and the participants, and includes detailed commentary on the transcript(s) with line-by-line notes pointing out significant linguistic and related cultural features. Useful references are provided at the end of each unit for readers who are interested in further analysis and research.

It should be recognised that the commentaries are by no means exhaustive. While aspects of pronunciation and intonation are noted, such an orientation is not a main focus in this book. Instead there is a particular concentration on those aspects of grammar, vocabulary and discourse patterning judged to be of significance for learners of English. However, even though there is no explicit guidance, the accompanying tape allows students and, where appropriate, their teachers to explore the articulation of the text in phonetic and phonological terms.

The provision of a tape has presented us with problems. As we noted above, it is a paradox of the study of authentic, 'real', spoken English that the clearer the quality of the recording the less likely it is that the tape will have been produced in completely naturalistic conditions with the speakers interacting unselfconsciously. From the pedagogic point of view of English language learning it is obviously important that the tapes should be as clear and undistorted as possible; yet at the same time it is important that exposure should be to data which is as natural as possible. Accordingly, we have left as many of the tape-recordings as possible in their original form even if some remain difficult to decipher. Where, on account of the impossibly poor quality of the recording, learners of English may have real difficulty in studying the text in relation to the tape, we have undertaken to re-record the tape using actors. However, the actors have themselves listened extensively to the original recordings and based their own versions faithfully on the originals. For Units 4, 6, 7, 10, 11 and 12 both the original recordings and the re-recorded versions have been included on the tape.

The book also has a glossary of terms. An explanation of the terms in SMALL CAPITALS can be found in the glossary. The fields of discourse analysis and conversation analysis have expanded rapidly in recent years and the glossary provides an opportunity to introduce definitions and exemplifications of new terms. It also allows an opportunity to redefine some grammatical and related terms in the light of their provenance within particular speech genres and according to their actual grammatical use in a range of different contexts. The glossary is not exhaustive but concentrates and elaborates on the terms used most frequently in the commentaries.

The units may be studied in any order and are not graded for difficulty.

Audience for the book

The intended audience for this book includes: teachers and teacher trainers (both native and non-native speakers of English), undergraduates and postgraduate students of language and linguistics, advanced learners of English as a second or foreign language, materials developers, language researchers, especially in the fields of grammar, vocabulary and discourse analysis and A-level English language students.

Glossary of important terms

Adverbs

Adverbs are a major class of words. Many adverbs are adverbs of manner such as *quickly* and *happily*; other adverbs (such as *extremely* or *rather*) operate as intensifiers and modify adjectives; others express place (*here*) and time (*now, afterwards*). Adverbs also occur as adverbial phrases or adjuncts (e.g. *in a moment, in the corner, with pleasure*). In spoken English certain adverbs play an important part in marking these relations but also in modifying whole propositions so that words like *basically, usually, literally, possibly, certainly, of course* are used frequently by speakers to indicate personal attitudes and judgements.

Back-channel

This refers to noises (which are not full words) and short verbal responses made by listeners which acknowledge the incoming talk and react to it, without wishing to take over the speaking turn. Typical back-channels in English are *Mm, Uhum, Yeah, No, Right, Oh*, etc. In our transcripts they are shown as occurring during the speaker's turn, though sometimes it is difficult to distinguish between back-channels and full speaking turns, and the decision to transcribe one way or the other is ultimately subjective. Here is an example with back-channels from speaker <S 02>, shown within square brackets [ ]:

> <S 01> Oh yes, yes, yes mind you my parents were really quite well-off when we lived in Ireland but the education in England was very expensive [<S 02> mm] and I can remember my mother had jewellery and silver and she used to keep selling it [<S 02> Really] to pay for our extra music lessons and tuition in this and that [<S 02>Mm] and er I it was, must have been difficult

Binomials

Binomial expressions are a sub-category of FIXED EXPRESSIONS. As the term suggests, they occur in a paired relationship and are fixed in that the order of the words cannot normally be altered or reversed. Examples of binomials include: *spick and span*; *ups and downs*; *swings and roundabouts*; *cash and carry*; *hit and miss*. Such expressions occur in both written and spoken discourse but are more extensive in spoken English (see McCarthy and O'Dell 1994, unit 77, for more examples and exercises). Trinomials also exist (e.g. *ready, willing and able*; *this, that and the other*; *morning, noon and night*), with three elements, but these are much rarer than binomials.

Deixis

This term describes what may be termed the orientational features of language as deixis involves words which point backwards and forwards in a text as well as outside the text to a wider extra-textual context. For example, words like *these/that/this/those* locate an utterance in relation to space and to the speaker's sense of closeness or involvement with something, words like *now* and *then* relate to the current moment of utterance and words like *we/you/they/him/I* relate to who is speaking, who is present, included, excluded, etc. Thus, 'I'd like to pop in to that little shop over there before we leave' contains deictics which orientate a listener interpersonally, temporally and spatially in relation to the proposition of the sentence. Certain contexts of language, such as language used to do things like packing, cooking, moving furniture, etc. involve a lot of deictics because the objects and other phenomena being dealt with are normally immediately visible to all speakers and thus forms of language such as 'Could we just move that into this corner here?' are relatively commonplace.

Delexical verbs

In general, the more frequent a word, the more likely it is that it combines with other words and that it therefore has less independent meaning. For example, the primary function of many common verbs such as *have* or *take* or *give* is to carry other nouns and adjectives: for example, *take a long walk*, *have a swim*, *have a good look*, *give someone a ring*. Delexical verb combinations such as these are common in informal language and in spoken discourse in particular.

Discourse markers

Discourse markers are words or phrases which are normally used to mark boundaries in conversation between one topic or bit of business and the next. For example, words and phrases such as *right*, *OK*, *I see*, *I mean*, help speakers to negotiate their way through talk indicating whether they want to open or close a topic or to continue it, whether they share a common view of the state of affairs, what their reaction is to something, etc. In telephone and other conversations the discourse marker *anyway* usually serves to indicate that the speaker wishes either the current stretch of talk or the whole exchange itself to be brought to a conclusion. In much informal talk the word *like* can be used to signal that some kind of exemplification is to follow. In conversation in general phrases such as *you know* or *I mean* or *you know what I mean* serve to check understanding and to soften and personalise the interactive style, keeping the listener(s) involved and on the same wavelength. *Right* often serves to indicate that participants are ready to move on to the next phase of business.

Discourse markers do not primarily carry information or propositional content and have, as a result perhaps, been regarded as examples of careless or lazy speech. For example, the word *then* can frequently signal the closing of a stretch of talk and have no obvious connection with the temporal meaning of *then*. However, all speakers use them to perform the essential task of structuring what they say and of signalling to their listener(s) how they wish it to be taken. Such is the importance of signalling and signposting discourse that speaking turns can sometimes consist entirely of a discourse marker or markers. For example:

A: OK then?
B: Right.
A: That's it then.
B: Fine.
A: Bye.
B: Bye.

Ellipsis

Ellipsis is pervasive in spoken discourse. It occurs in writing but functions textually to prevent repetition where structures would otherwise be redundant. For example, in the sentence 'We ran for the bus but missed it' where it is clear that 'we' remains the subject of both clauses; or in the sentence 'The chair was broken and the table too' where it is clearly unnecessary to repeat the verb phrase 'was broken'. Ellipsis in spoken English is mainly **situational** (i.e. affecting people and things in the immediate situation), and frequently involves the omission of personal subjects, where it is obvious that the speaker will remain unambiguous. This feature is especially common with verbs of mental process: for example, *think so, wonder if they'll be coming to the party, guess they won't be ringing after all* (with *I* omitted in each case), and so on. Such ellipsis also occurs with main or auxiliary verbs where meaning can be relatively easily reconstructed from the context. For example:

A: What's the matter?
B: Got an awful cold.   (ellipsis: *I've*)
A: Just seen Paco.   (ellipsis: *I've*)
B: Did he say anything?
A: Nothing.
B: Interesting isn't it?   (ellipsis: *It's*)

Ellipsis only rarely occurs in this form, however, with modal auxiliary verbs so that, while pronoun subjects are omitted, the force of the modal is normally retained (e.g. *must be difficult, might be the right thing to do*). Several elliptical structures are almost FIXED EXPRESSIONS, occurring as frozen lexical routines (*sounds strange, seems worth it, absolutely right, good job you did that* and so on).

Collectively, ellipsis of this kind is situationally rooted but is not random. It occurs across many speech genres and in almost all cases marks a degree of informality between speakers. Ellipsis of this kind is especially prominent in service encounters so that a perfectly normal utterance can be to ask for 'two first class [stamps] please' in a post office or ' [a] cheeseburger, please' or 'two ham and one cheese [sandwiches]' in a restaurant, and without the speaker feeling it necessary to include a phrase such as 'I'd like' or 'Could I have', though such a choice always remains possible and could impart a greater formality or possibly politeness, if the speaker wished to communicate this.

Fixed expressions

The term **fixed expression** describes language which is in some way preformulated or prefabricated, that is, language forms which are routinised and patterned. A significant proportion of all language comes into this category and, indeed, speakers would find it difficult to communicate if everything that was said had to be inventive and original. Fixed expressions play an important part in spoken language in particular in maintaining and stabilising relationships and in reinforcing shared knowledge and social conventions, and referring to common cultural understandings. Examples of fixed expressions include: *as a matter of fact, once and for all, at the end of the day, a good time was had by all, honesty is the best policy, carry the can, an open-door policy, as far as I am concerned*, as well as proverbs, quotations or cultural allusions such as 'A rose by any other name (would smell as sweet)' (a reference to Shakespeare's play *Romeo and Juliet*, Act 2, Sc. 2, l.43).

The expressions have varying degrees of fixity, some being collocationally fixed (e.g. *a fat salary*), some operate within frozen syntactic patterns (e.g. *have forty winks*), and some are quite fixed in discourse position or are semantically indecipherable (e.g. *carry the can* which means 'to carry responsibility'). Other fixed expressions allow greater internal modification and are more 'open' forms syntactically, lexically and discoursally (e.g. *take a chance*, which could occur as *I took the first chance I got*).

Fronting (or front-placing)

Fronting refers to the movement of an element from its 'canonical' position and its relocation as the first element in a construction. Taking the sentence 'I dedicated my life to that man and his music', we can front the indirect object as follows: 'To that man and his music I dedicated my life'. The process allows a focus or emphasis to fall on the fronted element (see also **Heads**).

General words

General words allow vague and indefinite reference. In the following examples the words *thing* and *business* are general words:

> The video's broken down again. That thing's driving me mad.
> The neighbours are complaining about the noise. I don't want to get involved with that business.

General words are normally nouns and are a subcategory of VAGUE LANGUAGE. General words enable a speaker to express attitudes and feelings without needing to locate an exact or precise referent. They are widely used in spoken discourse and as general words *thing* and *stuff* are among the most frequent words in spoken English. They frequently have an evaluative feel to them (as in the examples above).

Heads (or topics)

Heads perform a basically orienting and focusing function, identifying key information for listeners and establishing a shared frame of reference for what is important in a conversational exchange. Heads are a subcategory of FRONTING and normally involve placement at the front of a clause of a noun(s) or noun phrase(s) which anticipates a structure which then forms the main subject of the clause. Heads are in *italics* in the following examples:

> *That chap over there*, he looks like your brother.
> *This friend of ours, Carol, her daughter*, she decided to buy one.
> *The women in the audience*, they all shouted in protest.

Heads are almost exclusive to informal spoken English. They parallel TAILS, although tails generally serve a much more affective purpose.

Hedges

Hedging is a general term used to describe the strategy when a speaker or writer wishes to avoid coming straight to the point or to avoid speaking directly. Hedging can include the use of a wide range of language, including VAGUE LANGUAGE. Hedges occur commonly when a speaker expresses an opinion about somebody or something:

> He was *kind of* begging us to write but I *probably* won't do it.
> *Well, I mean*, I have, *you know*, never *actually really* liked her as a teacher.
> She was *sort of somewhat* mixed up in her feelings about him.

The hedges (in *italics*) allow speakers to personalise or otherwise soften the force of what they say, all in different ways, either because they have no wish to sound definite and authoritative, or because they believe the speaker not to be fully acquainted with their propositions or, very simply, because they do not know or are searching for the right word or expression. In most cases there is sensitivity to 'face', either for purposes of self-protection or because the speaker does not want to put the listener(s) or reader(s) in a face-threatening situation.

Hedges and modality in language are closely linked. Many modal verbs contribute to hedging (e.g. *may, might, could*) and there is an extensive range of adverbs which mitigate the force of what is written or said: for example, *perhaps, probably, generally, normally, slightly, basically, at least.*

Interactional

Interactional language is language which is primarily personal and social in orientation. Its effective use normally allows social and interpersonal relations to be maintained. In some contexts, such as service encounters or even sometimes in formal interviews, it is combined with TRANSACTIONAL language to soften and make less forbidding the business of getting certain tasks done.

Tags

Tags are described as strings of words consisting of an auxiliary verb and a pronoun with or without 'not' which are normally added to a declarative statement. The polarity of the tag is sometimes the reverse of that found in the main clause, that is, a positive clause takes a negative tag and vice versa. The following examples of tags (in *italics*) all meet this broad definition:

> Frascati's nice, it's nice to drink *isn't it?*
>
> She's a lovely girl *she is.*
>
> A: Have you noticed it always disappears?
> B: Yeah, it does, *doesn't it?*
> A: I've got two now, yes, it does always disappear *doesn't it?*
> B: Yeah right
>
> He isn't coming *is he?*
>
> Sound really bossy *don't I?*

In these examples there are also other features of tags to note, particularly in the longer extract: there is a general clustering of tags, together with a repetition and re-statement of propositions in tag-like forms; and words like *right* are, as it were, variants on tag forms. In the second example, two positive clauses are found together. Such forms do not necessarily demand a reply; instead they often serve just to establish a shared, mutual view of things. All the above data are taken from informal conversational interchanges. Tags are an essential feature of grammar in use in informal and intimate contexts of interaction and are particularly appropriate to contexts in which meanings are not simply stated but are negotiated and re-negotiated.

Tails

The term **tail** describes the slot available at the end of a clause in which a speaker can insert grammatical patterns which amplify, extend or reinforce what (s)he is saying or has said. These may be TAGS of the type exemplified above, or full noun phrases. Examples of tails include:

> She's a really good actress, *Clare*.
> Singapore's far too hot for me *it is*.
> They haven't mended the road yet *haven't those workmen*.
> They complain about it all the time *they do*.
> He's quite a comic *that fellow*, you know.
> It's not actually very good is it *that wine*?
> They do tend to go cold, don't they, *pasta*.

We should note also the extent to which such patterns (in *italics*) cluster with different kinds of tags, hedges and modal expressions and how they often serve to express, on the part of the speaker, some kind of affective response, personal attitude or evaluative stance towards the proposition or topic of the clause.

Transactional

Transactional language is language used in the process of conducting business and generally getting things done. It contrasts with INTERACTIONAL language.

Modality

This is a term used in grammatical and semantic analysis to refer to contrasts in meaning, signalled mainly by verbs but also by associated forms. The reference is basically to unrealised states and possible conditions of everyday situations, and covers verb phrases such as *must be, could be, ought to be, might have* and so on. Typical modal meanings are obligation, option, permissibility, possibility. A modal verb may express more than one kind of modality: for example, the sentence 'He must be in bed' can either be a conjecture (he must be in bed because he can't be found anywhere else) or an order/obligation (he must be in bed by nine o'clock). Modality can also be signalled by modal adverbs such as *possibly, probably, presumably, definitely*. Modal forms are an interpersonal aspect of grammar and are central to all spoken and written language use; in conversational discourse they serve to mark out personal relationships and to some extent to frame the nature of the interaction between speakers.

Vague language

Vague expressions are more extensive in all language use than is commonly thought and they are especially prevalent in spoken discourse. When we interact with others there are times when it is necessary to give exact and precise information (for example, concerning departure times for trains); but there are occasions where it would not be appropriate to be precise as it can sound unduly authoritative and assertive. In most informal contexts most speakers prefer to convey information which is softened in some way by vague language, although such vagueness is often wrongly taken as a sign of careless thinking or sloppy expression. Examples of vague language include phrases such as *or something, or anything, or whatever*, all usually in clause-final position:

> Can you get me a sandwich *or something*?
> Have they got mineral water *or anything like that*?

Vague expressions are common when factual information is given and where approximations seem more appropriate. Number approximations are common with times and dates and figures (e.g. 'They're coming in six weeks *or so*'; 'We'll arrive *around* eight in the evening'). Vague expressions such as *sort of* and *kind of* also serve to allow the speaker not to commit themselves completely to the truth value of a proposition:

> A: Do you think she's interested?
> B: Well, she's *sort of* interested.

Vagueness can also be created by adjectives carrying a '-y' suffix so that to describe hair as 'a bit wispy and straggly' is to be deliberately and expressively vague.

Note:

English and Englishes

The features noted above are recurrent forms in spoken British English and it is not claimed that they are prevalent in other Englishes. At the time of writing the CANCODE corpus mainly comprises British English but plans are already laid for developing the corpus to include other World Englishes and to undertake comparative analyses of such Englishes.

Notes on transcription

Any piece of spoken language can be transcribed in a variety of ways, depending on what level of detail one is interested in. Consider the following stretch of talk between a group of young female students, who are having tea together (see Unit 9 for the full transcript). In this book we have just transcribed the girls' words in normal, standard orthography, but in addition have indicated that speaker 3 <S 03> begins her reply before speaker 2 <S 02> has finished hers – a typical overlap in this situation, since speaker 1's question is addressed to 2 and 3, therefore either or both of them may answer. We have also distinguished between *yeah* and *yes* as two common forms of the affirmative reply:

<S 01> Does anyone want a chocolate bar or anything?
<S 02> Oh yeah yes please
<S 03>   └Yes please

We could have done a number of other things too. We might have been concerned as to whether speaker 1 fully articulated *does*, or whether it may have been more accurate to write it as *d's* or phonetically as [dəz] or even just as [zeniwən] to represent *does anyone* spoken quickly and informally. Equally *want to* could be transcribed as *wanna* to indicate its reduced, informal pronunciation. We could have transcribed all the conversations with full intonation markings, so that every line in the book might look thus:

<S 02> /oh yeah/ /yes please/

or with phonetics and intonation:

<S 02> /əʊ jéə / / jes pliːz/

Then what of the affective elements signalled in speech, such as exaggerated lengthening of sounds or a sudden raising of the pitch level:

<S 02> /əʊ jeə ːː / / jes pliːːz/

What we decided in the end was to adopt a fairly broad, simple transcription which would be easy to read, since the book also has a tape with it. It is therefore rather like ordinary written text, with some exceptions. These are:

1   Overlaps are indicated by extra indentation and a connecting line └.

2   Utterances that are butt-ended (i.e. when there may be just a very slight or no overlap at all, and no pause between speakers) are indicated with extra indentation and a connecting line ⌐.

3   Punctuation
     Speakers do not use punctuation in the way writers do, but
     punctuation is very useful in transcripts such as these. We have used
     punctuation items in the following way:

,   comma indicates that the speaker has re-cast what she/he
                     was saying, e.g.:
                     I went to, into town the other day
...   three full stops indicates a pause longer than one second
[8 secs]   times in brackets indicate long pauses in the talk
[laughs]   other items in square brackets include things like laughter,
                     coughing and other sounds on the tape, or when the tape
                     is simply inaudible

     We have also used question marks and exclamation marks where we
     feel these may be helpful.
4   Each speaker is numbered <S 01>, <S 02>, etc. These types of
     labels are often used in the study of language corpora using
     computers, since the computer can distinguish that these are not
     people's words and can locate a particular speaker if need be.
5   Every language has a series of sounds which are not full words, but
     which are used by the listener to acknowledge the speaker's words
     while she/he is speaking or after. These are difficult to transcribe, but
     we have tried to represent the variation found in English between
     acknowledgements such as *Mm, Uhum*, etc., and variants of 'yes' such
     as *yeah, yep*, etc. Also, sounds indicating hesitation or thinking-time
     may be transcribed as *er, erm*, etc., in order to try as faithfully as
     possible to render what can be heard on the tape.

We hope you will find the type of transcription offered in this book sufficient to
enable you to follow the tape and to get the full flavour of the conversations.
However, transcription is an extremely difficult and imperfect art, and the
willing ears and hands that have helped us with transcribing the tapes may
occasionally have missed something or been uncertain as to what they could
hear. Even the original speakers themselves are not always sure what it was
they said when they hear the tape! Our aim has been to produce a
transcription that will not distract you from the conversation nor increase your
difficulty in hearing what is already difficult enough, given that our tapes are
recorded naturally, and (with the exception of broadcast data and the
additional re-recorded versions of Units 4, 6, 7, 10, 11 and 12) without the
benefit of studio surroundings and high-tech equipment.

Dangerous childhood pranks

General: conversational story-telling

People often tell stories in conversation, and the ability to tell a good story is universally admired. All stories share certain basic ingredients, but a good story needs something extra. The basic ingredients are:

1   References to times, places and settings.
2   Characters involved in the events.
3   Some sort of plot or series of unusual, strange, funny, etc., events which make the story interesting.
4   Some outcome or conclusion to the events.

But a good, entertaining story often has, in addition:

5   Embellishments or decorations by the teller, for example, exaggeration, intensification, suspense, amusing details.
6   Features which make the story more vivid, such as dialogue, changing the tense from past to present.
7   Comments on the events, telling us how people felt, what their attitude to the events was.
8   Some sort of relevance to the conversation in which the story is told, for example linking it to an earlier story or something someone has just said.

What is more, the teller has to **begin** the story appropriately (the opening) and **end** it in a suitable way (the closing). This means that telling a good story in a foreign language requires a good deal of language skill.

Activity

While listening to the extract for the first time, and before reading the commentary, try to identify which of the features **5-8** you think occur in these stories.

Speakers and setting

<S 01>	male (48)
<S 02>	female (42)
<S 03>	male (47)
<S 04>	male (47)

<S 01> and <S 02> are brother and sister. <S 02> and <S 03> are wife and husband. <S 04> is an old childhood friend of <S 01> and <S 02>. The extract was recorded at <S 02> and <S 03>'s home. The speakers are reminiscing about dangerous childhood pranks.

Transcript

1	<S 01>	Anyway
2	<S 02>	So anyway
3	<S 01>	So anyway
4	<S 03>	So anyway erm my cousin Mervin that was in the REME er got me a 38
5	<S 01>	Gun
6	<S 03>	Wesson, Smith and Wesson special and Benny's, no it wasn't it was
7		Rick Holman's shed and Benny, Brian Beddingfields knew his dad had
8		some ammunition from the war and he found it and they were 38s
9		so we erm took it over the marshes and shot a couple of rounds off
10		that was great and then one day we were in, up Prospect Road near
11		the scout hut in a shed in a pre, erm Rick Holman's shed so there was
12		four of us in this sort of [<S 01> mm] eight by six shed ... and
13		we were playing about with the thing and and we messed about with
14		it and did the usu, you know and sort of said oh we'll put a cross in it
15		make a dum-dum of it and fired it in the shed at at the bit of wood
16		[<S 02> [laughs]] and this bullet went round the shed about three
17		times and we all just froze this bullet went round and round and
18		round [laughs] was absolutely outrageous we had no concept of
19		what could have happened
20	<S 04>	Yeah
21	<S 01>	God
22	<S 02>	Dear God

23	<S 01>	Remember that kid ⌐
24	<S 03>	└ And then the other one right the other one
25	<S 04>	You said he was in the REME
26	<S 03>	Yeah
27	<S 04>	What's that
28	<S 03>	Royal Engin, oh
29	<S 01>	└Royal Electrical and Mechanical Engineers
30	<S 03>	└Engineers
31		I'm sorry, the other thing that we used to do that Bernard
32		mentioned when I was a little kid, before erm the sea-front was all
33		different it was just open [<S 01> mm] we used to cycle down
34		especially on foggy days was the best [<S 01> mm] cycle straight
35		down Canute Road and straight off the prom into the sea because
36		we erm we'd make sure the tide was sort of in and, but you had to
37		get rid of your bike in mid-air
38	<S 02>	└But didn't you do that dreadful thing to that boy
39	<S 03>	Oh yeah
40	<S 02>	└Where you were all kneeling down as if to say come in
41	<S 03>	└It's about
42		an eight or ten foot dive in [<S 01> yeah] and you could dive at high
43		tide and Guss Hughes came along one day and we were always
44		taking the Mickey out of him he was you know he was one of these
45		the lads that always got taken, so we all knelt down [<S 01>
46		[laughs] Patsy] with the water up to about there he stood on the
47		top and said is it okay to dive we said yes but of course it was only
48		knee-deep and he dived [<S 04> [laughs]] and he stuck and he just
49		went crunch
50	<S 02>	Somebody actually broke their neck [<S 01> That sounds like] down
51		there didn't they
52	<S 03>	Oh that yeah [<S 02> yeah I suppose] that's since they put the new
53		brick part of it though but basically you know how we didn't kill each
54		other and all things like that I don't, it's incredible

Line-by-line commentary

ll. 1–4 Anyway occurs four times, here used in a rather jokey way. The speakers are returning to their story-telling after a brief interruption. *Anyway* is a common DISCOURSE MARKER in English, used to indicate a boundary in the talk, either, as here, when getting back to an interrupted topic, or, often, to indicate that the speaker feels the conversation is coming to an end. This often happens in phone calls, e.g.:

> Anyway, it's been good talking to you. I'll give you a ring again at the weekend.

l.4 *that was in: that is* frequently used in informal speech as an alternative to *who* in relative clauses.

l.4 The *REME*, a branch of the military forces in Britain, is explained later, in 1.29. Here the initials are pronounced like a word, which is usually called an **acronym**. Other common acronyms in English include:

> NATO /neɪtəʊ/ North Atlantic Treaty Organisation
> OPEC /əʊpek/ Organisation of Petroleum Exporting Countries

But not all sets of initials are acronyms, and most are pronounced letter-by-letter:

> She gave me an IOU for £20. (I-O-U: I owe you: a written promise to pay back money owed)
> Her brother joined the ANC. (A-N-C: African National Congress)

l.6 The use of co-ordinating conjunctions such as *and, but, so* is a frequent feature
–l6 of spontaneous oral narrative.

l.6 *Smith and Wesson*: A world-famous gun-manufacturing company.

l.8 *the war* here is the Second World War (1939–45).

l.8 The switch in pronouns here is from *it* (ammunition) to *they* (bullets).

l.8 *38s*: a size of bullet.

l.9 *over the marshes: over* is often used in informal speech with motion verbs such as *go* and *drive*, and simply indicates movement to a different place (not necessarily crossing anything). It occurs both with and without *to*:

> Let's go *over* to my place for a drink.
> I usually go *over* the park with the dog before breakfast.

l.10 *up Prospect Road:* The speaker is probably using *up* here in a personal sense, corresponding to his idea of his town as having some parts which are *up* from where he lives, and some which are *down*. This may correspond to north and south of where he is, but not necessarily, and there is no necessary implication that there are hills, with some streets going, literally, 'up'.

For further discussion and examples of these informal, often idiosyncratic uses of prepositions, see Unit 6, e.g. ll. 18 and 65.

ll.11 *There was four of us*: Two things should be noted here:
–12 *There's / There was* are increasingly used in spoken British English with plural complements, though traditionalists would probably object to such usage. Even highly educated people, including politicians and journalists, can be heard using *there's* on radio and television instead of *there are* with plurals.

Non-native speakers are often tempted to say 'We were four' in this situation. This is possible, but sounds terribly formal and literary. The usual informal construction is with *there is/are/was/were* + *(number) of*:

> There were six of us at the meeting.
> There are five of us in my family.

l.12   Note the use of *sort of*, which is frequent in informal spoken language when a speaker hesitates, or is searching for the right word, or wants to be a bit vague in the word chosen. The word does not have to be a noun; it can be any part of speech:

> It was sort of hanging in the air. (+ verb phrase)
> She lives sort of behind the shop. (+ prepositional phrase)

See l.14 for another example.

l.12   *eight by six*: Eight feet long and six feet wide (approx. 2.5×2 metres).

l.13   *the thing* here is not just a pro-form or substitute for *the gun*, but also tells us something of the attitude of the speaker towards the gun (somewhat dismissive/satirical). Other examples:

> Don't ask me to use the computer; I hate the thing.
> My car broke down and I had to push the thing all the way home.

l.14   *did the usual*: This is an informal FIXED EXPRESSION meaning 'what we always/typically did'. For example:

> A: Any holiday plans for this year?
> B: Oh, we'll probably just do the usual, you know, a package to Spain or somewhere.

Usual occurs in other expressions and with personal pronouns, e.g. 'I'll have my usual, please' (said to a barperson, describing the drink you usually order in a bar where you are a regular customer).

l.15   By cutting an 'x' shape in the head of a bullet, it can be made into a *dum-dum*, a lethal type of bullet that splits as it enters its target, causing terrible injuries.

l.17   *this bullet*: Note how the story-teller uses *this*, even though the events were a long time ago in the past. *This* is very frequent in stories and jokes, when characters and places are referred to. It brings them to life, making them more immediate and 'present' rather than distant and past. Other examples:

> There was this man, and he goes into this pub, ... (a typical way of beginning a joke)
> Suddenly, we saw this huge dog coming towards us.

l.17   *round and round and round*: This is an intensified version of the usual BINOMIAL construction *round and round*. Intensification of structures is part of the function of making the story more engaging and entertaining.

ll.21 *God* and *dear God*: These are typical reactions in conversation to startling or
–22 shocking information. *Dear God* is the stronger of the two. Other alternatives
include *my God, my goodness, goodness me, Christ almighty*, the last expression being
the strongest of all those listed here. It is important to note that expressions
containing the word *God* or *Jesus* and *Christ* may be very offensive to Christian
listeners. Swear words (e.g. *bloody hell*) will also be heard in such contexts.

l.23 *Remember* is an example of situational ELLIPSIS. (See also Unit 7, 1.2.) Here the
subject and auxiliary verb (*do you*) are understood. This often happens in
informal conversation in questions in the second person, with verbs such as
want, see, think and other verbs of 'mental processes':

> Seen my glasses anywhere? (Have you seen ...?)
> Think she's missed the bus? (Do you think ...?)
> Want another drink? (Do you want ...?)
> Know where to go when you get there? (Do you know ...?)

l.24 The speaker here is trying (unsuccessfully) to introduce his next story, which
he refers to as *the other one*. The DISCOURSE MARKER *right* is often used to mark
the boundary between the introduction to a joke or story and the actual
beginning of the story itself:

> Let me tell you this joke I heard, right, there's this vicar, and he goes
> into a pet-shop ...

The *right* may also occur just after the first piece of orientation information in
the story:

> Oh, I've got a story about camping, we were in France, right, and we
> were putting up our tent one day when ...

l.34 *especially on foggy days was the best*: Note here how the speaker changes his
syntactic plan as he goes along: the prepositional phrase *on foggy days*,
originally 'planned' as an adjunct suddenly takes over and becomes the
subject of the clause.

ll.31 Note the pattern of verb forms here. The speaker uses the *used to* form twice
–37 (*used to do* in l.31 and *used to cycle* in l.33). After that, he changes to *would* (*we'd
make sure* in l.36). This is typical of stories about regular or repeated events.
Used to comes first, to set the general scene, and then subsequent typical events
are told with *would*.

l.41 *about* is common in approximations involving numbers and times, especially in
spoken English. It is another example of VAGUE LANGUAGE.

l.35 *the prom*: An informal clipping of 'the promenade' (the road running along the
sea-front).

l.38   The story-teller's wife uses *that* twice here (rather than saying '*a* dreadful thing to *a* boy') because she has heard the story before. *That* signals the 'shared knowledge' between her and her husband.

l.44   *taking the Mickey out of him*: An informal idiom meaning 'to mock/to tease'. Notice here the use of *always* with continuous verb form. Continuous form acts as a marker of personal comment or attitude with adverbs of frequency, though the precise attitude expressed can usually only be identified in the particular context. Some examples:

> She's always giving me presents. (could be associated with surprise, irritation, suspicion)
> He was constantly upsetting everyone. (could be associated with reproach, exasperation)

l.45   *got taken* here means roughly 'was the victim/object of tricks and pranks'. Speaker <S 01> then interrupts with the word *Patsy*, which is a slang name for pathetic people who are easily teased or are frequently the object of ridicule.

l.49   *went crunch*: The verb *go* is frequently used in conversation to describe movements, actions, noises and so on in a vivid way; *crunch* here describes the noise of the boy hitting the sea-bed. Other examples:

> The wind blew and the door went 'bang'.
> I lit the gas and the flames went 'whoosh' and burnt my eyebrows.

l.53   Note how *though* comes at the end of the clause here. This is common in spoken language, but far less common in written language, where it would tend to come at the beginning. Clause-final *though* is an ADVERB here and has the meaning of 'however' and as such can also appear in a medial position e.g.

> The south of England though will be much cooler than in the past few days (weather forecast).

In most written usage though in clause-initial position is a conjunction and usually has the meaning of 'although'.

ll.52   Stories normally close with some sort of comment or general reflection on the
–54   events, with evaluative words like *incredible, amazing, horrendous, hilarious, disgusting, appalling* frequently occurring at such points, the choice of word depending on the type of story told.

l.53   *basically* is an extremely common ADVERB in spoken English, and usually means something like 'put simply'. (See also Unit 20, l.75)

Further reading

For a classic study of the structure and language of spoken story-telling, see Labov (1972).

On narrative structure and function in general, see also Toolan (1988).

For more on abbreviations and acronyms, with some practice exercises, see McCarthy and O'Dell (1994), unit 98.

For a further discussion of *used to* and *would* as they are used in spoken and written stories, see McCarthy (1997: ch. 3).

unit **2**

Flying over Budapest

Activity

Imagine that you are describing to others a particularly memorable experience. You will be reporting your experience in the form of a narrative. What would you need to concentrate on in order to make your narrative effective? What parts of your experience would you need to highlight and why? (See **General commentary** below.)

Speakers and setting

        <S 01>   female (78)
        <S 02>   female (30s)
        <S 03>   male (47)
        <S 01>   is <S 03>'s mother-in-law
        <S 02>   is <S 03>'s cleaning lady

<S 01> recounts how she was invited onto the flight deck during a return flight to the UK from a holiday in Cyprus.

Transcript

1	<S 01>	Well I I don't know how I got this honour really I had all the badges in
2		you know, I used to be in the air force and I'd spoken to two or three
3		but when we got on the plane they took me on first because er er
4		they'd had to lift me on you know [<S 02> yeah] with that lift and er
5		the pilot was sat in one of the seats there were nobody on the plane
6		but me and er I don't know, I must have said, either said something

7		funny about flying or he'd said some, noticed me badges I don't know
8		which it was, anyway that
9	\<S 03\>	⌐He saw your badges I think.
10	\<S 01\>	Yes I think he did ... erm that, I never thought anything more about it
11		... well we'd, how long had we been flying, about half way weren't
12		we?
13	\<S 03\>	Yeah it was about an hour or hour and a half
14	\<S 01\>	⌐About half way up, home
15		and the loo was just behind the, where the pilot
16	\<S 03\>	⌐The cabin
17	\<S 02\>	⌐Yeah
18	\<S 03\>	⌐The
19		cabin
20	\<S 01\>	And er I went down there queued up [\<S 02\> uhum] and then
21		when I came out somebody said to me the pilot says you can go in
22		the cabin you see, well me mouth dropped open [\<S 02\> [laughs]]
23		no idea you see now I thought oh, I'd had a joke with one of the er
24		girls you know [\<S 02\> yes] the stewardess girls and er maybe it was
25		her or there was a young man with us that had been in our hotel
26		maybe he'd said something somebody had anyway so they took me and
27		Jeanne went with me of course in case I fell [\<S 02\> yeah] right into
28		where the two pilots were it was absolutely fantastic
29	\<S 03\>	⌐Marvellous
30		wasn't it
31	\<S 02\>	Was that the first time you've ever been
32	\<S 01\>	⌐in the cabin
33	\<S 02\>	⌐Yeah
34	\<S 01\>	⌐Yeah
35	\<S 03\>	⌐Yeah
36		normally they only take children and V-I
37	\<S 02\>	⌐That's right
38	\<S 03\>	⌐And V-I-Ps
39	\<S 01\>	⌐Yeah
40	\<S 03\>	⌐So
41		I don't know which
42	\<S 01\>	Well this was a V-I-P
43	\<S 02\>	Yeah [laughs]
44	\<S 03\>	[laughs]
45	\<S 01\>	And er I went through this door and below was a city

46		all all the lights and that and it was fantastic
47	\<S 02>	What was the city
48	\<S 01>	Er I was just you know
49	\<S 02>	└Oh you're coming to that
50	\<S 01>	└And I kept thinking I wonder where we are
51		now just you know and er one of the pilots said you're looking down
52		on Budapest [\<S 03> mm] he said the top side of that river is Buda
53		and at this side is Pest that's why they call it Budapest
54	\<S 02>	Oh is it? I didn't know
55	\<S 01>	Well I'd never heard that before
56	\<S 03>	└Yeah it is two
57	\<S 02>	No I hadn't
58	\<S 03>	└Two towns
59	\<S 02>	Oh
60	\<S 01>	I was absolutely transfixed with that [\<S 02> mm] it was like looking
61		on Fairyland [\<S 03> mm]
62	\<S 03>	It was lovely wasn't it
63	\<S 01>	└And of course we talked about the air force he said oh all up,
64		you know I've been in a plane but not up er [\<S 03> yeah] [\<S 02>
65		yeah] during the war [\<S 02> ah right] I'd missed out on that and er
66		it was absolutely [\<S 02> mm] fantastic [\<S 03> mm] I felt like a V-I-P
67		[\<S 02> [laughs]] when I came out everybody were looking
68		at me
69	\<S 03>	└When she came [\<S 02> yeah] when she came out people
70		were looking at her and said to one or two people it's all right she
71		said I've, they've just let me drive for a while [\<S 02> [laughs]]
72	\<S 01>	I said I've I've just taken you through Budapest you'll be all right now
73		[\<S 03> yeah] shown them the way
74	\<S 03>	It was nice [\<S 02> yeah] wasn't it yeah
75	\<S 02>	Ah
76	\<S 01>	Oh it was
77	\<S 02>	└Finished the holiday off yeah
78	\<S 03>	└It was a lovely yeah lovely
79	\<S 01>	Yes it was lovely it was nice of them to do it [\<S 02> mm] whoever
80		done it
81	\<S 02>	Mm it was yeah
82	\<S 03>	Though though we were two and a half hours late weren't we
83	\<S 01>	Yeah yes we were late setting off [\<S 02> ah] and er they chatted to
84		me like I'm chatting to you

85 <S 02>   Yeah

86 <S 03>   Great

87 <S 01>   Yeah it was great

General commentary

In order to make an oral narrative interesting and involving to listeners, certain aspects of personal experience need to be highlighted. In particular, listeners need to be oriented. That is, they need to be able to recreate in their imagination something of the time the narrative was taking place, they need information about the setting and, where appropriate, other participants and they need to be able to understand the point of the narrative, why it is being told. The latter requirement puts a responsibility on the tellers of a narrative to evaluate their experience (see also the general commentary to Unit 1).

In this narrative the initial action revolves around a key piece of information concerning <S 01> which is that she wears, almost all of the time, WAAF (Women's Auxiliary Air Force) badges attached to her clothes. She served in the WAAF during the Second World War. The possibility that these badges might have been noticed by flight crew becomes a starting point for the story.

Line-by-line commentary

l.2   *I'd spoken to two or three*, and l.4 *because er er they'd had to lift me on* are both examples of past perfect tense (the form *had* + *past participle*). In spoken language, the past perfect is mostly used for background information and is frequently used when the speaker is giving reasons, excuses, justifications for events, and *not* just for ordering events one before the other. The speaker here is disabled; that is why she had to be lifted onto the aeroplane.

l.5   *The pilot was sat*: The speaker comes from the county of Yorkshire in the North of England and speaks in the dialect of that region. The standard English dialect equivalent would be *was sitting*.

ll.5   *There were nobody on the plane but me*: In Yorkshire dialects *were* is used to
−6   mark both singular and plural. See also l.67.

l.7   *noticed me badges*: The use of *me*, where a standard English dialect alternative would be *my*, is common both in Yorkshire dialect as well as in several other non-standard English dialects (e.g. some Irish-English dialects). (See also l.22.)

l.11   *about half way weren't we*: The speaker gives her crucial orientation for the listeners concerning more general time, duration and place. This is then followed by more specific orientation in respect of the setting *I went down there and queued up for the loo* (toilet) which serves as a frame or main point of departure for the narrative.

l.21 *the pilot says*: The use of the present tense is relatively common in narrative. It is known formally as an 'historic present' and certainly adds a degree of immediacy to the narrative recount. The use of the present tense stands out here in contrast with the more extensive use of the more usual simple past and highlights and gives prominence to the words of the pilot.

l.22 *you see* is a frequent DISCOURSE MARKER used to signal explanations and things that the speaker assumes the listener does *not* know. Compare it with *you know* (e.g. l.4; l.24), and *of course* (l.27), which signal an assumption that the listener *does* know what the speaker is getting at.

l.23 *no idea you see*: Ellipsis is not normally common in narrative, chiefly because the narrator cannot take too much for granted and has to be explicit throughout most of a narrative. Here a non-ellipted version would be 'I had no idea'. The presence of ellipsis adds a note of casualness and informality and also serves perhaps to establish a closer interaction with and involvement of the listeners. (See also l.77, where the listener says *(It) finished the holiday off*.)

l.25 *a young man with us that had been in our hotel*: The use of *that* as a relative pronoun, as an alternative to the standard English dialect version *who*, is common in many non-standard English dialects.

ll.24 *it was absolutely fantastic*: A positive evaluation of the experience which also
−5 serves to underline the point of the narrative. The evaluation is for the benefit of the listeners and, indeed, one of the listeners also contributes an evaluation (*marvellous wasn't it*), at the same time co-constructing the narrative (he was with the teller on the same flight).

l.38 *V-I-P*: An abbreviation which stands for Very Important Person.

l.46 *all all the lights and that*: The use of *and that* is quite common in spoken discourse; an appropriately vague piece of language, it allows the speaker to say that there were many other aspects involved without having to specify any more precisely. See also Unit 4, l.28.

l.60 *I was absolutely transfixed with that*: The teller here offers an unequivocally positive personal evaluation of the experience of going on to the flight deck, underscoring the point of recounting a unique individual experience.

ll.60 *it was like looking on Fairyland*: A concluding remark which generalises the
−61 experience so that others can better identify with it. It is a mark of a skilful narrator to move seamlessly from individual to more general, represented experiences.

l.63 The recounting of personal experience here is, as it were, collaboratively constructed. Informal spoken narratives are hardly ever 'monologues' and listeners do a lot of work, adding their own evaluations, asking for more details, helping the teller to finish the story and enabling all present to get out of 'story-world' and back to the 'conversational world' they were in before the story started. There is extensive BACK-CHANNELLING on the part of <S 02>

and <S 03> (e.g. 1.62 *It was lovely*; l.61 *mm*; l.65; *ah right*, l.69 *yeah*). Such insertions into <S 01>'s discourse are essentially supportive, encouraging <S 01>, indicating their enjoyment of her narrative.

ll.79 *whoever done it*: Another feature of Yorkshire dialects (and many other
–80 British English dialects) is that there is often no significant difference between past simple and past perfect tense forms. *Done* here functions as a simple past. Likewise the past simple form of Standard English can be used as past participle in some other dialects, e.g. 'I've *wrote* to her' (instead of *written*).

l.82 *though we were two and a half hours late weren't we:* At this stage in the narrative there is a shuttling back and forth between narrative evaluation and a re-establishment of setting and context. The time reference here is a kind of retrospective orientation.

ll.86 *great*: A strongly marked evaluative comment, repeated across a speaking turn
–87 brings the main narrative sequence to a conclusion.

Further reading

See the references to Labov (1972) and Toolan (1988) in Unit 1.

Wolfson (1979) and Schiffrin (1981) are perceptive studies of tense and aspect in oral narratives. Schiffrin notes that speakers will often switch between *simple* historical present and present *continuous* tenses (with the *-ing* form) in order to give a focus to particular events or actions.

Silva-Corvalán (1983) is a parallel study with particular reference to Spanish data.

Fludernik (1991) examines the functions of the historical present in narrative recounts.

There is extensive discussion of the discourse functions of language in narrative in McCarthy and Carter (1994: ch 3).

unit 3

Ken's mother

Activity

Somebody is telling you a story about a person they knew. They say that he/she was:

(a) 'a real character'
(b) 'the terror of the neighbourhood'

What sort of person is this? What sort of behaviour would be typical of him/her? You will find some suggested answers in the **Line-by-line commentary**.

Speakers and setting

<S 01> male: Canice (nicknamed 'Ken') (originally from Kilkenny, Ireland) (50s)
<S 02> male (South Wales) (40s)
<S 03> female (originally from Iceland, but has spent most of her adult life in Cambridge, UK) (50s)

The extract takes place at <S 03>'s house, Cambridge.

1	<S 01>	I'll tell you a little tale, er when me mother was alive in Cambridge
2		and erm we had some coal delivered, me mother was a terror if
3		anything was wrong you know and er it got some rocks and bits of
4		scale in it and I was going, I was quite young then and she said er get
5		a, get a, we had a a bag it was a, quite a strong bag she said fill it up
6		with some of the coal and stuff and we got it on the bus and we
7		went all the way to the bottom of Hills Road Bridge, was, er in fact
8		the building's still there the coal office and inside was an old table an

9		oak er front, was about as long as this room and er I didn't know
10		what she was going to do with it, just take it back and probably tell
11		them you know the coal's not very good and as she went she bent
12		down picked it up and WHOOSH! straight across the counter dust
13		coal everywhere take it back she said and come back and get the
14		rest of it they couldn't believe it I can see their faces today they
15		couldn't believe it [<All> laugh] mother was like that yeah [<S 02>
16		was that, was that] if she sent, if she sent us up the road to get
17		anything [<S 02> yeah] only the manager could could do it and you'd
18		go up to the shop and er you'd want bacon and they'd, the fella'd
19		shout out 'Mrs Dowling's bacon!' and the manager'd have to come
20		out and cut it and if he didn't get it right he got it the next day she
21		was terrible
22	<S 02>	⌐So Mrs Dowling was the terror of
23		the neighbourhood was she
24	<S 01>	Oh Christ yeah
25	<S 02>	God
26	<S 03>	She was a character she was really
27	<S 02>	Did you know her
28	<S 01>	⌐She had she had er pernicious anaemia and she went into er
29		Addenbrooke's and me brother'd just come back from Australia and
30		that particular Saturday he'd just got back she was coming out you
31		see and erm he said oh I'll give her a surprise and go down and and
32		and take her home and he went into the Spread Eagle for a drink
33		first and cos he used to go in there years ago before he went to
34		Australia and he met, funny enough he met some of the people he
35		used to know and they were talking within a group and one of them
36		was a nurse, a nursing sister he said I'm going in to pick my mother
37		up and she said oh what ward is that and what name and when he
38		said Dowling good God she said are we glad she's going today
39		[<S 03> laughs] she's taken over the whole ward and the most
40		hardened sister can't you know can't handle her [<All> laugh] once
41		she got better she started to take over things [<S 02> yeah] and er
42		telling them what to do and this and that
43	<S 02>	She's dead now is she
44	<S 01>	Yeah
45	<S 02>	When did she die long time ago
46	<S 01>	Eh
47	<S 02>	A long time ago

48	<S 01>	But she was a, oh yes twenty years ago … but she was a
49	<S 02>	⌐ Great
50		character eh
51	<S 01>	Oh she was a terror in the shops
52	<S 03>	[laughs]

General commentary

This is another pair of connected, typical, everyday stories, this time centred round a particular person rather than an event or set of related events (compare Units 1 and 2). In a typical narrative, the main characters are 'evaluated' (i.e. commented upon, judged and appraised) by both the teller and the listener(s). Note here that the teller (Ken)'s mother is evaluated as a 'terror' at the beginning of the story, again after the first story, where she is also called 'terrible' and 'a character', and then again at the end of the second story, where both evaluations are repeated.

The way Ken connects the events of his stories is very simple: note how many times he just uses *and*. Connectors such as *consequently, next, subsequently, therefore, later,* etc. are rare in informal everyday spoken narratives, and are strongly associated with written texts.

Line-by-line commentary

1.1   *I'll tell you a little tale*: The teller, Ken, announces that he is about to embark on a story. This gives him the right to be the main speaker, and it would be very difficult for anyone to interrupt and say 'No you're not', or 'Not now, Ken!' The others are socially obliged to behave as typical story-listeners, i.e. to laugh in the right places, to use BACK-CHANNELS and to join in the evaluation at the end of the story.

1.1   *me mother*: The use of *me* instead of 'my' is common in several English dialects in the British Isles. Here Ken shows his Irish origins with its use.

1.2   *was a terror*: This suggests that, when things went wrong, she lost her temper and terrified people around her, perhaps by shouting, being very assertive or aggressive. She was certainly not a calm, passive sort of person!

1.4   *scale*: Low-grade, non-burnable stony material mixed in with the coal.

1.6   *and stuff* is a VAGUE LANGUAGE marker referring unspecifically to the waste materials mixed in with the coal, which Ken does not need to repeat in detail.

1.6   *we got it on the bus*: got here means something like 'managed to carry/load/lift it'. *Get* is extremely common in informal spoken language and it has many meanings (see Unit 20 for further examples).

1.9   Note the ELLIPSIS of *it* (referring to the table) before *was*.

1.12   *WHOOSH*! is an onomatopoeic word indicating something sweeping through the air. It could be used, for instance, to describe a plane flying past very quickly and suddenly, or a strong gust of wind.

l.13 Note the position of *she said*, just after the first clause of the reported speech. This strategy (i.e. a few words of speech, the reporting clause, then more speech) is common in spoken narratives. It helps to dramatise the reported speech, isolating the key words at the beginning.

l.15 The use of *mother* without *my* gives a familiar, more personal tone to the word.

l.16 *up the road*: This does not necessarily mean up a hill. *Up* here could simply mean 'towards the town/towards where the shops were'.

l.17 Note the four uses of *'d* (i.e. *would*) here, to refer to past habitual actions. It
−19 can only be used once a past time-frame is already established (often following 'used to'). Compare:

> I used to love going to the beach as a kid. I'd spend all day building sandcastles.
> When he lived locally, he'd come and see us every Sunday.

It cannot be used for past states:

> I used to live in Johannesburg (not 'I would live …')

l.18 *fella* is a typically Irish (and some other dialects') way of saying 'fellow', a colloquial word for 'man'.

l.22 *the terror of the neighbourhood*: It is clear that Ken's mother had all the local
−23 shopkeepers scared of her and her extravert, aggressive, bombastic behaviour.

l.24 *Christ* is a taboo word used in exclamations and reactions to things. It is offensive to many people, not only to people with strong Christian beliefs, and so it is best avoided. Less strong and less offensive alternatives include *God* (see 1.25) *Good God!* (1.38) *Crikey! Cripes!* and *Gosh!*

l.26 Note the reinforcing TAG (*she was*); this type of tag is common in spoken language (see also Unit 12, 1.1).

l.29 *Addenbrooke's* is a famous hospital in the city of Cambridge in the UK.

ll.30 *you see* is a DISCOURSE MARKER used when you believe the listener does not
−31 already know what you are telling them. It contrasts with 'you know', which projects an assumption that the listener will be familiar with the situation.

l.32 *The Spread Eagle* is the name of a local pub in Cambridge, known to all Ken's listeners.

l.34 *funny enough* is a colloquial version of 'funnily enough' or 'strangely enough'.

l.38 Note the word order here. Exclamations often have so-called 'question' word-order, with falling intonation. Some other examples:

> Was my face red last night! (tells the listener it <u>was</u>)
> Didn't I get a shock when I saw her!

l.42   *and this and that* is an example of VAGUE LANGUAGE which enables Ken not to specify further details (he can assume his listeners will understand now that they know what sort of character his mother was).

l.43   Note the affirmative tag here, indicating that the listener thinks this is the case but cannot be sure. If he had been more certain, he might have said 'She's dead now, *isn't she*'.

l.45   *long time ago*: Note the ELLIPSIS of *a* here. Ellipsis of the first element is common with everyday fixed expressions in informal conversation.

ll.49
–50   Here the listener and Ken re-affirm their evaluation of his mother. *A great character* suggests she was different, memorable, fun to observe and know, as well as a *terror*.

Further reading

Bauman (1986) is a good source on spoken narrative in general.

On funny stories in particular, see Gardner and Spielman (1980).

Farrell (1986) also discusses story telling.

On speech reporting see McCarthy (1997: ch. 6).

On *used to* and *would* for narratives of habitual events, see McCarthy (1997: ch. 3).

On evaluation in spoken narrative, see Labov (1972).

unit 4

Two old friends meet up again

Activity

English has a system of tags which speakers can put at the end of what they say. For example:

> You're French, *aren't you*?
> He's coming tonight, *is he*?

What do you think these tags are for? Make notes and/or discuss with a partner why you think speakers use tags. Are there other types of tags apart from the two types in the examples above?

Speakers and setting

> <S 01> male (40s)
> <S 02> male (40s)

Two old friends who haven't seen each other for a few years are 'catching up' with each other. They are in a village pub garden on an exceptionally hot summer's evening, talking about <S 01>'s children.

Transcript

1	<S 01>	Are you still playing er
2	<S 02>	⌐Gui-tar
3	<S 01>	Irish music, yeah
4	<S 02>	No I don't play very much now, no, not at all
5	<S 01>	└I thought you were touring the

6		country at one point

6   country at one point

7 <S 02>   [laughs] No, I er ... we go, we listen to it quite a lot, every time we

8   go to Ireland we erm, you know, seek out good musicians and er do

9   quite a lot of listening and of course we still buy a lot of records,

10   bought a lot of records over the last few years, but erm, there's not

11   actually anybody to play with around here, you know [<S 01> mm]

12   there's a there's a session every Sunday night in Cambridge in a pub

13   and that's erm about it ... do you still listen to Scottish music?

14 <S 01>   Ver ... since this pair have arrived [<S 02> mm] very very little, cos

15   you just don't have the time, and with the new house, and with the

16   garden [<S 02> Mm] occasionally I take fits of putting stuff on, not as

17   much as before

18 <S 02>   They do I s'pose take up a lot of time, don't they, kids?

19 <S 01>   ⌊They take up a lot

20   of, I mean, normally, you get, if you're lucky they're all tucked up in

21   bed by eight-thirty [<S 02> mm] ... that's if you're lucky, and then er

22 <S 02>   Do they sleep all night without erm waking up, did they wake up last

23   night, they didn't [<S 01> no] did they, no, [<S 02> no] didn't hear

24   a thing

25 <S 01>   Jamie normally, you put him in his cot and he's ... he's gone

26   [<S 02> mm] he sleeps he's very good at sleeping [<S 02> mm]

27   Thomas is a bit of a pain [<S 02> ah] all sorts of things frighten him,

28   you know [<S 02> yeah] wakes up with nightmares and that

29   [<S 02> does he] yeah some nights we change beds about three or

30   four times, he comes into our bed and there's not enough room and

31   so I go into his bed and he comes back in so to my bed and his bed

32   and chopping and changing

33 <S 02>   It's extraordinary to think they have bad dreams, well, I suppose they

34   dream of images they've seen during the day, probably dream of that

35   bloomin' duck or something

36 <S 01>   Or it just might be a car, noisy car going past the window or

37   something, wakes them up

38 <S 02>   Mm ... it's going to be hot tonight ... in bed, isn't it

39 <S 01>   Mm

Line-by-line commentary

l.1   *Are you still playing ...?* This suggests a more familiar, informal relationship with the speaker than the alternative 'do you still play ...?'. Note that <S 02> still feels able to reply using the simple form *don't play*.

l.2   *Gui-tar*: The way the speaker pronounces this suggests he is mimicking a stereotypical Southern USA accent, associated with country music.

l.7   *We go, listen*: Switches from one verb to another are common in spoken discourse. Such 'on-line' monitoring of language choices is, of course, normally edited out in most written texts.

l.9   *Do quite a lot of listening* is an example of a DELEXICAL VERB. Delexical verbs such as '**have** a smoke', '**take** a walk' are more common in spoken than in written discourse. The 'do', 'have' and 'take' in each case are lexically weak and operate only as adjuncts to the main lexical items of 'listen' and 'smoke' or 'walk'. In written discourse the main lexical verb usually operates independently.

l.9   *of course*: Note this DISCOURSE MARKER, which means that something is obvious between speaker and listener, and can be assumed to be known by all parties. Non-native speakers (especially those speaking Germanic languages) sometimes misuse it and can sound arrogant or pompous, as in:

> A: Where did you go in the summer?
> B: Oh we went to Paris
> A: Oh yeah, did you go up the Eiffel Tower?
> B: Of course

B probably meant 'yes, sure' or 'yes, indeed' or 'yes, we did', but has given the impression of saying 'yes, how could you be so stupid as to ask me that?'. The English *of course* does not necessarily translate directly into its Germanic equivalents.

l.12   *a session* means an informal gathering of musicians where anyone can bring an instrument along and join in.

l.14   *since this pair have arrived*: *this pair* refers to <S01>'s two small boys; the use of the past perfect tense *have arrived* rather than the alternative simple past 'arrived' adds to the statement a degree of immediacy and relevance-to-the-moment.

l.15   *with the new house, and with the garden*: This use of *with* is very common in spoken English. It means roughly 'when you take into consideration ...'

l.16   *take fits of putting stuff on*: *take fits of* here means that now and again, the speaker plays music quite intensively, then has long periods without doing so. *Put on* here means 'play on the record player/CD player/tape player'. *Stuff* is an extremely useful general word which can mean almost any type of thing; here it means 'music/records/tapes/CDs'.

l.16   *or something, all sorts of things, I mean, I suppose, normally, occasionally, sort of*: Such items have a certain propositional content but their main purpose is to establish and support a high degree of interpersonal and interactive exchange between the speakers as they talk about more immediate experiences and introduce both a more markedly affective and personal note into their conversation and a context (the sleeping habits of <S 01>'s children) to which both can in different degrees testify. The extent of the hedging and mitigation may be surprising to learners of English whose text books would not normally use such naturally-occurring data but it is a more regular feature of casual conversation than is generally understood.

l.25   *Jamie, normally, you put him in his cot ...*: The use of a HEAD or right-branching structure with a pronoun (*him*) that repeats the topic word (*Jamie*) is a common grammatical structure in spoken discourse. It serves, here, in particular to give emphasis to *Jamie* as the new (sub-) topic.

l.25   *He's gone*: a colloquial expression for 'he's fast asleep'.

l.27   *a bit of a pain*: a colloquial expression meaning 'a bit of a nuisance/problem'.

l.28   *wakes up with nightmares and that*: *and that* is frequently used in informal conversation to mean 'and such things' (see also Unit 2, l.46); it is a useful piece of VAGUE LANGUAGE.

l.32   *chopping and changing*: this is a BINOMIAL expression meaning 'constantly changing in an irritating/exasperating way'. Binomials are a relatively frequent type of idiomatic expression in informal speech. Other examples:

> She's making *life and death* decisions.
> We got there *safe and sound* in the end.

l.35   *that bloomin' duck* is a grotesque plastic toy duck in <S02>'s garage that the kids spotted earlier that day. *bloomin'* is a quite mild swear word, far less strong or offensive than bloody.

Comments on activity

Tags in this extract:

l.18	They do I s'pose take up a lot of time,	don't they, kids?
ll.22–23	Did they wake up last night	they didn't [no]
ll.28–29	Wakes up with nightmares and that	<S 02> does he
l.38	It's going to be hot tonight ... in bed,	isn't it

Points to note:

Tags have a very strong INTERACTIONAL effect in the conversation, reinforcing intimacy and informality. In the first case (l.18), the tag is followed by a lexical repetition (with *kids*) of the subject pronoun *they*. This is an example of a TAIL. Tails are frequent when speakers are commenting and evaluating states of affairs, and often accompany tags.

In l.23, the speaker answers his own question (*they didn't*) and adds a checking tag (*did they*). Speakers often use tags to check or confirm information in this way.

In l.29, note that tags often occur in the listener's response, to express the listener's reaction, or just to provide an acknowledgement or BACK-CHANNEL.

In l.38, the speaker assumes agreement on the part of the listener, and signals this assumption with the tag.

Further reading

On delexical verbs see Sinclair and Renouf (1988).

McCarthy and Carter (1994: ch 3), discuss the function of tense and aspect across a variety of spoken and written texts, especially narratives, and consider the teaching implications of marked tenses and tense switching.

For an extensive treatment of repetition in spoken discourse, see Tannen (1989), especially chapter 3.

On hedging markers in casual conversation see Schiffrin (1987), which is the most comprehensive treatment of spoken discourse markers.

On tags see Hintikka (1982), Bennett (1989) and McGregor (1995).

Brazil (1995) is an extensive study of spoken narrative discourse.

unit 5

An elderly lady reminisces

Activity

Before you read and listen, consider why the following remarks would normally be thought of as rather *formal*. How could you say them in a more *informal* way?

> 1 A number of my schoolmates to whom I still write also went to University.
>
> 2 She used, in her younger days when she was a student, to spend her holidays in Norway.

Answers to the **Activity** will be found in the **Line-by-line commentary**. As you listen and go through the transcript, underline structures similar to these.

Speakers and setting

> <S 01> Jen (late 20s) (Glasgow)
> <S 02> Esther Hamilton (84) (Ireland/Somerset)

In this extract, Esther Hamilton, an 84-year-old Englishwoman brought up in Ireland, reminisces about her youth to her great-niece, who asks her questions about herself in an informal interview-style conversation.

Transcript

1	<S 01>	So what did you study at Oxford?
2	<S 02>	Erm I got into Oxford on Modern Languages, French and
3		German but I was always much more interested in social affairs
4		and politics and I realised I would not want to spend three years

5		doing ancient French grammar or anything like that so I switched
6		over to what Alan's reading now called the Modern Greats
7		[<S 01> mm] or PPE, politics philosophy and economics it was quite
8		new I only knew about it because when I, Cicely was very good to
9		me and used to have me up to stay at Somerville while I was still
10		at school and one of her friends was sort of, pioneered this new
11		school of study and I decided that was for me [<S 01> mm] and
12		very interesting it was too [<S 01> mm were there] quite a number
13		of my friends with whom I still keep up er also switched to that yes
14	<S 01>	Mm were there many other women at Oxford with you?
15	<S 02>	There were four colleges erm there were a hundred and
16		fifty in Somerville it's grown enormously since then and it now
17		takes men [<S 01> right] but there was no thought of men at any
18		of the four women's colleges in my day ... I don't think it made
19		any difference as far as erm studying went, in fact I think I
20		would have preferred it as it was because I'm sure I wouldn't
21		have concentrated so well if it had been a mixed college
22	<S 01>	[laughs] When you were living at home before you left
23		while you were at, in Bristol and in Ireland did you erm did you erm
24		did you have any help in the house or
25	<S 01>	Oh yes, yes, yes mind you my parents were really quite
26		well-off when we lived in Ireland but the education in England
27		was very expensive [<S 01> mm] and I can remember my mother
28		had jewellery and silver and things she used to keep selling it [<S 01>
29		really] to pay for our extra music lessons and tuition in this
30		and that [<S 01> mm] and er I it was, must have been difficult
31		for her because she was brought up in affluence you know and now
32		she had to be a very economical housekeeper we had two maids in
33		residence [<S 01> mm] erm a cook and a house parlour-maid so we
34		didn't really do anything ourselves in the house [<S 01> mm] I
35		suppose we must have had a gardener I don't remember that really
36		we didn't have much of a garden in Clifton anyway, not like the
37		one in Ireland
38	<S 01>	Right and what did you do during your summer holidays when
39		you were at school?
40	<S 02>	Well first of all in the Easter holidays we always went
41		to a farm in the Mendips [<S 01> mm] and that was absolutely
42		lovely we erm the farm people let us help with the animals you
43		know we were very keen scouts and guides and we used to walk the

44		Mendip hills talking to each other in Morse [laughs] [<S 01>
45		[laughs]] erm and then we we sketched, mother used to set us little
46		sketching competitions you know just for fun and then in summer
47		holidays we very often went to Brittany cos the rate of exchange
48		was in our favour and erm that was lovely er we would stay at a
49		hotel and have bathing and see the local Breton regattas you know
50		and erm Cicely was a great swimmer, and while we were on one of
51		those Breton holidays she swam out so far that she met the only
52		other person who could swim who turned out to be an Austrian and
53		that was the beginning of our link with Austria and the next day
54		Cicely went to Graz where this woman lived and er your grandfather
55		and I followed I think the next summer and spent the summer there
56		in Graz supposedly improving our German but er [inaudible] was
57		only interested in playing cricket games on paper [<S 01>
58		[laughs]] oh we had a wonderful time climbing mountains and so
59		on ... and then you see we really began to split up we were
60		terribly lucky because our parents were keen that we should have
61		our own careers [<S 01> mm] and not be tied to them ... mother
62		said never let it be said of me that I tied my children to home
63		and she used in her latter days when she was a widow to have
64		Danish au-pair girls so that we could go out and have our own
65		careers and [<S 01> mm] not be tied to looking after her and I
66		remember your grandfather going off on a bicycle tour when he was
67		just about nine, he was at prep school, all by himself [<S 01> goodness]
68		round the abbeys and cathedrals of Southern England and then Emily
69		and I were very keen guides and we went to guide camps every year
70		erm Cicely being a language student went a lot to France on her own
71		she ... erm and our elder brother Freddy who was destined for the
72		army but he didn't get in because er it was after the First World
73		War you see and they weren't recruiting many and it was very
74		difficult to get in and he didn't pass his medical [<S 01> mm]
75		because of his eyesight er so he was sent out to New Zealand on
76		a public school scheme which sent these young lads out at about
77		the age of eighteen whole batches of them to learn farming in New
78		Zealand [<S 01> oh] and he never came back [<S 01> mm] and
79		your grandfather and I went out just once after fifty-three years to
80		see him
81	<S 01>	Goodness me
82	<S 02>	Erm but all this was very untypical of er the people

83		among whom we lived, Clifton was a very pleasant leafy suburb of
84		detached or semi-detached large houses and erm people didn't
85		work, I mean the girls never thought of having careers the others er
86		they just lived at home [<S 01> mm] and I think they thought we
87		were very strange [<S 01> [laughs]] in fact I remember one of our
88		[laughs] neighbours said to, who had two grown-up children you
89		see well this was typical the girl stayed at home and the son
90		followed into his father's business [<S 01> mm mm] that was how
91		they, most of them, and then some of them married the girl next
92		door you know they were very conventional [<S 01> mm] they
93		always went either to Devon or Cornwall for their holidays
94		[<S 01> mm] they always trooped off to the same church on Sunday
95		mornings you know then one of these neighbours said to my mother
96		when your grandfather went off on his first Arctic expedition I
97		can't think why Richard wants to go to the Arctic when he's got
98		such a nice home [<S 01>[laughs]] we thought this was hilarious
99	<S 01>	Oh my [laughs]
100	<S 02>	Our houses were built around a tennis court and my
101		father arranged it that every family had a day you see in
102		rotation er but after six o'clock in the evening er anybody could
103		go out so we young ones all went out and we devised various games
104		like erm six-a-side tennis [<S 01> [laughs]] great fun and then
105		after that we used to play bicycle polo [<S 01> [laughs]] bicycle
106		hockey in the street you see it was off a main road it was just
107		a crescent [<S 01>mm] but some of the neighbours disapproved of
108		this and withdrew their daughters at that stage [laughs]
109	<S 01>	Goodness
110	<S 02>	We were the mad Irish [laughs] [<S 01> [laughs]] and
111		it really never entered the head of any of us that we should stay
112		at home, [<S 01> mm] I mean Cicely was very brilliant really and,
113		and erm what did she do first oh she did teach for a year and then
114		she went out to the States and had various jobs and went on the
115		stage and married a erm
116	<S 01>	So she was an actress she she acted?
117	<S 02>	Yes
118	<S 01>	└ I didn't know that
119	<S 02>	└ Yes she joined a professional
120		company she was always very good at acting as I say we did a lot

121   of acting at school yes
122 <S 01>   Mm

General commentary

Esther, the main speaker, is an upper middle-class lady whose speech combines quite informal features with some rather formal, perhaps old-fashioned features. Notice, nonetheless, that even though her speech is often formal, and even though she speaks with an upper-class RP (Received Pronunciation) accent, she still uses a large number of DISCOURSE MARKERS, as indicated in the line-by-line commentary. Some people think discourse markers are a sign of 'lazy' or 'uneducated' speech, but this is not so, and they are just as common in the speech of people like Esther as in that of any other social class of speaker.

Line-by-line commentary

l.1 and l.6   Notice how Jen uses *study*, while Esther uses the verb *read* to refer to the same thing. *Read* in this sense of 'study a university subject' is very much associated with the prestigious universities of Oxford and Cambridge and is thus a social class marker. *Read* with this meaning is becoming increasingly obsolescent.

l.2   *I got into Oxford on Modern Languages*: An informal way of saying 'I was accepted to study ...'; it can also mean that she was admitted on the strength of past performances in modern languages.

l.7   *Greats*: This normally means at Oxford University 'Classics', i.e. Latin and Ancient Greek, but here it has a special meaning combined with Modern, which Esther explains.

l.9   *up to stay*: People who study at Oxford or Cambridge usually refer to travelling to those places as going *up* to Oxford/Cambridge, and going *down* as going home (at the end of term, for example). These are purely cultural uses of the prepositions. Somerville is a college of Oxford University.

l.10   Note the use of *sort of* as the speaker searches for the appropriate word. This is extremely common in conversation and is here a marker of hesitation after a 'false start'.

l.12   *and very interesting it was too*: Note the word order here (complement-subject-verb-adverb). Word order is quite flexible in conversation, and Esther puts the adjective complement at the front here to emphasise it. The structure is also distinctive in the placement of *and* at the beginning of the clause and the stress which is given to the *too* at the end of the clause. It functions as a kind of parenthetical comment or afterthought and usually involves an evaluation, e.g. 'And very helpful she was too'.

ll.12 –13 This is one of the rather formal (typically written) structures in Esther's conversation, with the preposition and the *wh-* word at the front. Normally, in informal speech we would expect:

> A number of my friends (who/that) I still keep up with ...

(See **Comments on activity** below).

l.19 *as far as studying went*: the use of the verb *go* here is an informal version of 'was concerned'. Another example:

> As far as holidays go, I'm quite happy to stay in this country.

l.25 *mind you* is a useful spoken DISCOURSE MARKER meaning roughly 'it's important to say' / 'we should not forget'.

l.26 Esther says *the education* here. She could have just as well said 'education'. The use of *the* here seems to suggest 'the kind of education that you and I know would have been suitable for people like us'.

l.29 –30 *This and that*: A useful BINOMIAL expression meaning 'various unspecified things', as in, for example:

> A: What were you and Sandy talking about?
> B: Oh, this and that, nothing special.

A similar expression is the TRINOMIAL idiom 'this that and the other'.

l.31 Note how often the marker *you know* occurs (see also ll. 42, 49, 92, 95). *You know* as a signal that the speaker thinks the listener will share his/her view of the world contrasts with *you see*, where the speaker signals 'I am telling you something you may not be aware of', as in ll. 59, 73, 89, 101, 106.

l.36 *we didn't have much of a garden*: This construction is common in spoken language and it means 'not big/important/good, etc.', depending on the context. Other examples:

> That wasn't much of a film, was it?
> It wasn't much of an airport, just a runway and a few tin huts.

l.36 *Clifton* is a suburb of the city of Bristol.

l.36 *anyway* has the meaning of 'in any case' and functions here as an adverbial adjunct. In informal spoken English it is more commonly a discourse marker used to mark boundaries or different phases in the discourse. (See Unit 1 ll.1–4.)

l.44 *the Mendip hills*: A range of hills in the south-west of England.

ll.43 –44 *walk the Mendip hills*: Verbs such as *walk* and *run* are sometimes used transitively (and without the more 'normal' prepositions such as *along* or *in* or *through*) in connection with places or specific events. For example, 'they both ran the London marathon last year'.

l.44 *Morse*: Morse Code, a system of wireless communication using long and short pulses, named after its founder.

l.45 *mother* (see also l.61) is a rather upper-class way of referring to one's mother. More socially neutral would be 'my mother', or very informally, 'Mum', 'My mum'. (See also Unit 11, extract 3 l.7.)

ll.46 *in summer holidays*: This now sounds a little old-fashioned or formal, and we
–47 would say 'in the summer holidays' usually.

l.47 Note how even such a formal, educated lady as Esther still abbreviates *because* to *cos*. This is perfectly normal and correct in everyday conversation.

ll.58 *and so on* has the meaning here of 'and that kind of thing'.
–59

l.63 *She used ... etc.*: Interrupting *used to* in this way with two adverbial expressions is a very unusual construction for informal spoken language, and would normally be associated with rather formal written language. In conversation we would expect 'In her latter days when she was a widow she used to have ...'. (See **Comments on activity** below.)

l.67 *prep school*: Preparatory school: a private school for younger children before they go on to public school (l.76), which is also a private (usually very expensive) type of school, some of which are very ancient and famous.

l.67 *all by himself* is an informal way of saying 'all alone', as is *on her own* in l.70.

l.71 It is interesting to compare this narrative sequence (concerning Freddy) with other narrative sequences in Esther's talk (e.g. ll.28-32) or with narratives elsewhere in this book (e.g. Unit 1) and to explore the different use of conjunctions. The greater number of subordinating conjunctions (e.g. *who, because*) at particular points in narratives (which are linked mainly by co-ordinating structures (e.g. *and, but, then*)) seems to be connected with the need on the part of the narrator to set the scene or to provide background information relevant to a character.

l.76 *These young lads*: The use of *this/these* in this way is very common in narratives. Esther could have omitted it. They are used to focus on *the young lads* and to make them more immediate to the narrative; 'this/these' are less distant than 'that/those'.

l.81 *Goodness me* is an expression of surprise, as are *my!* in l.99 and *goodness!* in l.109. These would not normally be used by young people under the age of 25-30, who would probably say *wow!*.

l.82 *all this*: Note the difference between *this* and *that* when we are talking about different sets of facts or ideas or arguments. If we wish to emphasise or highlight something, or focus on it as a new or important topic, we usually use *this* (as Esther does here and in l.89); if we wish to distance ourselves from or dissociate ourselves from the facts or ideas, we use *that*, as Esther does in l.90.

ll.91 *If you marry the girl next door* (a FIXED EXPRESSION meaning to marry a next-
–92 door neighbour) you marry in a very safe, conventional (and by implication
boring) way, which means you lack a broader perspective on life.

l.94 *trooped off* is an informal verb meaning roughly 'went along together, rather
monotonously and regularly'.

l.110 Because the English are traditionally such stiff, reserved people socially, they
often think of the more outgoing socially relaxed nature of the Irish as being
'mad'.

l.114 *out to the States*: This is another cultural use of a preposition; *out* is often used for
going (usually for work) to the traditional centres of emigration from Britain
(e.g. the USA, Canada, Australia, Africa, India, New Zealand). See Unit 1 l.12
and Unit 6 ll.18 and 65.

l.120 *as I say*: Note the present tense here in this FIXED EXPRESSION, even though the
speaker is referring to something she 'said' earlier.

ll.1– It is worth noting in this narrative the use of verb forms for referring to
122 habitual past actions. As might be expected, the past simple tense is frequently
used; but note too the regular use of 'used to' and 'would' plus main verb.
Most of the narratives in this book provide valuable data for exploring such
forms in actual use.

Comments on activity

The answer to sentence 1 in the activity would be:

1 A number of my schoolmates (who/that) I still write to also went to University.

whom becomes *who* or *that*, or is omitted, and the preposition stays at the end, after
the verb. (See also l.83)

The answer to the activity sentence 2 would be:

2 In her younger days when she was a student, she used to spend her holidays in
Norway.

Further reading

On the difference between *it/ this* and *that* for referring to facts and ideas, see
McCarthy (1994).

The most comprehensive work on discourse markers is Schiffrin (1987).

On the use of binomial expressions in everyday conversation, see Norrick (1988).

For a detailed study of fixed expressions see Fernando (1996).

Doing a job

Activity

Before looking at the commentary, listen to the tape while reading the transcript. What do you think these people are doing? Why is it difficult to tell just from listening and reading the transcript? What clues are there as to what they are doing in the language they use?

See **General commentary** below for answers to this activity.

Speakers and setting

<S 01>	female (25) (Yorkshire)
<S 02>	female (37) (Yorkshire)
<S 03>	male (30) (Yorkshire)
<S 04>	male (47) (South Wales)
<S 02>	is <S 01>'s aunt.
<S 03>	is <S 01>'s husband.
<S 04>	is <S 02>'s partner.

The extract was recorded in <S 02>/<S 04>'s house.

Transcript

1	<S 01>	It should fit there cos it's not that big I don't think
2	[7 secs]	
3	<S 02>	It's warm in here shall I turn that down?
4	<S 01>	We've got the instructions anyway

5	[8 secs]	
6	<S 03>	Just put it by the
7		window or something
8	[4 secs]	
9	<S 04>	D'you want me to take that?
10	[4 secs]	
11	<S 02>	Ooh ... then there's bedding for about ten people here
12	[laughs]	
13	[12 secs]	
14	<S 04>	Ah
15	<S 01>	Oh I say, ah we've got some more instructions
16	[12 secs]	
17	<S 01>	That bit there's the bottom
18	<S 02>	D'you know you went up to erm Nottingham yesterday and
19		you still didn't take Roger's duvet
20	<S 04>	Well ... I wouldn't have had time to take it in any
21		case, haven't seen him
22	<S 02>	Does he know we've got it?
23	<S 04>	No ... oh look at that
24	<S 02>	It's not [inaudible]
25	<S 03>	it's not as difficult as it first seemed
26	<S 01>	She says you've got to twist these round and it makes
27		them solid or something
28	<S 03>	And all this just for you [<S 02> oh [laughs]]
29	<S 01>	There that's solid now
30	<S 02>	I think I've made it unsolid sorry I've done it the
31		wrong way round have I
32	[3 secs]	
33	<S 01>	Solid
34	[4 secs]	
35	<S 03>	[laughs] [inaudible]
36	<S 01>	Right now it's your end now
37	<S 02>	Oh I see right okay
38	[4 secs]	
39	<S 02>	No too much
40	<S 01>	There ... what's that in the middle?
41	[5 secs]	
42	<S 02>	Oh it's
43	[2 secs]	

44	\<S 03>	Found some more legs
45	\<S 02>	Mm ... is it legs or is it erm
46	[2 secs]	
47	\<S 01>	It doesn't tell you what that is
48	\<S 03>	[laughs]
49	\<S 04>	Yeah that looks right surely
50	\<S 01>	Yeah
51	\<S 03>	Yeah well done
52	\<S 02>	D'you like that?
53	\<S 03>	Yeah
54	\<S 01>	Oh aye
55	[4 secs]	
56	\<S 02>	Is that our washing?
57	\<S 01>	No that's the sheet
58	\<S 02>	└No └right ...
59	\<S 01>	now I think this is the bottom of it
60	[3 secs]	
61	\<S 02>	Now
62	\<S 03>	Good grief
63	\<S 02>	Pikelet
64	[3 secs]	
65	\<S 03>	That's low down
66	\<S 01>	└Look at this Holly
67	\<S 02>	└Is that erm being used?
68	\<S 01>	└I'm gonna get back-ache
69		lifting you in and out of here aren't I?
70	[3 secs]	
71	\<S 03>	There now you'd better sleep in that [laughs]
72	\<S 04>	Well I'm very impressed
73	\<S 02>	Yeah it's incredible isn't it
74	\<S 01>	[inaudible] ... no I won't put that on the top cos she
75		might be sick so I'll take that, mine's downstairs
76	\<S 02>	D'you want d'you want the sheet from us?
77	\<S 01>	No I've I've brought one
78	[7 secs]	
79	\<S 03>	Amazing isn't it
80	\<S 02>	How many er pillows do you have, one, two?
81	\<S 01>	I have one Graeme won't have any [laughs]
82	\<S 02>	You have one Graeme doesn't have any

83 <S 01>   Yeah

84 <S 02>   Yeah right okay good job you said

85 <S 03>   They end up being thrown on the floor or Lindsey

86   pinches them [<S 04> [laughs]] or used to propping, for propping

87   babies up in the morning

88 [3 secs]

89 <S 04>   What's that what's that eh [<S 03> oo] oo oh whoops-a-

90   daisy [<S 03> [laughs]] what you looking for, tissue?

91 <S 03>   └Tissue or

92   something

93 <S 02>   └ There was a tissue there there was

94 <S 03>   └Errgh

95 <S 04>   You must get used to this

96 <S 03>   Yeah

97 <S 04>   [laughs]

98 <S 02>   Constant mopping up

99 <S 04>   Yeah

100 [2 secs]

101 <S 03>   Should put her bib on to get to bed I think

102 <S 02>   └Think it'll be too warm

103   in here for her or is it going to be all right ... can you take

104   that off there?

105 <S 01>   It'll be all right

106 <S 02>   That's it

107 <S 01>   She only needs half of that anyway

108 <S 02>   It does get pretty hot in here actually ... no matter what

109   [7 secs]

110 <S 02>   Couple of towels for you there she said chucking them

111   on the floor

112 <S 01>   Right

General commentary

This extract is what we call 'language-in-action'. That is to say, the language used is almost all dependent on what the people are *doing* at that moment. It is very tied to the immediate situation. Here, a group of people are assembling a portable baby's cot in the bedroom of a relative's house (<S 02>) where <S 01> and <S 03> are staying for the weekend with their young baby.

It is difficult to decide exactly what they are doing because they do not mention the word *cot* at all. This is typical of language-in-action conversations, where people do not need to mention directly things and actions which are obvious and right in front of them at that moment. Also, quite long silences are common while the speakers are doing things. On the other hand, the speakers use a lot of words like *that, there, here* and *it* to refer to the things around them.

In this type of talk, the speakers also use a lot of DISCOURSE MARKERS (especially the word *right*) to organise their activity and a lot of ELLIPSIS of personal subjects, since the people referred to are present in the conversation (see examples in the commentary below).

Follow-up activity

Below is part of a word-frequency list for this extract prepared by a computer. It shows words which occur five times or more, and how often each word occurs.

Note the extremely high number of occurrences of *it* and *that*, referring to the cot and its parts. But *this* does not occur in our list, since it only occurs four times in the conversation. What could be the explanation for the difference between *this* and *that* here? Similarly, the definite article *the* occurs 12 times. The indefinite *a* only occurs once in the whole conversation. Why?

Word-frequency list

Total number of words in the conversation: 482

Words occurring five times or more:

it	27	is	7
that	22	no	7
I	13	oh	7
the	12	or	7
there	9	now	6
to	9	do	6
yeah	9	here	5
in	8	take	5
right	8	think	5
have	7		

Line-by-line commentary

l.1 Note how *because* is frequently reduced to *cos* (see also l.74). This is informal but not 'incorrect'. Even highly educated native speakers do it regularly (see Unit 5), although they may not be aware of it.

Note also the use of *that big*, instead of *so big*. Using *that* in this way is very common in informal speech, especially after a negative. The use of *that* here is as a marker of degree; it premodifies gradable adjectives and adverbs. *Not that big* here has the meaning of 'not particularly big'. Other examples:

> The water wasn't that cold that you couldn't swim.
> I think I can afford it. It's not that dear.
> A: How're you feeling?
> B: Not that good actually.

<S 01>'s turn ends with a double negative, which often happens when the phrase *I don't think* comes after its object. If we reversed the order, we would expect: I don't think it's that big.
The order here is frequent in informal conversation. Other examples:

> It's not very warm out, I don't think.
> He won't be late, I don't suppose.

l.3 *in here*: prepositions are often used with *here* and *there*, especially in informal conversation, for example 'up there', 'over here', 'out there':

> Come and sit over here, why don't you.
> There's a cat out there, is it yours?

l.7 *or something* is a useful phrase to make what you are saying a little more indirect or vague. If you say to someone:

> Are you going to the shop? Could you get me a cold drink or something?

it sounds less direct, and gives the other person a certain amount of freedom to use their discretion. Note how <S 01> uses it in l.27 to make her report of what someone else said a little less precise. See also l.92 for another example; *or whatever* is also used in some contexts with a similar meaning.

l.11 The use of *then* here simply connects the different parts of the conversation. It is a DISCOURSE MARKER. It does not mean 'therefore' or 'afterwards'.

l.15 *I say* here is just an expression of surprise. Note the stress: /i SAY/. The expression is common in Yorkshire, where <S 01> comes from, but is normally not used by young people. The phrase can also be used as an attention-getter, e.g. 'I say, excuse me, is there a taxi rank near here?'; as an attention-getter it has quite a formal and upper-class ring.

l.17 *that bit there: this/these* are often used together with *here* and *that/those* with *there* for more precise reference in spoken language, but are not normally found together in written language. More examples:

> That girl there reminds me of Sandra.
> D'you want this book here, or the other one?

l.18 *up to Nottingham*: In Britain, when speaking informally, you normally refer to journeys to places to the north of where you live as going *up* (e.g. to Edinburgh, Manchester, etc. if you are in London), journeys to the south as *down* (e.g. from Manchester to Southampton) and journeys east-west or west-east often with *over* (e.g. 'I have to go over to Birmingham' if you are in Nottingham). *Over* is also used for journeys across the sea (e.g. go over to France/Ireland for the weekend). Some people use *up* for journeys to London, wherever they are, because it is the capital city.

ll.20 Note how <S 04> uses the discourse marker *well* to soften the force of his
−21 answer, and also how he omits the subject *I* before '(I) haven't seen him'. This is an example of subject ELLIPSIS, which is very common in informal conversation (see especially Unit 7). Note that *well* can function in this position in part to appeal for a listener's understanding when a speaker is making an excuse or giving a justification, or responding with something that diverges from the desired or predicted direction of the discourse. For example:

> A: You shouldn't have given her the money.
> B: Well, she didn't leave me a lot of choice.

where the main meaning is one of 'that may be so, but...'

l.26 *she says*: The *she* here is the woman who has lent <S 01> the cot for the weekend. Observe that we often use present tense to report other people's speech when it refers to something factual or permanently true (in this case the instructions for the bed). Other examples:

> Nick says the exams are starting on the 27th.
> Clare says Rio's quite a dangerous city.

ll.29 *solid* here means 'rigid'/'inflexible', and refers to the way the frame of the cot
−30 becomes rigid when the legs are twisted a certain way. *Unsolid* is not an established word. Speakers often create words for humorous effect using prefixes (here *un-*) or suffixes (see l.63 below), as <S 02> is doing here. The normal word would be 'loose' or 'slack' for this situation.

l.36 *now* marks here a new stage in the action. It does not have a marked temporal meaning.

ll.36 In language-in-action conversations we find a lot of DISCOURSE MARKERS
–37 such as *right, I see, okay*, which accompany people's actions and mark the stages
of the process they are trying to complete.

l.40 *there* is used as a discourse marker here, meaning roughly 'that's it / 'I've
finished my task'. This is very common in spoken language (see also l.71).

l.44 *found*: Here we have ellipsis of both the pronoun *I* and the auxiliary verb *have*.
This is common with first-person singular:

> (I've) Just bumped into Mark. I didn't know he was coming.
> A: What's the matter?
> B: (I've) Lost my glasses.

l.54 *Aye* is a common alternative to *yes* in many parts of Great Britain, especially
Scotland and northern England. It is not normally used by middle- and
upper-class speakers.

l.62 *Good grief* is a common exclamation indicating shock or great surprise. Other
expressions with similar force include *Good God!, Good Lord!, Good Heavens!.* (See
also Unit 1 ll. 21–22.)

l.63 *Pikelet*, which means a kind of flat cake of dough usually eaten toasted with
butter, is <S 02>'s affectionate name for speaker <S 04>, who is called
Michael. Mike is the short form of Michael, and she creatively transforms
Mike → *Mikelet* → *Pikelet*, playing on the sound patterns.

l.65 *Low down* is another example of 'doubling' in speech for emphasis (as we saw
with *this here / that there* in l.18, above). Similarly, people often say *high up*:

> I don't like that picture where you've hung it, it's too high up.

l.66 *Holly* is the little baby girl's name. She was born on Christmas Day. The
evergreen holly tree traditionally provides branches for decorating people's
houses at Christmas.

l.79 *Amazing isn't it*: Note the ellipsis of '(it's) *amazing*' here, followed by the tag *isn't it*.
This is a very common structure in informal conversation with adjectives
expressing evaluation. Other examples:

> Interesting, wasn't it?
> A bit scruffy, isn't he?
> German, wasn't he?
> Reads a lot for her age, doesn't she?

l.84   (It's a) *good job*: This is a very common FIXED EXPRESSION in conversation, used when you are glad something happened because if it had not, there would probably have been problems. It very frequently has ellipsis of *it's/ it was*:

> Good job you booked a table, the place is packed! (if you hadn't, we may not have got into the restaurant)
> Good job you speak Spanish! (if you didn't, there could be problems)

l.86   *pinches*: 'pinch' is an informal word for 'steal'.

l.89   *whoops-a-daisy*! is a very informal exclamation used when you or somebody else drops something, or when somebody trips or falls (but not a serious fall). It is often shortened to *whoops*! or *oops*! (See also Unit 11: extract 1, line 6.)

l.93   *There was a tissue there there was* is an example of a TAIL structure in which the repeated dummy subject 'there' and the main verb are repeated for emphasis and reinforcement at the end of the clause (see also Unit 11: extract 1, line 1).

ll.101   Note further examples of ELLIPSIS here. In l.101 *I* is omitted before *should*. This
–102   is common with *must* and *should* in conversation:

> (I) Must get my hair cut, it's got really long.
> (I) Should ring my mother, I suppose, before she goes to bed.

(Do you) think in l.102 has ellipsis of the subject and auxiliary verb. This is common in second person singular with 'think', 'want', 'have got':

> Think it's too late to call at Dave and Ida's? What time do they go to bed usually?
> Want another drink?
> Got any letters for the post? I'll take them if so.

l.108   Note the use of *pretty* instead of 'rather' or 'quite'. This is very common in spoken English.

l.110   Note the ELLIPSIS of 'there is' / 'there are', which happens often, and of 'a' before *couple*. Once again, this is typical of the high rate of ellipsis we find in this kind of conversation.

she said is used by the speaker here to mock herself: she sounds as if she's handing them the towels, but really they have fallen onto the floor.

Further reading

On this kind of language-in-action text compared with other text-types, see Ure (1971).

On pronouns in spoken English, see Thavenius (1983).

On ellipsis in spoken English see Carter and McCarthy (1995a).

Cooking rice

Activity

The text examined in this unit was recorded in the kitchen of a family home; all the participants are members of the same family. Here are some brief conversational exchanges. Would you expect to find conversations such as this in a family kitchen?:

> A: Would you like a biscuit?
> B: I beg your pardon.
> A: Would you like a biscuit?
> B: Oh, yes please. Thank you very much.
>
> A: I didn't know you used boiling water to make rice.
> B: You don't have to use boiling water but it is reckoned to be quicker.

Write short notes explaining why you would or would not expect to find such styles of conversational exchange in the text examined in this unit.

Speakers and setting

<S 01>	female (45)
<S 02>	male (19)
<S 03>	male (46)
<S 04>	male (49)
<S 02>	is <S 01> and <S 04>'s son
<S 03>	is <S 04>'s brother

This extract takes place in <S 01>, <S 02> and <S 04>'s house. <S 03> is visiting them.

Transcript

1	<S 01>	Now I think you'd better start the rice
2	<S 02>	Yeah ... what you got there?
3	[4 secs]	
4	<S 02>	Will it all fit in the one?
5	<S 01>	No you'll have to do two separate ones
6	<S 03>	Right ... what next?
7	[17 secs]	
8	<S 03>	Foreign body in there
9	<S 02>	It's the raisins
10	<S 03>	Oh is it oh it's rice with raisins is it?
11	<S 02>	⌐No no no it's not supposed to be
12		[laughs] erm
13	<S 03>	There must be a raisin for it being in there
14	<S 02>	D'you want a biscuit?
15	<S 03>	Erm
16	<S 02>	Biscuit?
17	<S 03>	Er yeah
18	[9 secs]	
19	<S 04>	All right
20	<S 03>	Yeah
21	[10 secs]	
22	<S 04>	Didn't know you used boiling water
23	<S 02>	Pardon
24	<S 04>	Didn't know you used boiling water
25	<S 02>	Don't have to but it's erm ... they reckon it's erm quicker
26	[5 secs]	
27	<S 04>	Tony was saying they should have the heating on by about Wednesday
28	<S 02>	Just gonna put the er butter on
29	<S 04>	What you making Ian?
30	<S 02>	Mm
31	<S 04>	What's that?
32	<S 02>	Oh er just gonna do some rice
33	<S 04>	Mm
34	<S 02>	Doing some rice in the micro
35	<S 03>	So you put margarine with it
36	<S 02>	Pardon yeah little bit don't know why cos otherwise it'll
37	<S 03>	⌐Separate it

38	<S 02>	Mm not sure actually doesn't erm don't have to do it when you put it
39		on the er on the stove
40	<S 03>	How long does it take?
41	<S 02>	Erm
42	<S 01>	Oh that'll make a noise
43	<S 02>	⌐Takes about thirty-five minutes yeah that'll that
44		that'll destroy your tape
45	<S 03>	Thirty-five minutes
46	<S 02>	Yeah
47	<S 01>	Yeah
48	<S 03>	I thought the microwave did everything in about two minutes
49	<S 01>	You may as well turn it off now then
50	<S 03>	Yeah you can do it on the cooker for thir, in thirty-five minutes
51	<S 02>	Then if you have to watch it ... you just ignore it
52	<S 03>	Mm
53	<S 04>	You don't have to wash the saucepan either do you?
54	<S 02>	You don't have to wash the saucepan after [laughs] [<S 03> mm] you
55		don't have to erm don't have to drain the water off either
56	<S 03>	I didn't know that microwaves ran that long
57	<S 02>	Yeah you don't have to erm drain the water off either cos er
58	<S 03>	I'll switch it off when you turn that on
59	<S 02>	When Sahib used to come out and make rice and your saucepan
60		used to be it'd be thick about an inch thick on the bottom it would
61		and that was the best part of the rice
62	<S 03>	[laughs] I'll turn this off

General commentary

The family are cooking rice for a family meal. Different activities are involved: cooking, helping, or simply acting as an onlooker. But the main focus of the talk at this point in the recording is on the cooking of the rice and on the procedures involved in its cooking. In this respect the language activity is essentially one of **language-in-action**: language used in the execution of a task in which the participants are directly and materially involved. It is noteworthy, however, that during this process the members of the family feel free to introduce other more incidental topics which may or may not be elaborated upon.

Line-by-line commentary

l.2   *What you got there?* In this recording ELLIPSIS is pervasive. The ellipsis takes, as we shall see, many different forms. In this example the main auxiliary verb *have* is ellipted. Ellipsis is pervasive for a number of reasons: chief among these reasons are that the speakers, as members of the same family, normally conduct conversations with one another which are highly informal. Ellipsis is a linguistic concomitant of informality and easy-goingness in conversation. More specifically, the speakers are performing actions or are making references which are easily visible and apprehensible by all the participants. This kind of grammatical shorthand is perfectly appropriate, therefore, as the speakers have no need to elaborate; indeed, if they were to elaborate, much in their discourse would become unnecessarily redundant.

l.4   *in the one*: In most standard written grammars this structure does not occur. *One* is not normally cited as allowing an immediately preceding definite article. Other examples of the same usage from authentic data are:

> (at an airport check-in)
> Airline check-in stewardess: Is it just *the one* bag you're checking in, sir?
> Male passenger: Just *the one*, yes.

> (woman to man standing waiting outside toilet in a restaurant)
> Is there just *the one* toilet?

In all cases, the object referred to is immediately visible to the speaker and listener. We can only conclude, since the encounters are public and since none of the speakers was speaking in a non-standard dialect, that such examples are examples of standard spoken English and simply have not been observed or codified before. This structure also occurs with other numbers:

> (supermarket assistant to customer) Is it just the three boxes?

l.6   *what next?*: Verbs are ellipted here: either the verb 'to be' or an auxiliary verb. (e.g. what's next?; what do we do next?).

l.7   *[17 secs]*: Note the long silences throughout the transcript, when people are busy doing things. In the context of interchanges between members of a family silences are common. They are neither as disturbing nor perceived as impolite or as unsettling as they might if a stranger or someone from outside the family were in their company. For your convenience we have omitted some of the longer silences on the tape. This also applies to Unit 13, where long silences occur while a customer is having her hair washed at the hairdresser's.

l.8   *Foreign body in there*: Another example of ellipsis; on this occasion it is likely that the dummy subject *there* and the verb to be are ellipted (There's a foreign body in there.). The phrase *foreign body* means here 'strange-looking object that should not be there'.

l.13 *There must be a raisin for it being in there*: The speaker plays here on the sound similarities between 'raisin' and 'reason', echoing at the same time the relatively fixed phrase 'there must be a reason for ...'. Creative punning, word play and patterning and all kinds of similar inventiveness are quite common in conversational discourse. Indeed, many so-called ordinary, everyday conversational exchanges can be more 'literary' than is normally appreciated.

l.16 *Biscuit?*: This is a heavily ellipted version of 'Do you want / Would you like a biscuit?' and is thus a repetition of l.14. It is likely that the biscuit is physically offered – an act which makes a second fully elaborated question redundant. It is likely that the same formulations would even be used in more formal contexts too.

ll.22 *Didn't know ... / Don't have to ...*: These are further examples of ellipsis involving
–25 the deletion of personal pronouns. In formal and written contexts personal pronouns would normally be used but the speaker's choice in omitting them here simply marks the informality of the relationship and the dependence on the immediate context for interpretability.

l.25 *they reckon*: Although inaudible, it is likely that the speaker goes on to give some reason why boiling water is used in the rice cooking process. The use of *they* here is a generic pronoun. An attribution is made to an outside, unnamed agency but without the more formal, impersonal force communicated by a passive construction, e.g. 'it is reckoned that ...'.

l.27 *Tony was saying*: The use of a continuous past tense form is interesting here since most standard grammars indicate that only a simple past tense form can be used when reporting speech events. However, examination of naturally-occurring data reveals that the past continuous is a relatively regular phenomenon. The choice by the speaker here of the past continuous would seem to impart a deliberately indefinite tone which is in turn more in keeping with the relaxed and informal nature of the ongoing discourse. The use of 'said' here would by contrast impart a sense of definite commitment, factuality and authority. The continuous form is often used to introduce a new and interesting topic into the conversation rather than just to report someone's words. Other examples from real data:

> A: Alan was saying the village hall nearly burnt down last night.
> B: Really!
> A: Jennifer was saying they've discovered five mortar bombs at
>   Heathrow Airport.
> B: Oh God!

ll.29 *What you making ... just gonna do some rice*: There are yet further examples of
–32 ellipsis here, in this case again involving omitting both the verb *to be* and the main subject pronouns. The use of the verb 'do' here is interchangeable with 'make' or 'cook'; 'do' is a ubiquitous verb in spoken language which can be

made to collocate with a wide range of nouns, usually adding in the process a note of informality. It is noteworthy, too, that the phrase is headed by the adverb *just* which is itself a frequent marker of informal and casual discourse.

l.38   *not sure actually*: Although a further clear example of ellipsis, involving the omission of the personal pronoun and the verb *to be*, the phrase is actually something of a fixed, routinised expression, and is more likely than not to occur in this form in most informal spoken communication.

l.43   *that'll destroy your tape*: A reference to the tape – the speakers knew they were being recorded.

l.48   *You may as well turn it off now then*: *then* functions as a kind of summary word, marking the closing of an action or sequence of talk.

ll.40   This sequence of exchanges contains several examples of the seemingly
–57   random topic switching and topic overlapping which is characteristic of much informal conversation. Questions remain unanswered or the answers are postponed; questions and answers overlap; turns are punctuated by hesitations and false starts. On the surface there appears to be much divergence, disconnection and incoherence. However, there is nonetheless a large measure of convergence by repetition. For example, the speakers use each other's words, employ parallel syntactic forms and generally pattern questions and replies in such a way as to confirm that there is a strong sense of cooperation, as well as mutual support and common interest in their exchanges. For example, *take* (l.40/l.43); *thirty-five minutes* (ll.43/45/50); *do/did* (ll.48/50); *yeah* (ll.46/47); *drain the water off* (ll.55–57). And so on. The repetitions across speaking turns are clearly not the work of people responding non-creatively, disinterestedly and automatically; they serve to create a strong sense of rapport and interpersonal involvement.

l.49   *may as well*: This is an example of a composite modal item. It is not absolutely fixed: the alternative 'might as well', a more indirect form, is also possible.

l.54   The use of *after* here is typical of informal spoken language. More formal speech or formal written language would usually have 'afterwards'.

l.58   *I'll switch it off when you turn that on*: Demonstratives and other deictics occur relatively densely in examples of language-in-action. Many of the referents are immediately visible and deictic reference is entirely appropriate. Indeed, at several points here the presence of nouns would be redundant. See also l.60.

l.59   *When Sahib used to come out*: The use of *out* with *come* rather than the more usual 'come over' or 'come round' relates to the fact that the family lives on the outskirts of a town or city and that Sahib travels *out* from a point nearer the centre.

l.60 *it'd be about an inch thick on the bottom it would*: The presence of the repeated verb tag *it would* functions as a kind of reinforcement to the statement. Such structures have been called TAILS and they occur almost exclusively in spoken discourse, mainly as here for purposes of adding emphasis. Tails always occur in full rather than contracted form; that is *it would* and not *it'd*.

Further reading

For a fuller discussion of ellipsis in relation to spoken discourse see McCarthy and Carter (1995) and Carter and McCarthy (1995a).

For a discussion of creativity in conversation and the use of literary strategies in conversational exchanges see Tannen (1989), and Carter and McCarthy (1995b).

Tannen (1989) is also a seminal source of analysis of repetition in discourse, especially with reference to patternings across speaking turns.

McCarthy (1988) and (1992a) reaches similar conclusions with particular reference to vocabulary patterns and repetitions.

Ishikawa (1991) is a further study of repetition in discourse.

There is discussion of the function of silences in conversation in Loveday (1982).

A seminal article on 'tails' is Aijmer (1989) and there is further commentary in Carter and McCarthy (1995a). McCarthy and Carter (1997) is a re-assessment of tails using extensive data examples.

Family and relatives

unit **8**

Activity

Make a list, in order of significance, of the main language features which you would
expect to find in a conversation between a mother and a daughter talking in a
relaxed and easy manner about family matters and family arrangements. Some of
the features you might like to consider are: shifts in topic, use of evaluative words
and phrases, repetition, ELLIPSIS, DEIXIS.

Speakers and setting

    <S 01> female
    <S 02> female
    <S 01> and <S 02> are mother and daughter.

In this recording the two speakers are at home. The main subject of conversation is
'family tensions'. The mother's sister, who is staying with them with her family, is
upset because a party has been arranged and they are unable to be there due to
previous commitments.

Transcript

1	<S 01>	And erm so we thought we'd have someone to dinner and have a
2		party you know a dinner party over this coming weekend but they're
3		not going to be here so.
4	<S 02>	Well that would be boring
5	<S 01>	Don't ... Not quite sure when they thought we were going to do it
6		but there we are.

7	\<S 02\>	But she's saying that erm loads of people that they're meant to be
8		staying with can't remember [laughs]. Apparently erm someone's
9		moving well to a new job and someone else has got relatives coming
10		to stay. So they can't
11	\<S 01\>	Oh up in Suffolk?
12	\<S 02\>	Mm. Don't know. But anyway.
13	\<S 01\>	Oh. But they're not. I mean they knew we were away for that whole
14		week cos I wrote and told them.
15	\<S 02\>	What week? Easter week?
16	\<S 01\>	Yes.
17	\<S 02\>	Mm.
18	\<S 01\>	And they they'd already made their plans for various visits before
19		they arrived. It's called a hoof.
20	\<S 02\>	└What is that? [laughs] Is it rubber?
21	\<S 01\>	Yes. I think it's probably quite old and rather
22	\<S 02\>	Where'd you get it?
23	\<S 01\>	inflexible
24	\<S 02\>	Where's it from?
25	\<S 01\>	A chemist. Erm do you know the chemist which is now Boots in
26		Petswood?
27	\<S 02\>	Yeah.
28	\<S 01\>	That's where I got it. I mean they [laughs] ... you use it like this.
29	\<S 02\>	[laughs]
30	\<S 01\>	Push back the cuticle.
31	\<S 02\>	Mm.
32	\<S 01\>	And when I had a manicure free of charge
33	\<S 02\>	When did you have a manicure?
34	\<S 01\>	They were doing them free in the Army and Navy when I went to a
35		special shopping evening.
36	\<S 02\>	Were they?
37	\<S 01\>	Yes. So I had one.
38	\<S 02\>	Mm Mm
39	\<S 01\>	But she didn't like the way I filed my nails. She didn't
40	\<S 02\>	What would they make of mine? [laughs]
41	\<S 01\>	I take them too far down at the edges
42	\<S 02\>	Mm
43	\<S 01\>	You think I do as well do you?
44	\<S 02\>	Yes definitely
45	\<S 01\>	[laughs]

46	\<S 02\>	Can't believe it.
47	\<S 01\>	Anyway. So I can't celeb, can't have any celebration with them cos
48		we were going to have something this weekend and then they said
49		they were going to be away so
50	\<S 02\>	Well if they're going on Tuesday.
51	\<S 01\>	Yes but Dad won't be here will he.
52	\<S 02\>	You're the sister not him.
53	\<S 01\>	Eh?
54	\<S 02\>	You're the sister not him.
55	\<S 01\>	He wouldn't go to that place anyway.
56	\<S 02\>	Is it not er nice at all?
57	\<S 01\>	Oh some of the things are delicious yes. But it's a long way from here.
58	\<S 02\>	Just got to be careful what you choose.
59	\<S 01\>	It's a [inaudible] You can't choose. He just cooks them a meal. If they
60		ring up and say they're going, he serves a meal.
61	\<S 02\>	Where is it then?
62	\<S 01\>	[coughs] Battersea.
63	\<S 02\>	Is that Sally lives there or something?
64	\<S 01\>	Or Battarsia
65	\<S 01\>	Mm.
66	\<S 02\>	Battarsia. [laughs]
67	\<S 01\>	[laughs]
68	\<S 02\>	Erm where's Battersea ... Dogs' Home? It's not that far. It's on the way
69		out of
70	\<S 01\>	It's just south of Victoria.
71	\<S 02\>	Yeah.
72	\<S 01\>	Of Yes. Just south of Victoria.
73	\<S 02\>	I suppose it's a long way to go out for dinner though isn't it?
74	\<S 01\>	It is on a weekd weeknight.
75	\<S 02\>	Except he can go straight from work.
76	\<S 01\>	They wanted to go last time. They thought that we could go straight
77		from work ... and er they could ... because Dad has the car he could
78		then drive us all back.
79	\<S 02\>	I remember that. Remember a bit of a fuss.
80	\<S 01\>	And because I was coming home at lunchtime.
81	\<S 02\>	Why couldn't they ... they'd get the train and meet us there?
82	\<S 01\>	Erm [pause] I think they were going to be in London anyway during
83		the day so they would meet us there or have us pick them up on the
84		way.

85	\<S 02>	Mm. I see.
86	\<S 01>	But ... if we make a thing about duck pancakes
87	\<S 02>	Yeah.
88	\<S 01>	She says he always does lobster and
89	\<S 02>	Mm. Yeah. Something else nice.
90	\<S 01>	something else but I've never had lobster there.
91	\<S 02>	Lobster and?
92	\<S 01>	Prawns?
93	\<S 02>	No. No.
94	\<S 01>	Scallops?
95	\<S 02>	Scallops it might have been. Might have been scallops.
96	\<S 01>	I've never had anything like that there.

General commentary

This conversation is structured along the lines of 'comment-elaboration'. Speakers switch topics relatively freely commenting on each other's statements and elaborating briefly in response to follow-up questions or further comments. The elaboration not uncommonly involves evaluative remarks. Such a structure is frequent in informal conversations between speakers in the same family or between speakers enjoying close relationships. There is no marked overall purpose or outcome to the conversation. Because the speakers can take much for granted about their relationship and mutual knowledge, they do not elaborate and ellipsis is common. Mutual support and convergence is evidenced through widespread repetition.

Line-by-line commentary

l.5 *not quite sure*: Note the ELLIPSIS of *I* here. This is common with verbs of 'mental process' (such as 'know', 'think', 'be sure', 'suppose', etc.). Examples:

> A: What time is it?
> B: Not sure. *or* Don't know. *or* Think it's about five.

See also l.12; l.46.

l.6 *but there we are*: A fixed phrase meaning that there seems little more that can be done.

l.7 *loads of people*: The use of *loads of* with countable and uncountable nouns is very common in informal spoken language. 'Lots of' would be a little less informal, 'a lot of' would be rather neutral, and 'many' would sound absurdly formal in this context.

l.11   *up in Suffolk*: References to places in Britain are frequently made using the prepositions 'up' and 'down'. The geographical position of the speaker relative to the reference is usually significant. The speaker here is south of Suffolk. (See also Unit 5.)

l.12   *But anyway*: A fixed phrase similar to *but there we are* (l.6 above) which indicates that the speaker has little more to say on this topic and may wish to change the topic.

l.19   *It's called a hoof*: A sudden switch in topic, probably occasioned by a switch in the direction of the listener's gaze. A hoof is an instrument used for pushing back cuticle skin on one's nails. See Unit 10, l.52 for a similar switch.

l.22   Note how *where did you* is contracted to *where'd you*. This is perfectly normal and is not 'bad' English.

l.25   *Boots*: The name of a chain of department stores in Britain all containing a pharmaceutical section.

l.34   *They were doing them*: The use of an unspecific pronoun is not uncommon with reference to general processes which one undergoes.

l.34   *Army and Navy*: Army and Navy Stores is the name of a British Department Store.

ll.38   *Mm mm ... definitely*: Throughout this exchange there is much mutual support
–44   through encouraging back-channelling and explicitly positive verbal response.

l.43   *as well* is far more common in informal spoken language than 'also', which has a more formal, written feel to it; 'too' is also common in informal spoken language.

l.47   *Anyway*: Speakers regularly use this marker to go back to topics that have been interrupted or diverged from, or else to signal that the topic is coming towards its end.

l.50   *Well if they're going on Tuesday*: Subordinate clauses which stand on their own and which remain uncompleted are relatively common in informal conversations. There is an invitation to the other speaker to verbally complete or at least infer the content presupposed by the main clause which it is judged unnecessary to elaborate on.

l.51   *Dad*: This is the most common, informal way of referring to one's father. 'Father' would be very formal, and 'Daddy' is mostly used by little children. Compare the discussion of ways of referring to one's mother in Unit 4.

l.54   *You're the sister not him*: Her father cannot, of course, literally be a 'sister'. The daughter means that her mother should take the decision since the relative involved is **her** sister, and so it should not matter whether the father (her sister's brother-in-law) is present or not.

l.58   *Just got to be careful*: Another example of ellipsis involving an ellipsis of a personal pronoun subject. Additionally the auxiliary verb *have* is elliped.

l.63 *Is that Sally lives there*: A combination of three questions (a) 'Is that (where Sally lives)?' – a false start (b) ('Does Sally live there?' – not fully formed as a result of the previous false start and (c) 'Is (it) Sally (who) lives there?'

l.63 *or something*: The phrase is deliberately vague and invites the listener to specify further.

ll.62 –68 Battarsia: The speakers play with the pronunciation of Battersea. Battersea is not a particularly salubrious district of London. It is, for example, known primarily for its power station and its Dogs' Home (l.65). It can be made to sound more attractive by a change in pronunciation which lengthens the second syllable, giving an effect of elegance or upper-class speaking style. This is one further example of creative verbal play for humorous purposes. (See also Unit 6.)

l.70 *Victoria*: Another district of London, known for its railway station which links London with the European rail network.

l.75 *Except he can go straight from work*: This is another subordinate clause which stands on its own. However, the clause complements *It's a long way to go out for dinner* (l.73). As noted above (l.50), apparently self-standing subordinate clauses are frequent in informal spoken discourse. The 'completion' is either present previously in the discourse or is judged to be inappropriate because the other speakers can recover the main proposition for themselves and to be explicit is unnecessary. Speakers can also complete each other's utterances by providing a 'missing' clause. In this way conversational meanings are jointly or co-constructed.

ll.76 –78 *They … we … he*: There is a density of reference here which is perfectly clear to the speakers because the people referred to are clearly established but which would make the conversation almost completely incomprehensible to those 'outside' this conversation.

l.83 *have us pick them up on the way*: Pseudo-passive constructions such as this are common in spoken English though less common in written English. The structure is thus an informal alternative to 'be picked up by us on the way'. 'We could pick them up' is also possible but the choice of a passive or pseudo-passive possibly underscores a tone of slight irritation that her sister and family required things to be arranged for them and were imposing a little too much.

l.86 *make a thing about*: *thing* is one of the most frequent nouns in spoken English and regularly occurs in such phrases as 'make a thing about' which means 'draw attention to' or 'make a fuss about'.

ll.88 *does lobster*: The use of *do* as a ubiquitous transitive verb of action is frequent in spoken English. An alternative here would be the verbs 'cook' or 'prepare'. (See also Unit 12.)

ll.88 –95 There is a real effort here by both speakers to jointly construct meaning and to locate appropriate words. The conversational convergence is also reflected by repetition of words and phrases across and within speaking turns: *something else, scallops, might have been, there*. Repetitions like this are a common feature of conversations in which both speakers share presuppositions and are mutually supportive. (See also Units 7 and 9.)

l.95 *Scallops it might have been*: *Scallops* is front-placed and is thus foregrounded as of main topical significance. The front-placing is prompted by the speaker's question in l.94.

Further reading

For discussion of vague language see Channell (1994).

Bublitz (1988) examines back-channelling and White (1989) discusses cross-cultural differences in back-channelling behaviour between Japanese and American speakers.

On subordinate clauses in spoken language, see Schleppegrell (1992).

On *thing* in conversation, see Fronek (1982).

For an initial study of 'completing' structures in dialogue, see Lerner (1991).

Two teachers chatting

Activity

When two people talk about experiences of places, people or events which they both have in common, would you expect them to relate extended narratives? If so, why? If not, why not? If there are narratives recounted, what form would you expect them to take? To help you, read Units 1 and 2 first.

Speakers and setting

    <S 01>   male
    <S 02>   male

In this extract two middle-aged male teachers talk and reminisce about their days teaching together and, in particular, about time spent at a school, Broadlands School, which they have both recently visited.

Transcript

1	<S 01>	I was amazed walking into Broadlands School how it had changed
2		but it hadn't changed if you see what I mean?
3	<S 02>	Erm.
4	<S 01>	The old the old classrooms were still there and the little raised things
5		by the boss's, what was the boss's offices all brought back memories.
6	<S 02>	It's it's not changed vastly
7	<S 01>	No it was a strange sort of feeling walking into that place.
8	<S 02>	How did Olive speak of it, with certain contempt?
9	<S 01>	Yes I suppose she did speak of it. Yes I said I remember this when it

10		was a woodwork room [<S 02> Mm] her room and I said cor crikey
11		it looks as though it could do with one or two. Yes she said they
12		rearrange the deckchairs round the edges every so often but that's
13		as far as they go with the place. I think she does some superb work
14		for them. You just walk in.
15	<S 02>	She's good at what she does.
16	<S 01>	She's very good at what she does. I didn't realise how under underpaid
17		she is.
18	<S 02>	Well she's not
19	<S 01>	Well she's not on a big scale is she?
20	<S 02>	She's probably on the first allowance so she was probably earning
21		about
22	<S 01>	Eighteen thousand.
23	<S 02>	Erm.
24	<S 01>	Which is not a massive great amount is it? For someone of her
25		talents. [<S 02> Well she] She seems sort of content with that level.
26	<S 02>	Well she's like Aubrey was I mean Aubrey was the sort of person who
27		would never have made a great never a career.
28	<S 01>	No no that's true.
29	<S 02>	And there are people like that who who are very good at what they
30		do.
31	<S 01>	Yeah
32	<S 02>	I mean Aubrey is very talented both in and out of the classroom you
33		know good teacher good diplomat nice bloke I've often thought of
34		contrasting Aubrey and Stan Klebbenham you know because Aubrey
35		was the genuine article.
36	<S 01>	Absolutely.
37	<S 02>	Stan had sort of the appearance of the genuine article [<S 01> and
38		wasn't] who actually was a little creep who wanted to further himself.
39	<S 01>	Well look where he's got now he erm he's Clerk to the Governors I
40		think.
41	<S 02>	Yeah well that's erm that's what he should have been years ago.
42		[<S 01 yeah] I think he's ended up in the right job.
43	<S 01>	You're probably right. Be interesting to see what he looks like. A little
44		wizened hatchet-faced man.
45	<S 02>	I think he'll look. He's the sort of bloke who won't age much. He'll still
46		look like Willy Carson's grandfather you know refugee from a racing
47		stable or whatever. I shall never forget the time that there was this
48		there was this staff match that he refereed and I got more and more

49		and more and more frustrated and irritated by it. And I could
50		contain myself no longer. This is I think this was the beginning of the
51		time that he really really seriously began to dislike me you know on a
52		professional basis. Cos I went up to him afterwards. Cos I'd suffered a
53		fair bit and everybody had it was pathetic, I said Stanley
54		I said I should like to congratulate you on the way you handled that
55		game. And his eyes but unfortunately I can't and walked off and left
56		him, fuming. He had the knives out [inaudible]. But Aubrey was a
57		great player
58	<S 01>	He was super again there were people like Rob Lummel who
59		was of the same mould a nice character [<S 02> mm] who did his
60		job well who taught adequately erm.
61	<S 02>	Never get on.
62	<S 01>	Absolutely right.
63	<S 02>	Never get on.
64	<S 01>	I suppose in a way like me.
65	<S 02>	Yes.
66	<S 01>	But wasn't I'm not career minded I've been pushed on occasions well
67		you should be applying for deputy headship I wasn't interested.
68	<S 02>	Well you and Aubrey used to make me sick actually in the nicest
69		possible way because erm I worked for two people and the subjects
70		I taught I worked for two people who actually managed to be good
71		teachers and be popular.
72	<S 01>	Erm.
73	<S 02>	Which is something that I never cracked you know. I managed to
74		be a good teacher but I wasn't popular I thought to myself, I mean
75		how can you follow that.
76	<S 01>	Follow that one yeah.

General commentary

The speakers are reminiscing about shared experiences. Extended narratives could be expected to be out of place in such exchanges; instead, much can be and is taken for granted and there is therefore little need to identify people and places in any detailed way.

The exchanges are relatively staccato in organisation, with the speakers making a comment about a person or an event and then elaborating briefly upon it. There is extensive topic switching though the topics are all linked by the school and their time there about which the speakers are reminiscing.

Line-by-line commentary

l.4   *little raised things*: the use of *things* here is deliberately indefinite and vague (see VAGUE LANGUAGE). Too great a degree of precision may make the speaker sound assertive and authoritative and this would probably be inappropriate for the reminiscing in which the friends are engaging. (See also ll.52–53 and ll.66–67.)

ll.4   *The old the old; It's it's*: repetitions of this kind are common in spoken discourse.
–6   They allow a little more time to formulate what you want to say. (See also ll.69–70 below.)

l.7   *It was a strange sort of feeling walking into that place*: *walking into that place* is a TAIL. Tails are common in informal conversation in English and allow the speaker to elaborate an idea, at the same time emphasising that it is important. Tails are more common in structures where subjects and accompanying verbs are restated. For example: *He's a very nice person Carl is*. In this example a non-finite verb phrase elaborates the subject *it*. Notice that the tail can be put in subject position and that the resulting structure would sound more formal: '*Walking into that place* was a strange feeling'.

l.10   *Woodwork room her room*: this is not a 'tail' (see l.7 above) but sounds more like a restatement.

l.10   *Cor* and *crikey* express surprise or shock. The words are normally more common in the speech of middle-aged people. *Cor* is also sometimes written 'kaw'; both these words can be used on their own but used here together serve to intensify the feelings expressed.

l.11   *it could do with one or two*: an abbreviation of 'it could do with one or two coats of paint', meaning it looked shabby and needed painting.

l.12   *rearrange the deckchairs*: A deckchair is a collapsible chair normally used for sitting outside and in the sun. Such chairs are easily moved and rearranged. The phrase in English 'rearranging the deckchairs' is an abbreviation of 'rearranging the deckchairs on the *Titanic*', and has a further meaning, that trivial and easy things are being done when there are more important things that need doing. (The ship *Titanic* sank, even though it was thought to be unsinkable. Simply rearranging deckchairs when the ship is sinking is pointless.) The comment is a negative one. Idioms, fixed phrases and, as here, cultural allusions are often employed to evaluate actions, events and people.

l.19   *a big scale*: The reference here is to scales of pay for teachers. There are four main basic grades for classroom teachers and several higher grades for more senior teachers.

l.22   *eighteen thousand*: The word 'pounds' is frequently omitted in casual conversation.

l.24   *Which is not a massive great amount is it?*: subordinate relative clauses are quite frequent in conversation, normally across speaking turns with the effect that one speaker picks up on, or elaborates on or completes a statement made by a previous speaker. (See Unit 8 ll.50 and 75.) The structure is common in written advertisements and gives this kind of text a spoken feel. A further adverbial phrase *for someone of her talents* is then added as a kind of after-thought.

Note also the intensification *massive great*, which is very common in conversational language. Other examples:

> She had a *huge great* dog with her.
> It was just a *tiny little* road.

ll.33   *good teacher good diplomat nice bloke*: Notice how this structure involves the ellipsis of subject, verb and indefinite article. (*He is a* good teacher ...) The ellipsis makes things sound more informal and produces a listing, enumerating structure which pointedly focusses on Aubrey's qualities.

l.35   *the genuine article*: An idiomatic phrase used to mean that someone or something does not fake what they say or do and is a true representative of a particular quality or set of skills.

l.37   Notice the switch from formal vocabulary *appearance of the genuine article* to informal vocabulary *little creep*. Such switches can often mark satirically comic effects.

l.39   *Clerk to the Governors*: An administrative assistant to the governing body of the school, a committee consisting of people from inside and outside of the school.

l.43   *Be interesting to*: Notice the ellipsis of subject (*it*) and modal (*will* or *would*) and subject and verb. Ellipsis here gives the interaction a more informal feel.

l.44   *Wizened* means 'shrivelled', like a thin old person, usually said of someone's face.

l.44   *hatchet-faced*: With sharp features (a hatchet is a sharp instrument for chopping wood).

l.45   *bloke* is an informal word for *man*. American English speakers usually say *guy*, and *guy* is becoming more common in British English too. (See also l.33 above.)

l.46   Willy Carson was a famous jockey.

l.47   *or whatever*: is another example of an indefinite expression where a deliberate lack of precision serves to make the proposition a little more casual and informal. The phrase *and/or whatever* normally only occurs at the end of an utterance or sequence of utterances.

l.48   *there was this staff match*: *This* is often used in spoken narratives instead of the indefinite article *a(n)*; it makes the people and things it refers to more vivid and immediate.

l.53   *a fair bit*: The more formal, written equivalent would probably be *quite a lot*.

l.56 *he had the knives out*: An idiom meaning 'he was just looking for every opportunity to attack/criticise'.

ll.61 *Never get on ... never get on*: The two speakers revert to a simple present so
−63 that their comments are both in the manner of a generalisation as well as a specific comment on the individual (Rob Lummel). See also ll.75–76 for comment on repetition across speaking turns.

ll.66 *I've been pushed on occasions well you should*: Here direct speech is embedded within
−67 a report. *Pushed* operates as a reporting verb so that *well, you should* is represented as direct speech. This is a common feature of spoken narrative reports. (See also l.75 below.)

ll.68 *in the nicest possible way*: This phrase allows the speaker to soften the threatening
−69 aspect of what he says. It makes his direct comment about his interlocutor (and Aubrey who is absent) less direct and to some extent protects both speaker and hearer, allowing neither to lose face too much. Other expressions that protect participants' face include:

> What a boring crowd of people! *Present company excepted*, of course.
> I think a lot of people here, *myself included*, have been rather lazy of late.
> *No offence intended*, but I think you're making a big mistake here.

l.73 *Cracked*: An informal word meaning roughly 'succeed in' or 'find the solution to'.

ll.75 *follow that ... follow that one yeah*: This expression means roughly 'it would be
−76 difficult to outdo/improve on that'. The two speakers repeat each other's words relatively frequently in this exchange. See also ll.61–63 (*Never get on ... never get on*) and ll. 15–16 (*good at what she does ... very good at what she does*). Verbatim repetition and repetition with minimal variation across speaking turns generally indicate agreement between speakers, the kind of convergence where they simply reinforce, by restatement, what the other has said. Where repetition with variation does occur, the second utterance is normally intensified by the speaker. Either a stronger verb or adjective is selected or intensifying adverbs such as 'very' or 'extremely' are employed. Disagreement is normally signalled if different vocabulary items are selected.

Further reading

McCarthy (1984) and (1988) has observations on uses of vocabulary across speaking turns (what he terms 'interactive lexis').

On repetition across turn boundaries, see Tannen (1989: ch. 3).

On tails, see Aijmer (1989).

On subordinate clauses in spoken discourse see Halliday (1989), Schleppegrell (1992).

On the question of face, and how speakers may threaten it or protect it, see Brown and Levinson (1987).

unit 10

Students chatting round the tea-table

Activity

Because the conversation you are going to hear is a very informal one, a number of colloquial words and expressions occur. These are not always easy to find (or simply are not included) in dictionaries, because most dictionaries do not take everyday conversational language into account. Check the following list of words and expressions that occur in the extract. How many do you already know/understand? How many of them are in the dictionary that you use most frequently when you have problems with English words? Explanations are given for all of them in the **Line-by-line commentary**.

> *It's a toss-up between ... and ...* (idiom)
> *wodge* (noun)
> *fag* (noun)
> *dangly* (adjective)
> *wow* (exclamation)

Speakers and setting

    <S 01>   female (20)
    <S 02>   female (21)
    <S 03>   female (21)

All three are Art College students who share a house in Carmarthen, Wales. <S 01> and <S 03> are from the south-west of England. <S 02> is from South Wales. They are having tea at home on a Sunday.

Transcript

1	<S 01>	Does anyone want a chocolate bar or anything?
2	<S 02>	Oh yeah yes please
3	<S 03>	└Yes please
4	<S 02>	[laughs]
5	<S 03>	[laughs]
6	<S 01>	You can have either a Mars Bar, Kit-Kat or erm cherry Bakewell
7	<S 03>	Oh erm it's a toss-up between [<S 02> [laughs]] the cherry
8		Bakewell and the Mars Bar isn't it?
9	<S 01>	└Well shall I bring some in then cos you might
10		want another one cos I don't want them all, I'm gonna be
11	<S 03>	Miss paranoid about weight aren't you?
12	<S 01>	Yes but you know
13	<S 03>	You're not fat Mand
14	<S 01>	I will be if I'm not careful
15	<S 02>	Oh God
16	<S 01>	I ate almost a whole jar of raisins this weekend [<S 02> <S 03>
17		[laugh]]
18		my Mum gave me all these
19	<S 03>	└Look at her, look
20	<S 01>	She goes oh [inaudible]
21	<S 03>	What was that about, you said about you and your Mum don't get on
22		[<S 02>[laughs]] I'd say you got on all right with that big wodge of
23		food there
24	<S 01>	└We can relate to chocolate ... I think they're the little ones
25		actually so you can have one of them and one of them if you like
26	<S 02>	Oh those cherry Bakewells look lovely
27	<S 03>	They do don't they?
28	<S 01>	Oh they were ... gorgeous ... did you say you'd like a cup of tea?
29	<S 02>	Yes
30	<S 03>	All right then
31	<S 01>	Sound like a right mother don't I?
32	<S 03>	You do
33	<S 02>	But they would go smashing with a cup of tea wouldn't they?
34	<S 01>	They would yeah
35	<S 02>	Cup of tea and a fag
36	<S 01>	Cup of tea and a fag Misses, we're gonna have to move the table I
37		think

38	<S 03>	Yeah d'you like Sarah's table she's constructed of erm boots and and
39		a book?
40	<S 01>	Oh that's brilliant
41	<S 03>	Eh that's really good there look
42	<S 02>	and it's got the Milky Way wrapper as that little extra support
43	<S 03>	I like Sunday nights for some reason, I don't know why
44	<S 02>	[laughs] cos you come home
45	<S 03>	I come home
46	<S 02>	You come home to us
47	<S 01>	and pig out
48	<S 02>	Yeah yeah
49	<S 03>	Sunday's a really nice day I think
50	<S 02>	It certainly is
51	<S 03>	It's a really nice relaxing day
52	<S 02>	It's an earring, it's an earring
53	<S 03>	⌐Oh lovely oh, lovely
54	<S 02>	It's fallen apart a bit but
55	<S 03>	It's quite a nice one actually, I like that, I bet, is that supposed to be
56		straight?
57	<S 02>	Yeah
58	<S 03>	Oh I think it looks better like that
59	<S 02>	And there was another bit as well, another dangly bit
60	<S 03>	What, attached to
61	<S 02>	⌐The top bit ⌐
62	<S 03>	⌐That one
63	<S 02>	Yeah ... so it was even ⌐
64	<S 03>	⌐Mobile earrings
65	<S 01>	What, that looks better like that, it looks better like that
66	<S 02>	Oh what did I see, what did I see, stained glass, there was, I went to a
67		craft fair [<S 03> mm] erm in Cambridge and erm I know, I went to
68		a craft fair in Cambridge and they had erm this stained glass stall and
69		it was all mobiles made out of stained glass [<S 03> ah wow] and
70		they were superb they were, and mirrors with all different colours,
71		like going round in the colour, colour-wheel but all different sized bits
72		of coloured glass on it [<S 03> Oh nice] it was superb, massive

General commentary

This is typical of casual talk, where the topics drift from one to another, sometimes provoked by what the speakers are doing (e.g. eating and weight problems), or objects in the immediate situation (the discussion about the earring), or just something which springs to mind by association (the remarks about the craft fair), or the whole present situation itself (talking about Sunday). No one person is in control of the topics, and almost anything may be talked about.

Line-by-line commentary

l.1   *or anything*: The other girls understand what this vague expression means. For them it probably includes the possibility of a biscuit or a cake, anything which typically goes with a cup of tea. What do you think speakers might imply when they say the following remarks?:

> Are you going to the cafeteria? Will you get me a sandwich or something?
> Maureen said you've moved into your new office. Let me know if you need any notepaper or anything.

ll.2   Don't forget that British English speakers will always include 'please' after
–3   'yes' when accepting offers of food/drink; it may sound quite impolite to just say 'yes'. Equally, if someone is checking that you have what you need or want, it is normal to say 'yes thanks':

> A: Have you had coffee?
> B: Yes thanks.

l.6   *Mars Bar*: A best-selling chocolate bar with a soft caramel centre. *Kit-Kat*: another best-selling chocolate bar, but with a wafer-biscuit centre. *Cherry Bakewell*: a small cake or tart with a cherry on top, named after a town in the north of England.

l.7   *it's a toss-up between ... and ...*: A colloquial expression meaning *it's difficult to choose between ... and ...* (see **Activity** above). The reference is to tossing a coin in the air and having to choose which side will land upwards (e.g. at the beginning of a football match to decide which team will play from which end).

l.8   *isn't it*: This conversation contains a number of TAGS, which create informality and intimacy among the speakers. They do not necessarily demand a reply; they just suggest a shared view of the situation. (See also Unit 4.) The tags in this extract are:

line	context
l.8	It's a toss-up between the cherry Bakewell and the Mars Bar **isn't it**
11	Miss paranoid about weight **aren't you**
27	They do **don't they**
31	Sound like a right mother **don't I**
33	They would go smashing with a cup of tea **wouldn't they**

Note in particular how the tags often occur when the subject (and sometimes the verb) are ellipted, as in l.11: (*You're*) *Miss paranoid* ... and l.31: (*I*) *sound like* .... Other examples:

> Got a pen I could borrow, have you?
> Been staying out late again, has she?

Note also how in the case of l.31 and l.33, the other speakers reply with the corresponding tag / reduced form too (l.32: *You do*; l.34: *They would yeah*).

l.11   The use of *Miss* here is humorous/sarcastic. Other similar examples:

> He's real Mister I-know-best, he is.
> She's always playing the little Miss hard-done-by. ('hard-done-by' = badly treated by other people)

l.12   *Yes but you know*: Notice how sometimes a speaking turn can be no more than just DISCOURSE MARKERS. (See also Unit 6, ll.36–37.) It is not always necessary to say a full sentence with 'content'.

l.13   *Mand* is a short form of the girl's name, Amanda.

l.19   Although the tape is difficult to interpret here, this is an example of using 'go' to report people's words and/or actions, which is frequent in informal conversation. (See also Unit 20, l.42.)

l.21   *wodge*: A colloquial word for a large piece of something (usually food such as cakes, bread, pies, meat). (See **Activity** above.) Also used for a pile of money (notes).

l.25 *One of them*: When *them* is stressed (as it is here) it is used in informal conversation as an alternative for 'those':

> (In a cake shop)
> Assistant: Yes please.
> Customer: *(pointing to the cakes)* I'll have one of them and two of them, please.

However, when 'them' is used as an alternative for 'those' in structures such as the following the usage is generally regarded as non-standard dialect form.

> Them people over the road always make a lot of noise.
> Don't buy them CDs. They're not worth it.

l.28 *gorgeous* is a word many British English speakers associate with female speakers, although this may be changing nowadays.

l.31 *right* here is a colloquial alternative to *real/proper*. It is typically used in pejorative contexts by most southern British English speakers:

> He's a right idiot, he is.

But in the north of England it is also used as an adverb meaning *really* and is used in positive contexts too:

> We had a right good time in Spain last year.

l.33 *go smashing*: *smashing* is a colloquial word meaning 'wonderful' / 'very good'. It has no adverb form 'smashingly', and so is used in its adjective form here, to mean 'wonderfully' / 'very well'.

ll.35 *fag*: Colloquial word for a cigarette. (See **Activity** above). In l.36, the speaker
–36 is mimicking working-class speech (perhaps imagining a factory cafe or canteen, addressing a colleague).

l.40 *Brilliant* is frequently used in exclamations by younger speakers to mean 'great/wonderful'.

l.42 *Milky Way*: Another popular chocolate bar, this time with a very light, soft milky-textured centre.

ll.44 The repetition here is done in a semi-humorous, affectionate tone of voice.
–46

l.47 *pig out*: eat far more than you should.

l.52 One of the girls has clearly expressed curiosity (probably by her facial expression) as to what <S 02> is holding (a broken earring).

l.59　*dangly*: The -y suffix is often used to create informal, rather vague adjectives (see **Activity** above). Other examples:

> Sorry, this ice-cream's all runny. (it's melting and running like a liquid)
> They were made of elasticky sort of stuff. (something like elastic)

l.59　Note how *bit* is used as an informal alternative to *part*.

l.65　*That* and *it* are used one after the other here to refer to the same thing. *That* has a pointing function; *it* simply repeats something already referred to or obvious in the situation.

l.69　*Wow* is a frequent exclamation/reaction of amazement/appreciation used by younger speakers. (See **Activity** above.)

l.70　*They were superb, they were*: This is an example of a TAIL, where the subject + verb are repeated at the end of the clause. Other examples:

> She's a fool, she is.
> I'm always spilling my coffee, I am.

This structure is common when we are evaluating or commenting on something, rather than just stating a fact. One of the main functions of tails such as these is to reinforce the comment.

l.71　*The colour-wheel* is a circular chart used by artists and other people working with colour which shows the relationship between the different colours in the spectrum.

Further reading

On how topics shift and change in everyday conversation, see Gardner (1987).

On tails, see Aijmer (1989); Carter and McCarthy (1995a); McCarthy and Carter (1997).

Further examples and a discussion of the creative use of suffixes may be found in Carter and McCarthy (1995b).

unit 11

At the post office

Activity

Think of five things you might want to ask for at a post office in your country. If possible, compare your list with someone else's or with someone from a different country.

Are post offices generally friendly places? What factors might make the conversation between a customer and the assistant more informal/friendly in a post office or other kind of shop?

Extract 1

Speakers

      <S 01>   customer: male
      <S 02>   assistant: female

Transcript

1	<S 01>	Right, send that first class please
2	<S 02>	That one wants to go first class, right we'll see if
3		it is, it's not it's not 41, it's a 60, I thought it would be, I'd be in
4		the ... 60 pence [6 secs] there we are
5	<S 01>	Lovely thank you
6	<S 02>	Okay 70 80 whoops 90 100
7	<S 01>	Thanks very much
8	<S 02>	Thank you

Extract 2

Speakers

<S 01>   customer: female
<S 02>   assistant: female

Transcript

 1 <S 01>   Can I have a second class stamp please Les?
 2 <S 02>   You can ... there we are
 3 <S 01>   ⌐Thank you
 4 <S 02>   ⌐And one penny thank you
 5 <S 01>   That's for me to spend is it?
 6 <S 02>   That's right
 7 <S 01>   I bought a new book of ten first class when I was in
 8   town today and I've left them at home in me shopping bag
 9 <S 02>   Have you?
10 <S 01>   And I've got one left
11 <S 02>   Oh dear [laughs]
12 <S 01>   Bye
13 <S 02>   Bye

Extract 3

Speakers

<S 01>   customer: female
<S 02>   assistant: male

Transcript

 1 <S 01>   Can I post this second class please?
 2 <S 02>   You may. Put him over the bar, just there, look, where
 3   my finger is
 4 <S 01>   There [laughs]
 5 <S 02>   They're still tingling, thank you ... second class is
 6   thirty-six
 7 <S 01>   Right ... I need erm to get a TV licence for my Mum, can you do
 8   it month by month or do you have to pay for it all at once or?
 9 <S 02>   ⌐Er ... well at the

10		moment we've got no forms for you to do it month by month but er
11		if you write to TV, Bristol [<S 01> yeah] just TV Bristol, TV
12		Licences Bristol, I think they'll send you a form monthly
13	<S 01>	Right
14	<S 02>	They're doing it, they used to do it in book form years
15		ago [<S 01> yes] and I think they're starting it again
16	<S 01>	Right
17	<S 02>	So you, you know
18	<S 01>	Cos she's probably not going to be in her own home for a year so
19		we just want to do it for a month at a time to see how she goes
20	<S 02>	⌐That's right, that's
21		right, or if she ever leaves she can always change the address
22		at a post office where she goes to
23	<S 01>	Yeah
24	<S 02>	If she does take a yearly one out, you know
25	<S 01>	⌐Right okay, and the other
26		thing I need is this, a form for repayment and reinvestment of
27		savings certificates please
28	<S 02>	Yep [12 secs] that's that
29	<S 01>	Thanks very much, that's all, then I owe you for the stamp
30	<S 02>	Thirty six, yeah
31	<S 01>	I've got the six actually ... there we go
32	<S 02>	There we are
33	<S 01>	Lovely
34	<S 02>	Thank you
35	<S 01>	Thanks very much
36	<S 02>	Thank you bye bye
37	<S 01>	Bye bye

General commentary

These three samples go from a very simple service encounter to more complex ones. **Extract 1** contains the bare, essential elements necessary to complete the business the customer wants:

1   Request for service   (l.1)
2   Acknowledgement and stating price   (ll.2-3)
3   Handing over the goods   (l.4)
4   Giving money and receiving change   (ll.5-6)
5   Closing the encounter   (ll.7-8)

Extract 2 is different. As well as doing business, the customer enters into conversation with the assistant. The customer makes a joke (line 5) on receiving the change, which is only one penny (= less than 2 cents US$) and then tells the assistant about buying stamps earlier in the day. The assistant joins in the joke and responds sympathetically to the customer's story. This is typical of many service encounters where **interactional** (personal/social) language is just as important as **transactional** ('business') language.

Extract 3 is complex in the sense that three different requests for service are linked together in one transaction. The end of each transaction is clearly signalled by the customer with *right* (lines 7 and 25). In line 16, the customer seems to be indicating that the transaction has ended (*right*), but the assistant offers further information.

Line-by-line commentary

Extract 1

1.1 Note how *right* is used by the customer to mark the opening of the transaction.

Send that first class: Although this looks like an imperative verb, it is almost certainly an ellipsis of *'I'd like to send'* or *'Can I send'* (or something similar). Imperatives are considered very direct in British English and can often be heard as impolite. It would be very unlikely that a customer would use a simple imperative in this situation. However, ELLIPSIS is common in service encounters of this kind, and the assistant 'understands' that it is a request, not a command. Usually, in a post office, it is sufficient to say 'First (or second) class please', when handing over a letter.

First class (fast mail service) and *second class* (a slower service) refer to the two options you have when sending an inland letter in Great Britain. First class is quicker but more expensive.

Note the use of *please*, even in an insignificant service such as buying a stamp. The safest rule is always to use 'please' in Britain when requesting goods and services. Not using 'please' can sound rude.

1.2 *That one wants to go first class*: It is, of course, the customer who *wants* the letter to go first class, not the letter itself, but *wants* here is used more with the meaning of 'needs' or 'should', which is a frequent usage in spoken language (e.g. 'My hair wants cutting', 'This room wants decorating').

1.3 Note how the assistant changes from *it's not 41* to *it's a 60*, the use of *a* here refers to the different bands of letter-charges and means roughly 'it's a letter that falls into the 60-class'.

l.4   *there we are* (see also extract 2, l.2, and extract 3, l.32): This is a common phrase used when handing anything over to someone (not just in shops). Alternatives you will sometimes hear include:

> There you are.
> There you go.
> There we go. (see extract 3, l.31)

l.5   *Lovely* is often used just to mean 'good', 'fine' or 'thanks', as an informal acknowledgement when receiving something.

ll.5   Note that *thank you / thanks* occurs three times. Saying thanks several times in
−8   this way is an important means of marking that the encounter has finished. It is wrong to interpret it as 'over-politeness'.

l.6   *whoops* is typically said when you drop something (here probably a coin) or if someone stumbles or has a slight fall.

Extract 2

l.7   *book of ten first class*: This refers to a booklet containing ten first class stamps. When you want to buy a supply of stamps in a British post office, you can buy them in 'books' of first or second class stamps. A 'book' may contain 4, 6, 10 or more stamps.

l.8   *me shopping bag*: *Me* is a non-standard form of 'my', and is common throughout the Midlands and North of England, and in parts of Ireland.

l.11   *Oh dear* is a polite way of expressing sympathy when someone reports an unfortunate event.

Extract 3

l.1   Compare this with line 1 in extract 1: There are various typical ways of asking for a letter to be sent:

> I want to / Can I *send/post* this first class please.
> Can I *have* this second class please.
> I'd like this to *go* airmail please.

l.2   *You may* is a rather formal and polite reply to the customer's *can*.

l.2   *Put him over the bar*: The assistant is referring to the security bar on the post office counter, and wants the customer to put the letter on the weighing scales behind the bar to weigh it. Referring to the item as *him* is also typical of informal workplace situations such as this.

l.5   *tingling* here refers to the needle on the weighing scale. The needle has not stopped moving but the customer tries to remove the letter. The assistant wants the letter to stay on the scales until it is clear what the exact weight/price is.

l.6 You will hear a variety of ways of referring to prices in pence in Ireland and Great Britain:

> Thirty-six pee please.
> Thirty-six please.
> Thirty-six pence please.

l.7 *Mum* is the most common informal word for *mother* in Britain. In some parts of Britain and Ireland you may hear *Mam*, *Ma* or *Mammy* as alternatives. *Mummy* and *Mama* (mə'maː) are considered rather upper-class if used by adults, but *Mummy* is often used by little children. (See also Unit 5, and Unit 8 for a discussion about ways of referring to a father.)

l.14 *in book form* (compare extract 2, line 7): Formerly, it was possible to buy a booklet into which you stuck savings stamps (usually month by month or week by week) which could be used to pay for your annual TV licence when totalled up.

l.28 *Yep* is a very informal, but business-like alternative to *yes*.

l.29 *That's all*: This is said when you have finished your requests for goods or services.

ll.36 *Bye bye* is not compulsory in service encounters of this kind. Here it probably
−37 happens since the conversation has been quite a long one. It would be much less likely to occur in extracts 1 and 2.

Further reading

On service encounters in general, see Ventola (1987).

On how 'thank you' is used in shops, see Aston (1995).

unit 12

Ordering food in a restaurant

This unit has two extracts. Do the **Activity** and study the **Commentary** for extract 1 first; leave extract 2 until you have finished all the work for extract 1.

Extract 1

Activity

Before listening to Extract 1, think a bit about how the forms *'ll* (or *will*) and *be going to* (often spoken as *gonna* in conversation) are used in English for making 'decisions about the future'.

If you cannot think of a simple rule or guideline for using the forms, have a look in one or two grammar reference books or English coursebooks and see what advice is given there.

(For comments on this activity, see **General commentary** below.)

Speakers and setting

    <S 01>   customer: female (24)
    <S 02>   customer: female (24)
    <S 03>   female waitress: (20s)

Two old schoolfriends from South Wales meet up to have lunch in London, in a very informal restaurant, the type that serves hamburgers and other fast-food. At the start of the extract, they are looking at the menu. While they are discussing what to choose, the waitress comes up and stands silently, waiting for them to order.

Transcript

1 <S 01>   I'm gonna have er ... an Old Timer with cheese, I am
2 <S 02>   What's that?
3 <S 01>   The Old Timer burger, but I'm gonna have cheese with it
4 <S 02>   Oh right, I'm gonna have, I think I'm gonna have a
5   veggy one with barbecue sauce on it
6 <S 01>   Mm, are you gonna have a starter, what you gonna have?
7 <S 02>   └Yeah ... I'm trying not
8   to have nachos [5 secs]
9 <S 02>   I'm either gonna have nachos, buffalo wings or potato
10   skins
11 [11 secs]
12 <S 01>   I'm gonna have the deep fried mushrooms, you like
13   mushrooms, don't you?
14 [3 secs]
15 <S 02>   I'm gonna have to have nachos, I'm addicted to it ...
16   I want, they don't do cider, and I don't want a beer, [<S 03> Hi]
17   don't do cider, do you?
18 <S 03>   Sorry
19 <S 02>   Don't do cider
20 <S 03>   No
21 <S 01>   I'll have the deep fried mushrooms with erm, an Old
22   Timer burger, can I have cheese on it?
23 <S 03>   What cheese?
24 <S 01>   What's the difference?
25 <S 03>   Swiss, Monterrey Jack is an American cheese [inaudible] how would
26   you like it cooked?
27 <S 01>   Erm well done
28 <S 03>   Yes
29 <S 02>   Can I have the, er, nachos and, erm, I was wondering
30   whether to have a veggy burger or the normal burger, erm, are the
31   veggy burgers nice?
32 <S 03>   Yeah they're okay, they're not made on the premises though
33 <S 02>   All right I'll have, er, I'll have a normal burger then, with
34   barbecued beans
35 <S 03>   How would you like it cooked?
36 <S 02>   Erm medium
37 <S 03>   And drinks

38	\<S 02\>	Er, d'you have, er have you got pineapple juice?
39	\<S 03\>	[nods her head]
40	\<S 02\>	Can I have pineapple juice mixed with white wine?
41		Mixed together
42	\<S 03\>	└White wine
43	\<S 02\>	Yeah, in a big glass with loads of ice
44	\<S 01\>	[laughs] Erm, can I have, erm, mineral water, sparkling one?
45	\<S 03\>	Okay
46	\<S 01\>	Thanks

Extract 1

General commentary

In this extract, before they place their order, the two women are 'thinking aloud' about what they want to eat. They have probably already *decided* before the waitress takes their order, but at this stage, the decisions are provisional and personal and are simply statements of what they have decided to order when the waitress arrives. Note how their decisions are expressed by *be going to* when they are simply thinking aloud, but change to *'ll* (which is sometimes written as *will*) when they have to state their decision finally and 'externally' to the waitress.

Be going to is rooted in the present, what seems likely *now*, or what I intend *now* for the future, or what I predict based on the evidence *now*. It is a very **interpersonal** expression, in which *you*, the speaker, involve yourself personally. *Will* is more neutral, objective and simply states what the future is certain to be, or most likely to be, or what you have decided it is to be.

Sometimes both forms are possible or are used together, but with a different shade of meaning:

> It *will* be cold tonight, so be careful, those country roads *are going to* be icy.

This use of both forms together is very frequent in informal weather forecasts on British radio and television, and seems to express a contrast between 'scientific prediction' *will* and a more interpersonal warning *be going to*, reinforced by the use of '*those* country roads', a very familiar, informal use of *those*.

> I'm *gonna* have to go to bed soon.

This was said by a very tired hostess, late in the evening, to her dinner guests. She could have used *will*, but it would have sounded much more cold and neutral. *Going to* expressed well her personal feelings at that moment.

Line-by-line commentary

l.1   *an Old Timer*: a brand name for a particular type of hamburger sold in this restaurant.

Note here the TAG *I am* at the end of the turn, which re-emphasises the personal pronoun *I* at the beginning of her turn. The *I* is stressed, not the *am*. This type of tag is frequent in conversation. Other examples:

> She's a fool, *she* is.
> He emigrated to New Zealand, *he* did.
> They work with me, *they* do.

ll.1–3 Notice the switch from *an* to *the* before *Old Timer burger*. When ordering food it is very common to refer to something from a menu using the definite article. Compare:

> I'll have an orange juice. (where the speaker is not selecting from a list but is assuming that an orange juice is available)
> I'll have the chicken. (where the speaker is selecting a particular chicken dish from the menu)

l.3   'Hamburger' is usually shortened to *burger* in informal conversation.

l.4   Note how useful *(oh) right* is as an informal follow-up to an answer from someone, when you want to show you have understood clearly what they tell you. Other examples:

> A: Where's Hokkaido?
> B: In the North of Japan.
> A: Oh right.
>
> A: What time do we have to be there?
> B: Six-thirty.
> A: Right.

The presence of *oh* can also suggest an element of surprise in the speaker's reaction. *Right* in l.4 could also mean 'OK it's time for me to order now'.

l.5   *veggy*: A colloquial word for *vegetarian*. It is most often used for food, but can be used for a person too:

> A: I don't want any meat, thanks.
> B: Oh, you a veggy too?
> A: Yeah.
> B: Oh right, so am I actually.

l.6   *what you gonna have*: In very quick, informal conversation, as well as shortening 'going to' to 'gonna', speakers sometimes leave out the verb 'be'. Here the speaker does not say 'What **are** you gonna have'.

l.7   *nachos*: A spicy Latin-American crisp-type of snack often served as an appetizer.

l.9   *buffalo wings:* chicken wings *potato skins*: thin chunks of potato with the peel on,
−10   fried and served as an appetizer or starter.

l.13   Note here a different TAG, *don't you*. Compare it with the reinforcing tag in l.1. This type of tag, where an *affirmative* verb in the main clause is followed by a *negative* verb in the tag (or vice-versa), spoken with *falling* intonation, is used when you are reasonably sure that what you are saying is true, but you just want the other person to confirm it. If you use *rising* intonation on the tag, you sound less sure:

> You like mushrooms, don't you? (fairly sure, confirm)
> You like mushrooms, don't you? (not so sure, tell me)

See also the discussions of TAGS in Units 4 and 10.

l.15   Although *nachos* is plural, the speaker sees the word as the (singular) name of the dish, and so says *addicted to it*, not *them*. *Them* would have been quite correct, too.

l.16   The use of *do* here is common as an informal word meaning *sell* or *serve* in shops, restaurants, hotels, etc. (See also Unit 8.) Other examples:

> D'you do vegetarian food?
> You don't do children's clothes, do you?
> Do you do just bed and breakfast?

l.17   At this point, <S 02> has turned towards the waitress, and is directing the question to her. Note when she repeats her question in l.19 she does not repeat the whole question, just the verb and object. This is situational ELLIPSIS, which is very common in informal situations where things and people are present and fairly obvious in the context.

l.18   *Sorry* is very common in informal conversation in British English to indicate you have not heard or understood what the other person has said.

l.21   Note now the change to *'ll* as the speaker 'announces' her decision.

ll.26   This is a very frequent sequence in food-ordering in restaurants where steaks
−27   and hamburgers are concerned. The waiter/waitress asks 'How would you like it cooked?' or 'How would you like it done?' or even just 'How would you like it?'. Normally, the choice is between 'rare' (barely cooked, a little bloody), 'medium rare' (a little more cooked than rare), 'medium' (considered

'average', neither under- nor over-cooked), or 'well done' (fully cooked but not burnt). (See also ll.35–36.)

l.29 *I was wondering ...* is a very indirect expression, combining past tense and continuous form. It makes what you are saying less direct and sounds more polite in situations where politeness is important. The actual time reference is to the present. Other examples:

> I was wondering if I could have a word with you.
> We were wondering whether to write to her. What do you think?
> Were you looking for someone?
> I was thinking of going to the cinema.

l.32 Note the position of *though* at the end of the clause. In formal written text, it is more likely to occur at the beginning of the clause. A formal, written version of the utterance might be:

> The hamburgers are good, though they are not made on the premises.

The same is true of *then* in l.33, which is also common at the end of the clause in informal spoken language.

l.38 Note how the speaker uses two constructions with 'have' here. *D'you have ....?* means more or less the same as *Have you got ....?*, but the form with *got* is more informal, and very common in everyday conversation.

l.43 *loads of* is one of a number of informal expressions common in conversation for expressing large amounts or quantities of something. The speaker could also have said 'lots of' here. Other expressions you may hear in informal British English include 'heaps of', 'tons of', 'piles of', 'oodles of', 'stacks of', 'masses of'. But each expression tends to have its own typical collocations, so listen out for them and the kinds of situations in which they are used. (See also Unit 16, l.80.)

l.44 ELLIPSIS is common in ordering food and drinks and other types of goods and services. Here the speaker does not say *a sparkling one*, which would be expected in more formal, typically written grammar. Other examples:

> Cheeseburger please, with French fries. (understood *a* or *one*)
> Single to Oxford, please. (understood *a* or *one* single ticket)

Extract 2

Activity

This is a small part of another transcript of a recording made in a restaurant. *Note:* There is no recording on the tape for this extract. The speakers are again looking at the menu and deciding what to order, before the waiter/waitress arrives, but this time the situation is different. This time, <S 01> has invited <S 02> and is going to pay for her meal. How is this reflected in the speakers' choices of *be going to* and *'ll*?

Transcript

1	<S 01>	Well what are you going to have then?
2	<S 02>	Erm I don't want any salad
3	<S 01>	Not [inaudible]
4	<S 02>	No thanks no I think I'll have
5	[10 secs]	
6	<S 02>	I think I'll have the haddock

Extract 2

General commentary

<S 01>, who has invited <S 02>, uses *be going to* in her question to ask <S 02> what she is thinking of ordering, but note that <S 02> does not use *be going to* in her answer. This is because it might sound as if she presumes that she can have anything she wants from the menu. When someone is inviting you, it is normal to say to them 'I think I'll have …', which is (a) more neutral and (b) more indirect because of 'I think'. The person who is doing the inviting is free to say either 'I think I'll have …' or 'I'm going to have …'.

Line-by-line commentary

1.1 Note again the final position of *then* (see extract 1, l.33). In this usage, however, the meaning is different from the final *then* above. It is equivalent to sentence-initial 'so' and marks the beginning of a topic. For example, a doctor-patient interview may start as follows:

> Hello, do come in … sit down. So what can I do for you? (*or* What can I do for you then?)

Further reading

For an account of *will* and *be going to* which has a good explanation of the present-orientation of *be going to*, see Haegeman (1989).

On the different types of tags and their functions in English, see Quirk et al (1985: 810–14) and Bennett (1989).

unit **13**

At the hairdresser's

Activity

When you sit down in the hairdresser's or barber's chair, what is likely to be the first question he/she will ask you? Imagine what *you* would answer for yourself in this situation. See the **Line-by-line commentary** for answers to the first part of the activity and note what the young woman asks for.

Speakers and setting

      <S 01>   hairdresser: female
      <S 02>   customer: female (21)
      <S 03>   hair washer: female

This extract was recorded at a hairdresser's in Beeston, Nottinghamshire.

Transcript

  1 <S 01>   Hello.
  2 <S 02>   Hiya, I've got an appointment for half past three.
  3 <S 01>   Jodie?
  4 <S 02>   Yes, that's right.
  5 <S 01>   D'you want to hang your jacket up there?
  6 <S 02>   ⌐Okay, thanks.
  7 <S 01>   Okay, do you want to take a seat across here?
  8 <S 02>   Thank you.
  9 [3 secs]

10 <S 01>   Alright? What?

11 <S 02>   ⌐Yeah.

12 <S 01>   How much do you want off?

13 <S 02>   Ermm [2 secs] Well I like to keep the top quite long [<S 01> yeah]

14   ermm, but I like the back nice and short and the sides nice and short

15   It's just got a bit, you know, a bit grown out of shape.

16 <S 01>   ⌐Too heavy

17 <S 02>   Yeah.

18 <S 01>   Do you have your sides feathered?

19 <S 02>   Yeah, yeah.

20 <S 01>   ⌐So whispy there

21 <S 02>   Yeah.

22 <S 01>   Now, this back bit do you tend to have that bit clippered?

23 <S 02>   Yeah, and I have, I tend to have it like graduated at the back, right at

24   the bottom really short and then kind of graduated up, you know

25   not like a line as such, just [<S 01> Right] graded up

26 <S 01>   ⌐So, right yeah.

27 <S 02>   And I generally style it, but it's 'cos it's got so, I generally have like a

28   maybe side, side-ish parting

29 <S 01>   ⌐Parting going over that way

30 <S 02>   ⌐Yeah,

31   just to give it a bit more

32 <S 01>   Do you have the front bit thinned slightly?

33 <S 02>   Yeah, yeah, it's got so heavy

34 <S 01>   ⌐How long would you say it is since you've had it

35   cut?

36 <S 02>   I know I had it done on the last day of January, so that's

37   [<S 01> right] but my hair grows really quickly and really

38   thickly as well so

39 <S 01>   So about six weeks or so [<S 02> yeah] so off your ear there

40   [<S 02> yeah] and then if I taper that out slightly so it's shorter

41   there, clipper that slightly and taper it slightly down [<S 02> yeah]

42   so you haven't got such a line [<S 02> yeah] and then just take a

43   bit through your layers

44 <S 02>   Yeah, that would be great yeah

45 <S 01>   [inaudible] for you

46 <S 02>   ⌐'Cos it just needs some more umph you know so

47 <S 01>   ⌐It's just

48		laying heavy [<S 02> yeah] okay, do you want to take a seat

48   laying heavy [<S 02> yeah] okay, do you want to take a seat

49 <S 02>   ⌐Thanks a lot

50 <S 01>   I'll pass you the bowl

51 <S 02>   ⌐Thank you

52 <S 01>   Take a seat in the middle

53 <S 02>   Right, thank you

54 [17 secs]

55 <S 01>   Here we are

56 <S 02>   ⌐Thanks [4 secs] Thank you

57 [16 secs] [laughter]

58 <S 02>   She's one step ahead of you in't she?

59 [6 secs] [phone rings]

60 <S 02>   Thanks [6 secs] Have you been busy today or has is it just quietened

61   down?

62 <S 03>   Well, I didn't start until one [4 secs] and I'm here till nine

63 <S 02>   Oh yeah, it's late night opening tonight isn't it?

64 [49 secs washing hair]

65 <S 02>   The shampoos always smell so nice, don't they?

66 <S 03>   Yeah [6 secs] The conditioners are nice as well [<S 02> yeah]

67   [inaudible] ... [laughs]

68 [28 secs washing hair]

69 <S 03>   Is that water okay?

70 <S 02>   Yes, fine

71 [1 min 5 secs]

72 <S 03>   Do you want to come over here?

73 <S 02>   Right, thanks [3 secs] thank you

74 <S 03>   Tea or coffee?

75 <S 02>   Can I have a tea please?

76 <S 03>   Do you want some sugar?

77 <S 02>   Er no milk or sugar, just black thanks

78 [19 secs]

79 <S 01>   Right

80 [4 secs]

81 <S 02>   I hate it when your hair just gets so, you know a bit long

82   [<S 01> yeah] and it's just straggly

83 [2 secs]

84 <S 01>   Right

85 [13 secs]

86 <S 01>   It just gets to that in-between stage [<S 02> yeah] doesn't

87		it where you think oh I just can't stand it anymore [2 secs] I think
88		when it's shorter it tends to, you notice it growing more anyway
89		[S 02> mm] you know it tends to grow all of a sudden [inaudible]
90	<S 02>	Mine's just grows so thick though [<S 01> yeah] quickly and
91		really, really thick and heavy and you just [<S 01> yeah] you know
92		have to have it thinned out.
93	<S 01>	[laughs]

General commentary

This transcript is a typical mix of TRANSACTIONAL and INTERACTIONAL discourse. The hairdresser and customer have to agree on how the hair will be cut and styled (the transactional), but they also chat to each other about various things just to be sociable (the interactional). The transactional parts involve the specialised vocabulary connected with hair and hair-styling.

There are long silences on the original tape where actions are taking place (washing the customer's hair). We have cut these in the tape accompanying the book.

Line-by-line commentary

ll.1 and 2: Compare *hello* with the more informal *hiya* or *hi*, which is very common among young people.

ll.5 and 7: Note this polite use of *Do you want to* ..., which is a more informal way of saying 'Will you ...'. (See also ll. 48, 72.)

l.12 *How much do you want off?* is usually the first question a hairdresser/barber will ask you when (s)he starts to cut your hair. It means 'How much do you want me to cut off?' (see **Activity** above).

l.18 *feathered* here means made into light, feather-like tufts. This is what the hairdresser means by *whispy* in l.20.

l.20 Conversations in service encounters are often ELLIPTICAL. Here the hairdresser reduces the message:

> So *(you'd like it)* whispy there?

Other examples:

> *(you want a)* parting going over that way (l.29)
> so *(you'd like it)* off your ear there (l.39)
> *(would you like)* tea or coffee (l.74)

l.22   Note the use of *tend* to indicate what one typically/habitually does. Using *tend* in this way is extremely common in everyday conversation, especially among younger speakers. Notice how the customer uses it in her reply too (l.23). (See also l.89.)

l.22   *Clippered* means 'cut with clippers', one of the hairdresser's cutting instruments that has teeth that move quickly from side to side.

l.23   Note the use of the DISCOURSE MARKER *like*, which is a very common vague language marker when you do not wish to be very precise.

l.26   Notice how the hairdresser's turn here consists entirely of discourse markers (*So, right, yeah*). This is quite common in service encounters and in language-in-action types of conversations. (See also Unit 6, l. 37.)

l.28   *Side-ish parting*: The suffix *-ish* is quite common in everyday conversation. It is extremely useful when you do not want to be terribly precise. It can be used quite freely with almost any adjective or number, and with many nouns too. Other examples:

> Come round about five-ish. (it does not have to be exactly five o'clock)
> She's about 30-ish I'd say. (she could be any age between about 28 and 32)

l.32   *the front bit*: *bit* is a very useful word in informal speech, meaning *part*.

l.32   *thinned* means cut with a special pair of scissors which has overlapping teeth.

l.39   *six weeks or so*: *or so* is useful VAGUE LANGUAGE for expressions of number and time. Other examples:

> We'll probably stay for a week or so.
> There'll be twenty or so there, I should think.

ll.40   Note how the speakers construct the *if-conditional* structure between them: the
–44   hairdresser speaks the *if*-clause (ll.40–43), and the customer adds the *would*-clause. Creating a 'sentence-structure' jointly in this way is typical of conversational language. It is a signal of the degree of trust and security which the speakers have developed during the course of their short conversation that they can have a hand in sharing in the grammar of this complex utterance.

l.46   *umph* is a slang word meaning 'body/solidity/substance'; her hair is too weak and floppy at the moment.

l.48   *It's just laying heavy*: Note how native speakers often confuse 'lie' and 'lay': traditionally correct grammar here would demand 'it's just *lying* heavy'. In informal speech, confusing these verbs usually does not matter, and is very common indeed.

l.58   *in't she* is a non-standard dialectal form of 'isn't she'.

l.62 *till nine*: Note how times on the hour are often stated ELLIPTICALLY in informal conversation, without 'o'clock'. This also sometimes occurs with 'half past' which is reduced to 'half', e.g. 'I'll be round at about half three, okay?'.

ll.65 The hair washer repeats the customer's use of *nice* in her reply, but note how
–70: repetition is by no means always the case. Observe how the customer does not repeat *okay* in her reply, but intensifies it to *fine*. This is very common in conversation. Other examples:

> A: Good meal wasn't it?
> B: Yes, great/very good/wonderful.
>
> A: Horrible weather!
> B: Yeah, ghastly!

l.82 *straggly* is an informal word meaning 'hanging in a very untidy and tangled way'.

l.82 The word *just* occurs frequently in this stretch of talk. The talk is relaxed and secure and the word *just* has a softening effect, maintaining a friendly and supportive tone; its omission would make the ideas more definite and direct and the interaction less positive.

Further reading

On how speakers repeat and vary one another's words across speaker-turns, see McCarthy (1988).

On ellipsis in these types of conversations, see Carter and McCarthy (1995a).

On the mutual completion of sentences by speakers see Lerner (1991).

unit **14**

Local radio phone-in

Activity

Before reading the transcript or listening to the tape which accompanies this unit, write a brief definition of a radio phone-in. In writing this definition try to answer some of the following questions:

What is the purpose of inviting members of the public to phone a radio station to discuss points of interest rather than inviting guests to the studio?

Are radio phone-in programmes rehearsed?

Who talks the most in radio phone-ins?

Can it be a genuine discussion when only two people, the presenter and the caller, are involved in the discussion?

Speakers and setting

        <S 01>   Ed Doolan: presenter
        <S 02>   John Robinson: caller

This extract is from a radio phone-in programme broadcast by a West Midlands Radio Station in England. It features Ed Doolan, the programme presenter, and a caller, John Robinson.

Transcript

  1 <S 01>   Did you hear me darling? Love a glass of water. Would kill for a glass of
  2   water. Alright? Thank you. [laughs] Where would I be without Sue
  3   Kelly. Ten and a half to two and John Robinson's in Lichfield. Hello John.

4	<S 02>	Hello Ed.
5	<S 01>	Yes.
6	<S 02>	Er just the usual. I've driven over from West Bromwich to Lichfield.
7		And I'm amazed literally amazed in these weather conditions that
8		people are still driving around without lights on.
9	<S 01>	You're joking.
10	<S 02>	No honestly.
11	<S 01>	I can't. I can't you see it is amazing to think that there is anybody left
12		in the world who can be so thick as to drive in this weather without
13		the lights on. I'd have thought the first thing you do when it gets as
14		dark and as wet and as miserable as this. You turn your lights on and I
15		don't mean the parkers. I mean the lights.
16	<S 02>	It's absolutely unbelievable.
17	<S 01>	But I don't understand how how can it tell me how can there be
18		anybody left in the world that hasn't heard that's what you do.
19		[laughs] Tell me.
20	<S 02>	Can I ... Can I pose a question Edward? These same people drive
21		around without the window wipers going
22	<S 01>	God knows. God knows. It is I don't understand it. I don't
23		understand
24	<S 02>	I mean I I know you've mentioned it several times in the past but it's
25		it still doesn't seem to get through to people.
26	<S 01>	I dunno. Well th th they it's none of my listeners mate. [<S 02> well]
27		There isn't one person listening to this at the moment in the car that
28		hasn't got the full lights on. Right? So we don't have to worry about
29		that.
30	<S 02>	Mm. Right
31	<S 01>	But I'm worried about the others.
32	<S 02>	And I am Ed.
33	<S 01>	Okay matey.
34	<S 02>	Okay thanks.
35	<S 01>	Good luck to you. [radio jingle] Nine minutes to two. Oh Sue. I think
36		I love you. I realise that's not money in the bank but it's nice.

General commentary

In Britain radio phone-ins may differ in format, formality and function according to the particular radio station, the style of the presenter and whether the programme is a national or local radio programme. The programmes can therefore range from formal discussion and debate on matters of contemporary significance (in which several contributors phone in, in turn) to rather more informally presented viewpoints on local issues. Some calls on some radio phone-in programmes are also taken as opportunities to discuss personal problems and seek personal advice. Some contributions may therefore be a little closer to the genre of comment -elaboration (see pp. 9 and 10) than to debate and argument.

The general format of the radio phone-in programme is that individuals phone the radio station and are 'interviewed' live by the programme presenter. The presenter controls the turns and manages the discussion as far as possible for interest value. In some programmes listeners who telephone are made to feel very much a part of a genuinely interactive and participatory event.

Line-by-line commentary

l.1   The use of ELLIPSIS here by the programme presenter has been commented on several times in this book. (See in particular Units 5 and 6.) Its main function is once again to mark informality between speakers, here the presenter and his personal assistant (Sue Kelly).

l.1   *Would kill for a glass of water* is a deliberately exaggerated humorous expression indicating how desperate he is to drink some water. The use of excessive hyperbole is a relatively common feature of the lexis of informal, highly interpersonal spoken discourse (see also below l.3).

ll.2–3 *Ten and a half to two*: This very precise time reference (ten minutes and thirty seconds to two o'clock) is not uncommon in radio programmes.

l.3   *and John Robinson's in Lichfield*: The caller to the programme is identified by name and by the place from which he is telephoning (Lichfield is a town in the West Midlands of England, about forty kilometres from Birmingham).

l.5   *Yes*: This simply invites the caller to say why he is calling.

l.6   *just the usual*: This is a FIXED EXPRESSION indicating that the same thing has been said or the same action performed on several previous occasions. The use of *just* here also modalises the expression, allowing the statement to appear casual and tentative, even routine, rather than too assertive. It is not uncommon to hear the expression *just the usual* spoken by customers in a pub when ordering a drink which the barperson will know to be their usual preference or in a hairdressing salon where the hairdresser knows the requirements of the customer.

l.7   *literally amazed*: *Literally* is very common in spoken language and is not really the opposite of *figuratively/metaphorically*. It usually just serves to emphasise the words/phrases it qualifies. (See also l.11.)

l.10   *honestly*: An affirmative, indicating that the speaker is serious and is not joking in any way. *Honestly* and *literally* (see above) are interpersonal markers of stance/attitude/evaluation, which we can expect to hear in a context like this one.

ll.11 —12 *that there is a anybody left in the world*: This is an example of deliberate hyperbole, or exaggeration, which allows the speaker comically to underline the strength of his position and the absurdity of the characteristic behaviour he is describing. The expression is repeated almost verbatim in l.18. It is worth noting that advertisers make use of hyperbole in advertising slogans and captions. For example, a recent advert for the Edwardian Hotel, Heathrow, London, claims it to be 'a million times more comfortable'. The absurdity of the claim and that it cannot possibly be substantiated means that no legal challenges can be made to the proposition by its competitors. Deliberately bizarre exaggerations, especially involving numbers and measurements, are not uncommon in informal conversation. They can be used to underline arguments but also for comic and ironic effects. For example, 'The person who can help is not a million miles from here' – which means that they are present or very close by.

l.12 *thick* here is an informal word used pejoratively to mean 'stupid'/ 'unintelligent'.

l.13 *I'd have thought*: A common grammatical structure for the reinforcement of a point of view. It allows the speaker to presuppose what is reasonable behaviour but then not associate such behaviour with the persons and their activities which are being criticised.

ll.13 —14 Comments are here chained together by association rather than by explicit cohesive linkage. For example, *I'd have thought the first thing you do when it gets dark ... You turn your lights on.* A version appropriate to written English or to more formal talk would have more complex linking. For example: I would have thought that the first thing you do ... is to turn your lights on / is that you turn your lights on.

l.15 *the parkers* here means parking lights or side lights on a car (as opposed to the main lights, the headlights, the *full lights* as the presenter later refers to them in l.28).

l.16 *absolutely unbelievable*: Another example of lexical hyperbole. It imparts, as above, a personal attitudinal marking to the propositions which it precedes or follows.

l.26 *I dunno*: An informal version of 'I don't know'. A similar example is 'I'm gonna' for which the written text orthographic equivalent is 'I'm going to'.

l.26 *Mate* as an address form marks solidarity between speakers and is almost exclusively used between male speakers. The use of *matey* (l.33) (as is frequently the case with -y endings in lexis, address terms and names in English) normally marks an even greater informality and sense of shared values and viewpoints.

l.28　*Right?* is a DISCOURSE MARKER used here to check understanding and agreement. However, in ll.26-34 *right* is used, together with *well* and *okay* to signal that the conversation should now end and that it is Ed's wish that it should.

l.36　*I realise that's not money in the bank*: An idiom 'That's/It's money in the bank.' meaning 'it's something you can absolutely bank on/rely on'. This is modified to a negative form and used by the speaker here to evaluate his own statement. He is referring here to the fact that Sue, his assistant, has obtained for him the glass of water which he had previously said he would 'kill for'; he says 'I love you' but admits she can't bank on that. These further exaggerations, together with the use of the word *darling*, add to the playful, bantering tenor of the presenter's discourse.

Further reading

See Cook (1992) for discussion of hyperbole in advertising language.

Stubbs (1986) and Carter (1987) discuss the informality of -y endings in lexis and in discoursal interaction in general.

McCarthy (1992b) and McCarthy and Carter (1994: ch. 3), Moon (1992) and Fernando (1996) discuss the function of idioms for evaluative purposes.

unit **15**

Student discussion

Activity

Student discussion can take several forms. Imagine a classroom discussion in which a teacher or lecturer asks a student to give a prepared talk on a topic and then invites other students to comment. Now imagine a voluntary discussion group, set up by like-minded students with common interests in which they support one another by discussing both individual and general problems.

List three main characteristics of the use of language in each type of discussion group. What are the main factors which determine the kind of language you would expect to encounter in each case?

Comments on activity

Comments on this activity are contained in the **General commentary** and in the **Line-by-line commentary** where differences between formal and informal discourse in academic settings are examined (e.g. ll.27–28, 30, 56–57).

Speakers and setting

    <S 01>   female
    <S 02>   male
    <S 03>   female
    <S 04>   male
    <S 05>   male
    All are aged 18–23.

unit **15**

Student discussion
unit **15**

Student discussion

This discussion takes place in an informal atmosphere in a student study-bedroom in a university hall of residence. The participants are all members of a student Christian group. The students have each put down on paper their answers to a series of questions about their personal attitudes to their religion. The first question they are discussing is which aspects of their daily lives *are* and which *are not* affected by their religion. <S 01> is the chair of this informal meeting and starts the discussion.

Transcript

1	<S 01>	Okay what have you got
2	<S 04>	⌐That directed at me
3	<S 01>	⌐in the, let's do the not-affected one first
4	<S 03>	Mm
5	[1 sec]	
6	<S 04>	Well I've gone for a huge cop out but then I have I always do. I put
7		erm relationships with non-Christians.
8	[1 sec]	
9	<S 01>	Yeah.
10	<S04>	Yeah well, [<S 03> mm] I mean in some ways you know I think you
11		should make the difference but it's being pernickety as well because
12		when I have you know when I do go out with the guys and just talk
13		to them and just be around hall generally with non-Christians, I try to
14		just sort of just hope my life isn't affected, by you know by my faith in
15		that sense but, then my behaviour and attitudes are always gonna be,
16		you know are always gonna be affected by my faith, you know I'm
17		not always gonna get overly overly excited in the alcohol
18		department and er, you know go round abusing and kicking things in
19		because, you know as as some of my friends did the other night you
20		know
21	<S 01>	Mm really?
22	<S 04>	Yeah well one of them did a bit too much and broke his leg [<S 01>
23		hmm] but, erm you know because my behaviour and attitudes, but
24		when I'm just sort of conversing with them now I don't openly think
25		my life's affected in that sense but, I hope you see where I'm sort of
26		coming from but
27	<S 01>	Yeah
28	<S 03>	Mm
29	<S 01>	Do you think then that the way you relate to like people who aren't
30		Christian, and your attitudes towards them like whether you decide

31		to accept certain people and [<S 04> mm] you know get a bit peed
32		off with other people and stuff like that, do you think it is affected by
33		your faith, like you were saying you [<S 04> mm] have kind of moral
34		standards of not [S 04> mm] like hooliganising and things I mean do
35		you think that's because of your faith or do you think that's because
36		well because of society or whatever
37	<S 04>	I I think it's because of my faith um because, I I like to do what's right
38		[<S 01> yeah] and you know I don't do that very well I don't do that
39		as as often as I'd like to but there's some sort of certain things such
40		protocol I wouldn't you know go into I think you know you don't do
41		that and then I think about well why, why don't you do that and I think
42		well first of all it's you know just wrong to do so [<S 01> mm] you
43		know you have no right to go and kick in someone's property or you
44		have no right to hit someone or
45	<S 03>	But is that because of your faith or because you've got a bit of a
46		conscience?
47	<S 01>	Mm
48	<S 04>	Well I see I don't know I think I think it is my faith because it comes
49		from that the feeling of doing wrong
50	<S 05>	Isn't our faith isn't our conscience affected by our faith
51		[<S 01 & S 04> yeah] for Christians?
52	<S 01>	Yeah but
53	<S 02>	The thing is I think
54	<S 02>	But you could
55	<S 03>	We were saying that some people people who are not Christians
56	<S 02>	Might go round who will all go round kicking
57	<S 03>	⌊Who will all go round, kicking
58	<S 04>	No no I'm not trying not to generalise in that sense
59	<S 03>	No
60	<S 04>	Oh yeah a lot of people have got very good morals who aren't
61		Christians, I mean you can be a good person and not a Christian we
62		all know that
63	<S 01>	Yeah but that that shows there must be somewhere else you get
64		ideas of morals from, other than Christian
65	<S 04>	⌊Oh sure [<S 02> mm] but I
66		don't know I mean like you say you just ask me does it come from
67		my faith but I honestly couldn't answer that
68	<S 03>	Yeah it's very difficult it's very difficult isn't it
69	<S 01>	You can't distinguish cos if you, I suppose if you've been like brought

70		up in the church and stuff and have been for all your life maybe that's
71		just what you do isn't it so you don't know which comes ... well
72		where it comes from isn't it
73	\<S 03\>	Mm

General commentary

The discussion is markedly symmetrical. The participants operate cooperatively and collaboratively, seeing each other as equals with equal speaking rights. A more teacher-led discussion (see Unit 16) would be more asymmetrical, with speaking rights controlled and assigned rather more by a single person (the teacher). A teacher may also want to polarise discussion for purposes of learning whereas in this discussion many of the linguistic choices signal mutuality, consensus and interpersonal support.

Line-by-line commentary

l.2 *That directed at me*: This is an example of ELLIPSIS and means 'Is that question directed at me?'.

l.6 *gone for a huge cop out*: 'Go for' is an informal version of 'choose/select'. As a verb, 'to cop out' means not to take responsibility. It's a highly informal expression. It can also, as here, be used as a noun in expressions such as 'It's a cop out', which indicates a strongly negative judgement.

l.11 *pernickety*: An informal word, more commonly used in spoken English. The word means to be too fussy or picky. Written equivalents would be *over-fastidious* or *too discriminating*.

l.13 *hall*: A university hall of residence, a hostel for students, usually on or near the university campus.

l.14 *just / sort of* are HEDGES which enable ideas or thoughts to be expressed more indirectly, politely and non-assertively. (See also *like* in l.29 below.)

l.17 *in the alcohol department*: The use of the word 'department' here serves to divide −18 up human actions or behaviour into different sections. The 'alcohol department' is time spent drinking alcoholic drinks. *I'm not always gonna get overly excited in the alcohol department* is an indirect, ironic way of saying that he will not normally drink too much. The use of quite formal, rather elaborate words to substitute for more direct alternatives is a form of over-lexicalisation which can allow speakers to refer to things with some measure of ironic distance. Another example:

> She's a bit lacking in the subtlety department. (She's not very subtle/tactful.)

l.26 *coming from*: A verb normally only used in progressive forms and which means 'to express a particular point of view'. 'I could see where he was coming from' is a more informal alternative to 'I could understand his point of view/his line of argument'.

ll.27 –28 *Yeah, mm*: In the early stages of the discussion other speakers are reluctant to intervene with comments of their own; however, verbal and non-verbal BACK-CHANNELLING takes place to give support to the speaker. Later in the discussion there is less back-channelling and more direct interventions and comments on the part of the other participants.

l.29 *Then* is used here as a summarising word rather than as a marker of time.

l.30 *Like* here has the meaning of 'for example'. This use of *like* is common in conversational English.

ll.31 –32 *peed off*: A verb formed from a slang word for 'urine' (pee). A stronger, more vulgar alternative is 'pissed off'; a more acceptable alternative expression for less informal contexts is 'fed up with'.

l.32 *stuff like that*: A common VAGUE EXPRESSION. A similarly frequent expression is *things like that* or *and things*, as in l.34. Speakers select vague language as here so that they do not have to specify precise examples – a procedure which would be necessary in more formal discussion in most academic contexts but which is not a prerequisite for informal discussion. In informal discussion among equals speakers deliberately do not want to sound too authoritative.

l.34 *like* is used here as a conjunction with a meaning similar to 'as' or 'for example'.

l.34 *hooliganising* is not an established word-form. The speaker has created a verb on the basis of the noun 'hooligan' (a noisy ill-mannered person who causes damage and trouble).

l.36 *or whatever*: This is another VAGUE EXPRESSION. It allows the speaker to sound deliberately imprecise and unspecific.

l.40 *I think you know you don't do that*: Verbs such as *think, ask, tell* can be followed by forms of language which serve, as it were, to reproduce direct speech. Here the words *you don't do that* are reproduced almost as if they were actually said. In formal written use quotation marks would be used or a more 'distant' alternative preferred; for example: 'I think that people don't do that'; 'I think that that isn't done'. Such strategies create a directness and immediacy for the reported process of thinking or saying. The reporting verb can be in either present or past tense form; in fact, in this example the verb *think* is, as is commonly the case in speech reporting, in the present tense, though habitual past actions are being recounted. (See also ll.66–67.)

l.53 *The thing is* is an extremely useful and common spoken expression meaning 'the problem is/the real question is/the point is'.

l.55 *We were saying*: The use of the past continuous tense here is frequent in conversations in which the participants wish to create deliberately indefinite, imprecise and informal interaction. Compare the effect produced by the more complete and definite 'we said'. It is also used here to suggest that the topic is on-going.

ll.56 *who will all go round kicking*: The reference to *kicking* here and *kicking in* (l.18) may
–57 or may not refer to the physical act of students kicking people or property. It may, for example, act as a kind of metaphoric expression for anti-social behaviour. The repetition of this subordinate clause of <S 02> by <S 03> indicates a convergence of viewpoint between the speakers; it also reveals a greater confidence to intervene, to overlap and to complete or attempt to complete the utterances of other parties in the discussion. This increased involvement illustrates that the speakers have now become more relaxed, the enhanced participation contrasting with the more hesitant contributions earlier in the discussion.

ll.66 *You just ask me does it come*: see discussion at l.40 above. The speech report
–67 here embeds what is effectively a direct, almost unmediated recount of the question 'does it come from your faith?'.

Further reading

For a recent discussion of a wide range of forms of speech reporting see McCarthy (1997: ch. 6), who draws on spoken examples. See also Yule, Mathis and Hopkins (1992).

See Thompson (1994) for a discussion of speech reports in written English.

Channell (1994) is a thoroughgoing study of vagueness in language use, drawing on recent work in pragmatics.

Fowler (1986), Halliday (1989) and Carter (1987) discuss the effects of different degrees of under- and over-lexicalisation.

unit **16**

School discussion

Activity

Make a copy of this transcript, having first removed any reference to the speakers at the beginning of each utterance. Show the transcript to at least three of your fellow students and ask them to identify the speakers in this discussion. Can they recognise when the teacher is speaking and when the students are speaking? If so, how do they do this? What clues are there in the language the speakers all use?

See the **General commentary** for comments on this activity.

Speakers and setting

    <S 01>   teacher: male (37)
    <S 02>   pupil 1
    <S 03>   pupil 2
    <S 04>   pupil 3
    <S 05>   pupil 4

In this text a small group of secondary school pupils are working together with their teacher. The students are all girls aged 14–15 years.

Transcript

1	<S 01>	What do you have to do, then, in the evenings, if you want to go out,
2		where?
3	<S 02>	On the underground.
4	<S 01>	Down the underground? What's the underground?
5	<S 02>	Yeah ... that's where ... boys do the popping

6	<S 03>	Popping.
7	<S 01>	Where's that?
8	<S 05>	It's an area ... where all the boys get together ... and they er pops
9	<S 02>	Underneath Russell Sports.
10	<S 05>	and dances.
11	<S 01>	What in the arcade off John Foss Square?
12	<S 02>	No underneath Russell Sports.
13	<S 01>	Underneath? That's ... under the car parks.
14	<S 03>	Yeah.
15	<S 01>	And what's body-popping exactly?
16	<S 03>	It's dancing.
17	<S 01>	What ... describe it. I don't know. I've never seen it.
18	<S 05>	It's just a new style of dancing, American style.
19	<S 01>	But ... er ... if it's in the car park, um, how do you dance? Where's the
20		music come from?
21	<S 04>	Bring a tape-recorder.
22	<S 05>	They bring a tape-recorder, they put lino in the floor and
23	<S 04>	So they put all graffiti all over the walls.
24	<S 01>	So they spray paint the walls, they put lino on the floor and then they
25		just do this body-popping in the car park like that? Why do you have
26		to do it in the car park?
27	<S 02>	Cos nowhere else to go.
28	<S 03>	The police it's cold
29	<S 05>	The police allows them to um go there ... the people in ... it's
30		underneath Russell Sports and, um ... everytime ... they come and
31		bring things in, um, from Russell Sports and they says 'Hi' to us ... and
32		they don't mind long as we keep the music down.
33	<S 01>	So as long as it's not too loud the police are quite happy for you to
34		go there? No-one chases you away?
35	<S 03, S 05>	No
36	<S 01>	But you have to go there because there's nothing else to do?
37	<S 05>	Nothing else.
38	<S 01>	Well, if you had this £10,000, then, which someone's going to give,
39		what could you do with that £10,000 to make life rather better for
40		you, to give you more things to do?
41	<S 05>	They could make it a place for body-poppers to go and, like a youth
42		club and ... special room for all that
43	<S 03>	Leisure Centre.
44	<S 05>	Yeah.

45	<S 01>	We're having a big leisure centre which is costing millions but you'd
46		like to have a building where you could go yourselves, would you?
47	<S 03>	Yeah ... in the nights, like, when, it's cold.
48	<S 02>	And you could sleep there.
49	<S 03>	Mm.
50	<S 01>	You could stay there as well? So what kind of things would you like to
51		see in this building that you could have? Body-popping is one – a
52		room for that
53	<S 04>	Space invaders ... stuff like that.
54	<S 01>	But can't you get these in ... in arcades in town? Or do you have to be
55	<S 04>	Yeah but you've got to be older.
56	<S 05>	You got to be 18.
57	<S 04>	You got to be over 18.
58	<S 01>	So you'd like to have an arcade where you could go ... without having
59		to be over 18
60	<S 04>	Yeah.
61	<S 05>	Not gambling machines, though, just the games.
62	<S 01>	Just the Space Invader games. You like those.
63	<S 05>	Mm.
64	<S 01>	You think they'd be popular [pause] That's £10,000, I don't think it
65		would cost £10,000 just to have body-popping and Space Invaders;
66		what else could you have?
67	<S 05>	You could have a variety of things
68	<S 03>	Snooker tables
69	<S 01>	Yes?
70	<S 03>	Table tennis
71	<S 01>	Do you think people would go there to play table tennis and
72		snooker?
73	<S 03>	Yes.
74	<S 01>	Do many people go and watch the body-popping down there?
75	<S 04>	Quite a lot
76	<S 05>	Quite a few ... yeah
77	<S 04>	Every Saturday they has a challenge at Maskell's Leisure Centre.
78	<S 01>	So you're saying there's a lot of young people your age, then, who
79		have nowhere to go and nothing to do.
80	<S 05>	Mm. There's loads of people who does it ... but ... there's nowhere to
81		go ... really ... and
82	<S 01>	So you'd have table tennis there, snooker there, body-popping ...
83		somewhere to stay overnight as well you think.

84	\<S 03\>	Mm.
85	\<S 02\>	Yeah. Got to.
86	\<S 01\>	Why do you think that's necessary?
87	\<S 02\>	Something to do, init? Nothing to do. You know.

General commentary

This is a transcript of a discussion between an English teacher and a small group of Year 10 (aged 14–15) secondary school pupils. The teacher has asked them to consider how they would spend £10,000 'for the benefit of the local community', and makes it clear, in response to a question, that this 'community' included people of their own age.

There are marked differences in the styles of speaking which the teacher uses and which the pupils use. It is noticeable, for example, that it is the teacher who has the most 'turns' and speaks more, even though he is outnumbered by the pupils. The teacher also asks most of the questions, with contributions to the discussion from pupils mainly taking the form of answers to the teacher's questions.

The teacher also tends to use complete, fully-formed clauses, whereas many of the pupils' contributions are elliptical and are understood only in the context of the teacher's utterances. The tone of the discussion is quite detached and impersonal. Everything is controlled (dominated even) by the teacher. Personal pronouns are not much used by teacher or pupil.

The discussion conforms to what discourse analysts have termed an IRF interchange:

Initiation (I)   an utterance, mainly teacher-led

Response (R)   mainly a pupil response/reply

Feedback (F)   mainly a follow-up comment by the teacher which also often evaluates or rephrases or expands what the pupil has said.

This discussion shows a tightly-structured teacher-led discussion, even though the setting is relatively informal and the pupils feel sufficiently relaxed to use a number of informal expressions. A further example of the teacher's control is not just the frequency of his interventions but his use of discourse markers to regulate what is said, when topics are to be changed and how the statements of others are to be reformulated and summarised. It is noticeable that, while the pupils often use each other's words, the teacher evaluates or summarises in different words.

Line-by-line commentary

l.1   The use of *then* indicates that a new stage in the conversation has been reached. The speaker signals either that a new topic is to be introduced or that a different phase of the existing topic is to be entered. In this use *then* is a DISCOURSE MARKER. It does not mean 'afterwards' or 'next' or 'at that time'.

l.5   *do the popping*: This is a typical DELEXICAL use of *do*. Compare everyday uses such as 'do the cleaning', 'do some gardening', etc.

ll.8   *they pops … and dances*: See notes ll.29 and 31 below.
−10

l.11   It is worth noting that *what* can be used in informal spoken language to check information about time and place and circumstances as well as 'things'. For example:

> A: These friends of mine climb mountains at night.
> B: What, in the dark?
> A: Yeah.
>
> A: You know, that Chinese restaurant as you come into town.
> B: What, on the left?
> A: Yeah, that's the one.

l.11   *off John Foss Square:* The use of *off* here is a colloquial or informal alternative to 'near' or 'next to'.

l.18   *It's just a new style of dancing, American-style.* This type of reformulation or apposition allows expansion of the main headword. Similar examples would be:

> Have you tried that new coffee, Columbian coffee?
> They've brought out a new Ford Mondeo, a turbo-diesel.

In written English the expansion would typically operate as a pre-modifier; for example: 'They've brought out a new, turbo-diesel Ford Mondeo'.

ll.19   *Where's the music come from?* Some grammars claim that 'does' is not normally
−20 reduced in English to '*s* as this is a form exclusive to the verb 'to be' (e.g. Where's he from?) and sometimes 'have' (e.g. She's gone out.). Such contractions are, however, frequent in informal, spoken English. See also Unit 17, l.7.

l.21   *bring a tape-recorder:* ELLIPSIS of the subject pronoun is common in informal speech. The teacher establishes a greater formality by inserting the pronoun into his parallel phrase.

l.22   *lino* is a shortened form of 'linoleum' – a kind of shiny, hard-wearing floor-covering.

l.24   *So*: In informal speech *so* is used as a DISCOURSE MARKER. It signals that some kind of summary of what has been previously said is to take place. It does not mean 'in order to' or 'so that'. See l.33 and l.50 for similar uses of *so*. It is similar in function to *well* l.38 (below).

l.27 *Cos nowhere else to go*: *Cos* is frequent in informal speech. It is a normal, reduced form of 'because' and is not incorrect. It is a form frequently used by all native speakers. (See Unit 5, l.47.) The ELLIPSIS of 'there is' is also frequent in casual conversation. It is often reduced to 'there's'.

l.29 Notice how a simple present tense is used to record repeated actions. (See also l.31 below.)

l.31 *they says*: *Say* is a common verb for reporting action and for reporting speech in particular. The more informal the context, the less likely it is that it will be differently inflected. 'I says', 'he says', 'we says', 'you says' are common, overlapping as they do with several local dialect forms. The speakers here speak a local mid-western British English (Shropshire) dialect.

l.32 *long as we keep the music down*: Note the ellipsis of *(so / as) long as*, which is infrequent in informal speech. But note that the student uses the reduced form; the teacher reinstates the more usual, complete form *so long as*.

l.38 *Well* is used as a discourse marker and is similar to the uses of *so*. (See ll.24, 33, 50). It functions to mark a boundary between one stretch of talk or one section of the topic and another stretch of the same talk. It can also mark a new or different topic.

ll.39 *to make life rather better for you, to give you more things to do*: It is not uncommon in
—40   spoken discourse for clauses to be chained together in parallel structures. Such patterning allows the speaker the opportunity to reformulate, refine or otherwise be more precise than composing in real time normally allows. Chaining of this kind occurs in writing, not uncommonly to create a more spoken, 'interactive' rhetorical structure for the writing. (In writing, however, the reformulations do normally lead to additional information content rather than simple topic restatement.)

ll.45 *you'd like to have a building ... would you?* The teacher makes quite frequent use of
—6   a structure in which an affirmative clause plus a tag question is used as a way of asking questions.

l.47 *in the nights, like, when it's cold*: *like* is used here, informally, as an alternative phrasing for 'for instance' or 'for example'. Such uses of *like* would not normally be appropriate in most written discourse.

l.53 *stuff like that*: *stuff* is a common item of VAGUE LANGUAGE. In conversational English contexts, too great a degree of precision would be likely to sound excessive. Similar vague expressions found in similar structures include 'things like that', 'that' or 'something like that'. See also Unit 15.

l.54 *But you can't get these in arcades in town?* Another example of questions being put by means of an affirmative statement.

l.62 *You like those*: As in ll.45–46 and 54 above the teacher puts questions by means of an affirmative structure. Note that in l.58 and here it is not used together with a tag. The teacher varies how he puts a relatively long sequence of questions; this structure enables him to elicit information a little more indirectly.

ll.75 *quite a lot … quite a few*: These sets of expressions are relatively common in
−76 informal spoken English and they are further examples of vague language. In most conversations very imprecise reference to numbers and to quantities allows speakers deliberately to hedge **or** to add emphasis without expecting to be taken literally.

l.80 *There's loads of people who does it*: Rules for subject verb concord vary in different dialects of English. Here *people* is accompanied by what would be singular verbs in most standard dialects of English, though there is some evidence to suggest that *there's* is a more frequent structure in English and is used irrespective of the noun or nouns which follow it, even by highly educated speakers in public life, in the media, etc. (note that the teacher himself uses it in l. 78). *Loads of* is a very common expression for expressing large quantities or numbers in English (with countable or uncountable nouns). 'Many' would sound terribly formal and 'written' in this context. 'Many' and 'much' are often overused in spoken language by non-native speakers.

l.83 Note the use of *as well*. Along with 'too' it is far more frequent in spoken language than *also*.

l.85 *Got to* is another example of ELLIPSIS in which the normal subject and auxiliary verb are deleted.

l.87 *Nothing to do*: As in l.85 another elliptical construction which marks deliberate casualness in the reply. Note also the colloquial *init*, a reduced form of 'isn't it'.

Further reading

The teacher-pupil IRF structure is explained in Sinclair and Coulthard (1975).

How the IRF exchange structure is further elaborated and manifests itself in other types of situation is discussed in Hoey (1991).

For a detailed study of naturally-occurring conversational discourse, including reference to data in educational settings, see Tsui (1994).

unit 17

Kid's stuff

Activity

Before you listen to the tape, consider for a moment how little children manage to learn their first language. Which of these ways do you think children use to learn their mother tongue, and which do you think is/are most important?

1 Imitating things they have heard adults say.
2 Just quietly practising sounds and words on their own without the help of adults.
3 Having conversations with adults.
4 Being corrected by adults when they make mistakes.

Now listen to the tape and read the transcript. What evidence is there that the little girl is engaged in any of the ways of learning language listed above?

See the **Line-by-line commentary** for comments on this activity.

Speakers and setting

<S 01>   female (37) (Yorkshire)
<S 02>   female (24) (South Wales)
<S 03>   male (47) (South Wales)
<S 04>   female baby (2) (South Wales)

<S 02> is the niece of <S 01> and <S 03>, and mother of the baby, <S 04>. The speakers are chatting in the kitchen of <S 01> and <S 03>'s house, in Cambridgeshire, while dinner is being prepared.

Transcript

1	\<S 01\>	D'you get out more now that she's a bit older
2	\<S 04\>	/ʙəgəbəgəbəgəbə . . . ʙəgəbəgəbəgə/
3	\<S 01\>	Don't know what that was but I know what it sounded like
4	\<S 03\>	⌊Sounded like
5		something you heard your father say
6	\<S 04\>	/ʙəgəbəgəbəgəbəgə/
7	\<S 01\>	What's that ... what what's that mean ... mm
8	\<S 04\>	He burn me he burnt it
9	\<S 02\>	He burnt you ... you caught your hand on the book did
10		you naughty book
11	\<S 01\>	It's the paper that was a bit
12	\<S 02\>	⌊Naughty book ... oh don't
13		break Rosie and Jim book
14	\<S 04\>	Oh he bit me he bit me
15	\<S 02\>	He bit you did he
16	\<S 01\>	The book bit you
17	[8 secs]	
18	\<S 03\>	It must be the biting humour of the story
19	\<S 02\>	[laughs]
20	\<S 01\>	Ya-ha-ha-ha
21	\<S 02\>	We don't go out that much now we we you know occasionally
22		Mum'll baby-sit if we've got anything special on but
23	\<S 01\>	⌊Yeah
24	\<S 02\>	Quite often some of the neighbours'll just come over
25		[\<S 01\> yeah] and we'll get a takeaway or something and
26		[\<S 01\> yeah] have a drink in the house
27	\<S 01\>	Yeah
28	[10 secs baby babbling]	
29	\<S 01\>	Probably just feel like having a quiet night in after
30		a day of running round after a [\<S 02\> yeah] little girl with
31		a foul mouth
32	\<S 02\>	I don't know where she got that from what what you
33		doing to that oh no that's horrible you don't do that to books
34	\<S 04\>	No
35	\<S 02\>	No
36	\<S 04\>	My my dummy
37	\<S 02\>	You want your dummy you big baby

38	\<S 03\>	[laughs]
39	\<S 04\>	Want my big book
40	\<S 02\>	You want your big book there
41	\<S 04\>	Want my book back what in the drawings
42	\<S 03\>	What
43	\<S 04\>	crayons
44	\<S 03\>	What what do you want
45	\<S 02\>	Read read in there read all tell me everything that's in that book tell
46		me that you, what pictures what's that ... drawing
47	\<S 03\>	Is there any ponies in there like you saw this afternoon
48	\<S 02\>	There is what's that's like you saw isn't it what's that
49	\<S 04\>	Gee-up
50	\<S 02\>	Gee-up yeah and what's that
51	\<S 04\>	Dolly houses
52	\<S 02\>	Yeah d'you know what those are
53	\<S 04\>	Bottles for green dolly
54	\<S 02\>	Bottles for the dollies is it and what's that
55	\<S 04\>	Colourings
56	\<S 02\>	Colourings yeah it's like what's that though
57	\<S 03\>	No wonder all those child language acquisition studies
58		have got them just saying what's that that's a horse cos it's the
59		only way they can get them to talk on the tape-recorder [laughs]
60	\<S 01\>	⌐Get them to talk yeah ⌐all
61		this business about [\<S 03\> yeah] you know two word sentences
62	\<S 03\>	⌐Interactive discourse yes yeah it's
63		not yes exactly they have all the sentences but they only ever
64		record two-word sentences cos it's the only thing they say when
65		the tape-recorder's on
66	\<S 02\>	⌐What's that
67	\<S 01\>	Yeah
68	\<S 04\>	Very hot it's very hot
69	\<S 02\>	It's hot yes ... and what d'you do with that
70	\<S 04\>	Play with it
71	\<S 02\>	Play with it
72	\<S 04\>	I pour it
73	\<S 02\>	Pour it
74	\<S 04\>	I pour it
75	\<S 02\>	You pour it do you
76	\<S 04\>	Yes [inaudible]

77	\<S 02\>	You pour a cup of tea
78	\<S 04\>	Yeah
79	\<S 02\>	Yeah

Line-by-line commentary

l.1   *get out* is a colloquial alternative to 'go out'.

l.2   The sounds the baby is making suggest the word 'bugger', which is a taboo word used as a negative comment on people and events:

> He's an awkward bugger, Jim.
> It was a bugger, that exam; I'm sure I've failed it.

As with all taboo words, you should understand it when you hear it, but take great care with regard to using it, as it can cause offence.

Little babies and toddlers like this one often spend a lot of time just 'cooing' and 'babbling' to themselves, i.e. making sounds and combinations of sounds and repeating them, as if practising them. This clearly has some role to play in the way they learn language. On the other hand, it is possible she is imitating adults whom she has heard saying the word 'bugger'. Both 'practising' and imitation probably play a significant role in learning language.

l.3   Note the ELLIPSIS of *(I) don't know*. This is very common with 'mental' verbs in informal conversation. Other mental verbs which often attract ellipsis are 'hope', 'think', 'guess', 'wonder', etc.:

> Wonder if she'll be at the party (I wonder if ...)
> Know what happened to that tin-opener we had? (Do you know ...)
> Think I'll go home now (I think I'll ...)

See also *feel like* in l.29.

There is another ellipsis in l.4, this time of 'it' (*It sounded like* ...). This is also common in informal conversation with verbs such as 'sound', 'look', 'seem':

> Seems he's not coming after all (It seems he's ...)
> Looks as if they've left already (It looks as if ...)

l.7   *What's that mean*: here 'does' is contracted to *'s*, which happens in very informal talk (see Unit 16 ll.19–20):

> What's he do for a living? (What does he ...)
> When's it have to be ready? (When does it ...)

ll.8 –9   The little girl is obviously having trouble constructing the right grammar for her message, but her mother does not openly 'correct' her or tell her she is wrong. Instead her mother just says the appropriate form. Parents and carers often seem to concentrate more on acknowledging the **content** of what little children say rather than its grammatical correctness. But repetition of the correct form by the adult probably influences how the child learns.

l.13　*Rosie and Jim* is the name of a series of story books for very young children.

l.18　This is a rather silly joke which plays on the collocation of 'biting' with words such as 'sarcasm', 'humour', 'comments', etc., where 'biting' means 'sharp' or 'very strong'.

l.22　Note the use of *will / 'll* to indicate tendencies or typical or predictable events in
–25　the present. Other examples:

> Normally I take the bus but occasionally I'll get a taxi.
> About once or twice a week my sister'll ring me up.

Note also the use of 'to have something on' (*if we've got anything special on*), a colloquial expression meaning to have a social appointment or date:

> D'you have anything on on Saturday? Fancy going to the cinema?

l.25　*get a takeaway*: Buy a meal from a 'take-away' restaurant (you take the food home to eat it).

ll.32　Note the ELLIPSIS of *what (are) you doing ...?* *Are* often gets ellipted in very
–33　informal talk in similar constructions:

> Where (are) you going?
> Why (are) you looking so miserable?
> What (are) you worrying about?

l.45　Now the mother starts to interact with the little girl rather in the way teachers often do with their pupils, asking them 'display' questions (i.e. questions to which they already know the answer) and giving the child feedback on her responses, reinforcing her answers and praising her – the IRF structure mentioned in Unit 16. This kind of 'learning through interaction' with adults is obviously very important for the child's development and the learning of language.

l.47　Note the use of the singular *Is there ...?* with a plural noun (*ponies*). In present-day British English, this usage is very common, even among highly educated speakers, and can often be heard on radio and television, used by journalists and politicians.

l.49　*Gee up*: This is what one shouts to make a horse go faster. In 'baby-talk', horses are often called 'gee-gees'. Also, the suffix '-y' is often added to words in baby-talk: e.g. 'doggy', 'piggy'. This happens with *dolly* in l.51.

ll.60   *all this business about* ...: This expression is a very useful one in informal talk, and
−61   can be used to refer to a 'topic' or 'issue':

> What do you think of all this business about fishing damaging the
> environment? (all the debate/discussion in the papers/on TV).

Further reading

On how children learn language, see Elliot (1981) and the papers in Snow and
Ferguson (1977).

For more on ellipsis in informal talk, see Carter and McCarthy (1995a).

For further guidance on the use of *will* to refer to predicable/typical events in the
present, see Quirk et al (1985: index).

unit **18**

University tutorial

Activity

What differences would you expect there to be between planned and unplanned talk on a specific topic? (In each case, you have a good knowledge of the topic in question.) Consider both general and specific linguistic differences. Pay particular attention to vocabulary. For example, which of the following words and phrases would you consider more likely to occur in planned talk?

> On the one hand; firstly, secondly; well; dodgy; dunno; contribution; military interventions; funny; 'cos.

Would you expect formal talk to be characterised more by nouns or by verbs?

See **Line-by-line commentary** for comments on this activity.

Speakers and setting

> <S 01>   student: male
> <S 02>   tutor: male
> <S 03>   student: female

This is an extract from a recording of a university seminar on European politics. The main participant is an undergraduate student who has been asked to give a presentation on a specific topic: does France need Africa as much as Africa needs France?

During the presentation there are very limited interventions by the tutor and by other students. At the end of the presentation more general and informal discussion ensues among the tutor and the group of students. The student who gives the presentation has had time to research the presentation and to write it out in advance in the form of both continuous prose and, in places, detailed notes. The talk is therefore written to be spoken and is an example of planned talk.

The views expressed in this extract are not necessarily those of the authors and publisher.

Transcript

1	<S 01>	When President De Gaulle ensured that France had a prominent
2		role in Africa, it was part of his strategy to try and make France a
3		world power along with membership of er NA ... what ...
4		membership of NATO at the time but ... had a seat on UN Security
5		Council and his nuclear weapons. How has francophone Africa
6		benefited from this policy? Well it doesn't appear economic growth
7		is anything any better in francophone Africa than anywhere else
8		despite the large sums of aid given by France to the region. The vast
9		majority of the population have not seen their lives improve as a
10		result of a relationship with France. It cannot be said that African
11		populations have benefited from French support for authoritarian
12		and oppressive regimes, President Bongo in Gabon or Mobutu in
13		Zaire. Support of corrupt governments have ... has done little to
14		promote development; much of the aid provided has been either
15		mismanaged or embezzled. The crisis in the relationship began during
16		the late 1980s as France's so-called fading affair with Africa. Towards
17		the end of the 1980s, France's enthusiasm with Africa began to cool.
18		Instead of a financial benefit from its dealings with er francophone
19		Africa, it began having a deficit, its balance of payments went in
20		deficit and so did the Franc Zone. The French government ended up
21		subsidising its former colonies. The failure of the economies of er
22		French Africa led to a lot of blame being placed on France and its
23		failure to promote development is quite is er important role in Fre in
24		African governments earning large sums of aid pumped in. The
25		end of the cold war focussed the attention on the French
26		government's policy of propping up authoritarian and corrupt
27		regimes. People began to question the er benefit of propping up
28		such governments especially as er Eastern Europe began to have a
29		weight with democracy. Africa began to lose its appeal to French
30		industry, especially as the European Community became more
31		important in French exports. Also with the opening up of Eastern
32		Europe to Western Europe there's even more attraction in Europe
33		for French business. In the last month France devalued the CFA

34		Franc deciding its subsidising of Francophone Africa. Some believe
35		this is a clear sign that France is abandoning its Africa commitment
36		in favour of Europe and other areas. An example is the fact the new
37		right wing French government is not willing to fund these corrupt,
38		bureaucratic governments. But despite this there seems some
39		continuation in the policy. Despite the intentions to promote
40		democracy as President Mitterrand said in 1990 summit with the
41		African leaders, it appears France is unable to break its old habits.
42		The previous socialist government in its last few months in office was
43		humiliated by African leaders. President Bongo, an authoritarian,
44		is still in power; Mobutu is still in power. France did little to .. to er
45		punish Zaire despite the French ambassador being murdered by
46		Mobutu's henchmen. [a student laughs] ... armed guard
47		... or whatever
48	<S 02>	Armed guard
49	<S 01>	Armed guard was it? Nothing was done by the government in
50		reaction to the 1993 election in Cameroon despite the result being
51		claimed to be fixed and there was ... dunno ... dodgy dealings.
52		Cameroon therefore is still receiving a recipient of French aid
53		despite threats of aid being linked to democracy and Cameroon is
54		one of the richest countries in francophone Africa so the newer
55		aspect of aid policy doesn't seem to be doing much. The French
56		political parties still need African leaders for France as they've always
57		done, funded by or partly funded by African leaders ... so ... it's a
58		habit that's hard to break. However does Africa need France still?
59		Despite the favourable noises about democracy and freedom,
60		France has done little to promote either. Devaluation will hit African
61		people hard. The only people who will benefit from the CFA franc
62		devaluation are the big trading and export companies which are
63		often foreign owned and controlled anyway. The mass of people face
64		an ever greater drop in living standards. French aid policy has failed
65		to benefit the majority. Instead it has pandered to the interest of
66		French business and corrupt African leaders. African leaders in the
67		past have needed France. Military interventions or the threat of
68		them has helped keep many of them in power. An example of this
69		at the moment French troops have helped to prop up the routed
70		Rwandan army after its er defeat ... and that is it.
71	<S 02>	Good. Thank you very much indeed. Okay so there's about three or
72		four major points you want to talk about ... right ... which you were

73		going to try and identify.
74		The first of them is ... just to go into the basis of the relationship that
75		Ian started with. Why is it that France didn't want to break with
76		Africa? Why is it that France didn't want to let Africa em become
77		independent 'cos they clearly didn't I mean it was '58 where they had
78		that sort of funny referendum, oui ou non and er then we went on
79		to the 60s situation; why? ... why not? Why did they ... what was ...
80	<S 03>	[They] saw it as part of France itself ... Like the British didn't really
81		see their colonies as like a part of Britain, France very much saw it as
82		an integrated part of the nation.
83	<S 01>	The plan was always ... The plan was never to let go but to er
84		assimilate em the Africans into a er sort of wider France. The plan
85		was always beginning with the French [inaudible] or whatever was to
86		er assimilate the Africans into a larger France, never to sort of ... like
87		Britain. The plan was, I mean they saw an end to the road, they never
88		said they would hold on to it

General commentary

This teaching situation is marked by extended, prepared contributions by individual students directed in advance of the session by the tutor. It therefore contrasts markedly with the kinds of interchanges found in Unit 17 where speaking turns are shorter, less complete and less planned.

Time to plan what to say and to draw on books in preparation in addition to knowledge of the requirements of formal seminar presentations result in more formal talk. In terms of *vocabulary* more written, precise, infrequent and specialised items can be expected and are, indeed, to be found in the transcript above. In this context of language *written* to be spoken it is interesting to ask if there are words which are peculiar to spoken discourse. The specific commentary which follows examines some aspects of this question. It is also interesting to compare this transcript with the data in Unit 5 which mixes formal and informal features.

Line-by-line commentary

ll. 1–5 The speaker is finding his way into his argument at this point and the talk is thus characterised by one or two false starts (*anything any better*) (*er, what*), an informal discourse marker (*well*), and some lapses in syntactic ordering (*when ... but had a seat on UN Security Council*).

l. 10 *It cannot be said that*: The speaker has now located an appropriate formal style which approximates to written English. Impersonal passive constructions such as this are common in most forms of written argumentation.

l.34 *Some believe ...*: This is another impersonal formulaic phrase which allows views to be ascribed to others. It is a strategy for making an argument more subtle and is common in informal or written discourse. In informal discussion and debate the phrase is more likely to include the verb 'say' ('some say', 'some people say').

l.39 *... continuation in the policies*: In informal speech it would be unusual for nouns such as *continuation* to occur. The process of turning different parts of speech into nouns, particularly verbs into nominal forms, is a characteristic of written discourse or of discourse which is written to be spoken. In speech this expression would be more likely to be formulated as '... the policies seem to have continued' or '... they seem to have continued the policies'.

l.41 *it appears* is a marker of tentativeness. There is, however, still only minimal intrusion of the speaker's personal views (compare 'it seems to me'/'it appears to me'). Compare also the density of structures which indicate tentativeness when the discussion becomes more interactive and individual contributions are evaluated (see l.71).

l.48 *armed guard* is a prompt on the part of the tutor in response to the student's use of *or whatever*, which indicates he is uncertain of how accurate his statement is. The tutor still controls the situation even though the student holds the floor. It would be unusual for any of the other participants to provide a prompt at this point.

ll.51 *dunno ... dodgy dealings ... a recipient of French aid*: The talk enters a phase here in
–52 which spoken and written modes are mixed and interspersed; *dunno* is an informal form of 'I don't know'; *dodgy* is a word normally used in informal talk (a written equivalent would be 'dubious' or 'suspicious'); *recipient* is a more markedly 'written' form, nominalised from the verb 'receive' so that a more spoken alternative would be 'Cameroon still receives (or gets) French aid'.

l.52 The student here starts with a verb, *receive*, then changes to the very formal noun, *recipient*. This is another example of the nominalisation found in formal discourse. See comments on l.39 above.

l.63 *anyway* is here used adverbially and in clause-final position. An equivalent phrasing would be 'in any case'. In clause-initial position, *anyway*, in spoken discourse in particular, regularly functions as a marker of shift from one topic to another or as a signal to close a conversation.

l.71 *good*: The tutor here positively evaluates the presentation of the student. The option to evaluate is in this kind of institutionalised educational context very much the preserve of the teacher. It would be very unusual, for example, for speakers <S 03> or <S 04>, also students, to evaluate at this point the contribution of fellow students.

ll.72   *seem to, 'cos ... right*: The whole discourse becomes here much more
–77   'unscripted' and less planned. The use by the tutor of the shortened form of
        'because' (*cos*), the false starts (*er, the first of them is ... just to go into*) and the self-
        monitoring checks (*I mean*), indicate a less structured, more dynamic and
        developing discourse which contrasts with the more ordered 'written'
        character of the student's presentation; *right* serves as a kind of discourse
        organiser. With a rising intonation pattern it can serve to check understanding.

l.78   ... *sort of funny referendum*: The speaker here begins to use more informal lexical
        items (*funny*) and to qualify assertions by the use of informal 'spoken'
        disclaimers (*sort of*).

ll.80   *like* is a very common DISCOURSE MARKER of exemplification in informal
        spoken English. A formal, written equivalent would be 'for example' or 'for
        instance'. It can also commonly function as deliberately VAGUE LANGUAGE.

ll.83   The discussion is now becoming far more informal and interactive. The
–88   student is hesitant, he reformulates his utterances, he uses VAGUE MARKERS
        such as *whatever, sort of*, and the interactive marker, *I mean*.

Further reading

For one of the fullest explorations of the differences and distinctions between speech
and writing see Halliday (1989). This study gives further examples of what Halliday
calls 'grammatical metaphor' (see also Halliday 1985; 1994) – linguistic
representations by which processes which are typically reported by verbs in spoken
English are encoded as nouns in formal written English.

For further valuable explorations of spoken/written continua see McCarthy and
Carter (1994: ch.1); Chafe (1982); Tannen (1989).

For a core article on planned/unplanned discourse see Ochs (1979).

Nattinger and DeCarrico (1992) analyse the role of fixed phrases in formal and
informal talk. See also Lewis (1993).

Stenström (1990) and Carter and McCarthy (1988: ch. 5) analyse lexical items
peculiar to spoken discourse, and lexis in discourse respectively.

On the language of lectures and formal presentations, see Coulthard and
Montgomery (1981); Swales (1990) and Bhatia (1993).

Coulthard (1995) is an interesting study of the spoken and written characters of
statements made to the police. Coulthard makes particular use of measures of
lexical density.

For a detailed study of naturally-occurring conversational discourse, including
references to data in educational settings, see Tsui (1994).

unit **19**

Planning a family holiday

Activity

You are going to listen to about 900 words of conversation where a married couple are at home planning their summer holiday with a guide book and with the help of a friend who is staying with them.

How good are you at predicting how often certain words might occur in this conversation? Given that the speakers are making plans, they are likely to suggest things, decide things, agree and disagree over possibilities.

Below are some frequency figures for certain verbs in this conversation, counted by a computer. Only one of the figures is correct for each verb. Which one?

	can	could	shall	should	must	suggest	think	reckon
frequency	10, 2, 6	8, 4, 0	6, 0, 11	9, 1, 2	12, 1, 5	8, 4, 0	10, 5, 2	6, 0, 1

Turn to page 146 for the correct answers, and note the comments on each verb in the **Line-by-line commentary**.

Speakers and setting

    <S 01>   female
    <S 02>   male
    <S 03>   female

Recorded in <S 01>'s and <S 02>'s home. <S 03> is a house-guest. At the beginning of the extract, the speakers have just been discussing whether it would be better to take their car across the English Channel or to go by train and ferry.

Transcript

1	\<S 01\>	Yeah we'll just leave the car behind and go on the bus go on the trains
2	\<S 02\>	I reckon that's what we should do [\<S 01\> yeah] the only problem
3		that we've got then is carrying luggage
4	\<S 01\>	Yeah I won't take any
5	\<S 03\>	Just take a ruckie
6	\<S 01\>	Yeah just take one, just take a Sainsbury's bag
7	\<S 02\>	Well this is what we usually do I haven't got a rucksack
8	\<S 01\>	Well what we need to take we've got the cool bag so we'll take that
9		and just so we can keep, it's only small take things in that and we
10		can get go to Zebrugge get the train down to Brugge and then 'cos
11		it's only a wee bit south then take the train back up and go into Delft
12		and up to Amsterdam and there's somewhere else nice on the way
13		go up to Amsterdam and then just get it back again, is Delft in
14		Holland or Belgium
15	\<S 03\>	Delft Holland
16	\<S 02\>	Holland
17	[5 secs]	
18	\<S 01\>	And it says in my book the train's quite cheap
19	\<S 02\>	The only problem I suppose if we do go by train is the hassle of
20		finding the right buses and coaches and
21	\<S 01\>	Nah cos the train stations'll be in the cities won't they it'll be fine
22	\<S 02\>	The ferry
23	\<S 01\>	And the ferry
24	\<S 03\>	Well you've done inter-railing haven't you
25	\<S 01\>	Yeah and they're in the towns
26	\<S 03\>	But they do a Benelux tour rail card 'Which enables you to travel on
27		all Dutch, Belgian and Luxembourg railways or buy a voucher for a
28		specified 17 days'
29	\<S 01\>	Wow how much is that
30	\<S 03\>	It costs erm [6 secs] hmm [6 secs] 80 quid that's a lot isn't it
31	\<S 01\>	That's a lot … each
32	\<S 03\>	Must be
33	\<S 01\>	That's a lot
34	\<S 03\>	But it does, I mean that would give you loads, that's if you go for like
35		17 days [\<S 01\>mm] you're probably just better to get your tickets
36		when you're there
37	\<S 01\>	Mm

38	<S 03>	For wherever you wanted to go
39	<S 01>	Yeah probably won't be dear
40	<S 02>	It might be worthwhile taking the car you know
41	<S 01>	Oh I don't know I can't be bothered with the hassle
42	<S 02>	I'll do the driving I like driving
43	<S 01>	It's not that it's the parking and trying to find things
44	<S 03>	If you go to Amsterdam it would be a nightmare to take the car
45	<S 01>	Trying to sort out everything
46	<S 02>	Because originally when we thought we were going I thought we
47		were just going to Amsterdam and that was it we were just spending
48		our week in Amsterdam cos there's loads to do
49	<S 03>	⌐We're not we're not
50		though
51	<S 02>	Which makes it more difficult
52	<S 01>	We are going to Brugge now as well
53	<S 03>	Did you know British Rail operate services to Amsterdam from
54		Liverpool Street and Victoria Stations
55	<S 01>	Yeah it's 49 pounds return each
56	<S 02>	Are you sure you want to go to, I mean we can go for a city break in
57		Brugge
58	<S 01>	It's dead expensive it's dear it's so cheap if you go, it's the same price
59		for the two of us and the car return to Zebrugge or Hook of
60		Holland either, as it is to go as foot passengers it's no cheaper or
61		dearer
62	<S 02>	But then you've got to add on 50 pounds a night wherever we stay
63	<S 01>	Don't you want to do that anyway
64	<S 02>	But you don't if you've got one of these city breaks it's all inclusive
65		isn't it
66	<S 01>	Yeah but then you're talking about 220 quid each aren't you instead
67		of 30
68	<S 03>	And you could base yourself in Amsterdam and just go to Brugge
69		for the day
70	<S 01>	How far is it how far's Brugge from Amsterdam
71	<S 03>	Don't know probably miles
72	<S 01>	[laughs]
73	<S 02>	You could do that you're right
74	<S 03>	⌐Don't know
75	<S 02>	⌐You could do that
76	<S 03>	You know like if you got the earliest train in the morning

77	<S 01>	Oh that's true yeah
78	<S 03>	└And then just got the last train back at night
79	<S 02>	The only thing is when I opened that up at Brugge first thing it said
80		in it was don't stay in Brugge ... no it says don't stay in Brugge cos
81		it's dear
82	<S 01>	Is it
83	<S 03>	└Yeah
84	<S 02>	└Yeah it does say that
85	<S 03>	Page 363 that was in the *Let's go* it said that it's difficult to find a
86		reasonably priced meal
87	<S 01>	Well maybe then we could do that go to the Hook of Holland, go to
88		Amsterdam cos Delft isn't far from Amsterdam is it that would be, if
89		you could go there for a wee jaunt
90	<S 02>	I thought Delft was miles from Amsterdam
91	<S 01>	Don't think so
92	<S 02>	Well I mean it's only, Holland's only small, it's not a big place
93	<S 01>	It's not I don't think it's far alright well we'll do that
94	<S 03>	Well it says 'you would be mad to come to Flanders and miss this
95		place' Brugge
96	<S 01>	It is the Venice of the north of Europe
97	<S 03>	'Its museums are named as one attraction hold some of the
98		country's finest collections of Flemish art'
99	<S 02>	You see I'd never get her into a museum to look at art
100	<S 03>	Yes well Jen could go and look at something more interesting while
101		you go and
102	<S 01>	Ah yes
103	<S 02>	└Jen could go and, you could go and look at things like glass buoys
104	<S 01>	Yeah that's okay
105	<S 02>	While I go and look at Flemish art
106	<S 01>	Good idea
107	<S 02>	That's separating our cultures
108	<S 01>	Yeah I'll go and sit in a cafe, street terrace bar somewhere and drink
109		beer, Belgian beer and eat chocolates and you can go and look at
110		paintings
111	<S 02>	You can pay 40 pounds for a Belgian beer
112	[4 secs]	
113	<S 01>	Well maybe we should do that

General commentary

When people are negotiating and planning in very informal or intimate situations like this one, verbs such as *suggest, agree,* and *disagree* are unlikely to be used very frequently. Instead, speakers simply state their position, but usually soften it by using modal verbs, especially *could* in this case, as well as other softeners such as *maybe, think* and *reckon*. These words are commented on as they occur, in the **Line-by-line commentary**. Words such as *suggest, agree* and *disagree* are more likely to occur in more formal settings such as debates, meetings, etc. (though even in those settings they are not as frequent as language coursebooks sometimes suggest). *Suggest, agree, disagree* are, in short, likely to be more useful for *reporting* such functions rather than actually performing them.

Line-by-line commentary

l.1   *We'll just leave the car*: Note here the *'ll* form used for making informal decisions. It is often not clear whether such uses of *'ll* are a short form of 'will' or 'shall', and it may be better to think of *'ll* as an independent form in conversational grammar. The use of *'ll* with *we* to announce informal decisions in this way is quite common. (See also l.8.)

l.2   Two softeners occur here: *reckon* and *should*; *reckon* (meaning 'think' or 'guess') is very common in informal conversation.

l.5   *ruckie*: Short form of *rucksack*. The '-y/-ie' suffix is often used to create informality, and in language used to or by young children. Other examples:

> doggy, horsy, froggy (used to/by children)
> Trekkie (a fan of the science fiction TV series *Star Trek*)
> Tommy, Maggie, Charlie, Micky, etc. (informal versions of personal first names)
> Biccie, ciggy, bevvy, lolly (biscuit, cigarette, alcoholic drink [*bev*erage], lollipop)

l.6   *Sainsbury's*: A major chain of supermarkets in Britain.

ll.8–9 *can* occurs three times here as the softener for the speaker's suggestions.

l.10 *wee*: This speaker is Scottish. *Wee* is standard Scottish and Northern Irish English for 'small', but is sometimes used by other English speakers (e.g. 'Could I have a wee bit more milk in my coffee please?').

l.19 *hassle*: An informal word meaning 'problem'/'nuisance'/'difficulty'. (See also l.41.)

l.21 *Nah*: This form of 'no' often sounds slightly scornful or dismissive.

l.26 *They do a Benelux card*: Note this informal use of 'do' used to refer to services provided by shops/companies, etc. (see also Unit 12, l.16).

l.29   *Wow*: An exclamation of surprise, normally used by younger generations.

l.30   *quid* is the normal, everyday colloquial word for a pound sterling in Britain. (See also l.66.)

l.32   Note the ELLIPSIS of *it* with *must be*, and the same with *won't be* in l.39. In l.71 and l.74 *I* is elipted before *don't know*, and in l.91 the same happens with *don't think so*. These are typical ellipses with everyday routine expressions.

l.34   *loads* is a common, informal word meaning 'a lot'/'many'. It can be used with plurals or uncountables:

> She's got loads of money.
> No need to rush, we've got loads of time.
> There's loads to do. (l.48)

l.35   *you're probably just better to* ...: This construction would not normally occur in writing, where we would be likely to find 'It would probably be better if you just ...'.

l.40   *might* is one of the most indirect softeners of all. 'May', 'could' or 'would' are all stronger alternatives here.

l.47   *that was it*: 'that was all, nothing else'.

l.51   *Which makes it* ...: In spoken language, speakers often tag on subordinate clauses in their next speaking turn; they do not have to start a 'new sentence' each time they speak. The structure is common in advertising language:

> Which is why you should always drink Fortuna beer.

Such usage allows the adverts to sound distinctly interactive and conversational in tone.

l.58   *dead expensive*: *dead* here means 'really'/'very', and is a very informal intensifier:

> That film was dead boring.
> I was just dead tired and couldn't concentrate.

Note also how the speakers alternate between *expensive* and the less formal *dear*.

l.66   *you're talking (about)*: This is an informal way of saying 'that means'. Other examples:

> For two weeks you're talking 300 pounds.
> You're talking thousands for a car like that, even ten years old.

l.68   *could* is the most common softener for making suggestions in this extract. Note its use here and in ll. 73, 75, 100 and 103 (twice).

l.76   Note the use of *like*, which is a very frequent discourse marker in informal conversation. Speakers use it when they are exemplifying, or often just as an alternative or accompaniment to 'you know'.

l.79　*The (only) thing is*: This is a frequent conversational expression meaning 'the only problem is'.

l.89　*a wee jaunt*: A *jaunt* is an informal word meaning 'a pleasant excursion/day out away from home or where one is staying'.

l.92　*Holland's only small, it's not a big place*: Speakers often use antonyms (opposites) in the same utterance to make their meaning clear. Other examples:

> The countryside's hilly, it's not flat.
> It's quite smooth, it's not at all bumpy.

ll.94 –95　The guide book obviously uses quite informal language (probably because it is aimed at young people), not dissimilar from conversational style, e.g. the use of *mad* ('crazy').

l.99　*get her ...*: an informal construction meaning 'persuade her to go to ...'. Other examples:

> You'll never get me into an amusement arcade.
> You'd never get him to go to church, not in a million years.

l.103　*glass buoys* here are marine buoys made of glass. Jen (<S 01>) collects them.

Answers for frequency activity

	can	could	shall	should	must	suggest	think	reckon
frequency	6	8	0	2	1	0	2	1

Further reading

On the use of modal verbs in real language compared with language teaching text books, see Holmes (1983, 1988).

McCarthy (1988) has further examples of how speakers use synonyms and antonyms to elaborate meaning in conversation.

Sinclair (1991) contains much fascinating material on lexical frequencies and related matters.

Publisher's planning meeting

Activity

The word 'get' (and its other forms 'getting/got') occurs quite frequently in the extract (as it does in spoken language in general). How many different meanings/uses does the verb 'get' have in English? Make a list of its different meanings and, if possible, compare your list with a partner's.

The occurrences of 'get' and approximate meanings/uses are given in the table at the end of this unit. How do they compare with your list?

Speakers and setting

<S 01>   informal meeting chairperson: female (30s)
<S 02>   male (mid-20s)
<S 03>   male (30s)

This is an extract from an informal meeting held at an educational publisher's office. The meeting consists of a small group of close colleagues who are planning the production schedules for educational materials.

Transcript

1	<S 01>	Erm can we keep these intermediate cassette schedules
2		as draft until [4 secs] erm [3 secs] because I, I have to erm
3		get a confirmed date for the tapescript from the author and stuff
4	<S 02>	⌐Yeah that's fine
5	<S 01>	Cos the authors have to finalise the tapescript and

6	until they do that erm
7 <S 02>	└Yep it's not a problem
8 [6 secs]	
9 <S 01>	I can't really say that all this is going to work [sounds of pages
10	rustling] and then *Changes* ... which is finally getting moving [4 secs]
11	now erm can we change the film date for Teacher's Book One
12	to the 30th of May because we're we're putting in some extra
13	pages ... so I'm waiting for typescript for those extra pages
14 <S 02>	What's the extent
15 <S 01>	[whispered] the extent
16 <S 02>	Is it going to remain the same
17 <S 01>	Yeah it should be one-seven-six ... yeah I think we've
18	got spare pages it's not a problem
19 [3 secs]	
20 <S 02>	Fine
21 <S 01>	Erm [sound of paper tearing] [4 secs] and we need
22	stock by July, early July we have to be a bit careful with these
23	three now because the the Loescher warehouse closes from the
24	first of August to the 22nd so ... we must allow time for things
25	to get there and get into the warehouse before it closes
26 <S 03>	How do you spell Loescher is it L-O-E-S-C-H-E-R
27 <S 01>	Yeah erm ... but I mean that seems that I mean based
28	on the printing time we've allowed here we should get stock
29	[<S 02> mm] early July [<S 03> yeah] anyway so that's a month to
30	get to Italy [3 secs] so that one's going okay, we've got ...
31	Workbook Book Two film okay by the 29th of May, shouldn't be any
32	problem at all in fact should be, should be quite a lot earlier
33 <S 02>	Do I need to do price fixes for Teacher's Book One
34 <S 01>	└Oh gosh erm
35 <S 02>	Do, don't I
36 <S 01>	└Yes actually Workbook Two's probably the
37	most urgent now [4 secs] I reckon we'll probably have film ...
38	in about three weeks for Workbook Two
39 <S 02>	Right ... it's not going to change in quantity is it
40	I mean I think we've bought the paper for it already
41 <S 01>	└Change in quantity ... no
42 <S 02>	Fine ... this is the bit where Kate goes oh it's
43	actually a hundred-and-ninety-six [laughs mockingly]
44	[<S 01> no no no] don't mean that erm right fine great so I'll just, I'll

45		leave it as on schedule
46	<S 01>	Oh hang on sorry
47	<S 02>	Oh no what
48	<S 01>	No the extent is not ninety-six
49	<S 02>	What is it
50	<S 01>	It's eight more ... sorry that's not a very nice extent
51		is it but
52	<S 02>	It isn't but erm
53	<S 03>	What er what I can't add that what does that take us
54		to hundred and four
55	<S 01>	└Er ninety, hundred and four
56	<S 03>	Hundred and four
57	<S 02>	Yeah
58	<S 01>	Is that hideous
59	<S 03>	Yeah
60	<S 02>	It is a bit of a problem
61	<S 03>	└Yeah it is
62	<S 02>	└Well, have to see what they come
63		up with
64	<S 03>	We'll see what we can do
65	<S 02>	Oh it's the, it's the mono one so it'll be less of a
66		problem
67	<S 01>	You know there was just no way [<S 03> mm] I could
68		squeeze it in
69	<S 03>	Don't worry don't worry we'll sort it out
70	[3 secs]	
71	<S 01>	Erm and Teacher's Book Two we've got yeah film end of
72		May again that's what I'm aiming for still
73	<S 02>	Shall I do a price fix for, estimate for that
74	<S 01>	Price fix estimate yes have you got costs from Tony
75	<S 02>	No well basically yeah
76	<S 01>	Erm sorry I was sending you hundreds of messages
77		before, while you were away about getting disks of things to Tony
78	<S 02>	For *Changes* which we've actioned
79	<S 01>	└He must now have the Workbook
80		because he's [<S 03> We've done them] so he's got Teacher's Book
81		Two and Workbook Two and those bits of artwork for Teacher's
82		Book One
83	<S 02>	└He hasn't got the bits of artwork yet for Teacher's

84		Book One Teacher's Book Two G&E are finding the disks and sorting
85		that out for us
86	<S 01>	Oh right and he's got Workbook Two hasn't he 'cos he
87		said he was, he would print it out
88	<S 02>	⌊He's got Workbook Two he's got the fonts he
89		needed he hasn't got the artwork he needed G&E are looking into
90		that at the moment
91	<S 01>	Right okay but it's all under control
92	<S 02>	It's actioned
93	<S 01>	Jolly good there's something else I wanted to ask you um
94		... when are you going to start handling reprints cos I need some
95		advice about reprints for *Changes*
96	<S 03>	Erm I won't, I couldn't offer you any intelligent
97		advice on reprints until I actually get it and probably even then
98		it would take me about three months I would think to get an angle
99		on it but I'm not getting it until June
100	<S 02>	⌊Linda's coming in in June yeah
101	<S 03>	⌊So until June
102	<S 01>	So I have to talk to Hamish
103	<S 03>	⌊Everything is Hamish yeah
104	<S 01>	Right
105	<S 02>	I mean Linda's doing them as we speak all new ELT
106		reprints are being handled by Linda
107	<S 01>	⌊It's Linda not Carrie
108	<S 02>	That's right
109	<S 03>	That's right
110	<S 01>	Erm

General commentary

The extract is quite informal, since the people at the meeting know each other well and work closely together every day. Business meetings between people who do not know each other are likely to display more formal features of language. Here the speakers have to arrive at a number of decisions regarding book production. As there is no one 'authority' figure, they have to negotiate their way to the important decisions. This transcript includes several examples of the problem-solution pattern, where problems are presented and possible ways of solving them are evaluated by the participants, for example, the problem of getting books to one of the company's distributors (ll. 22–30).

Line-by-line commentary

l.1   Note the use of *can* to make a polite but firm proposal; it is almost like an instruction here, and does not really give the others much room to say 'no'. See also *can* in l.11.

l.3   *and stuff* is a very informal way of saying 'and so on'/'and things like that'.

l.4 and l.7   The speaker does not repeat himself but uses *that's fine* and *it's not a problem* more or less synonymously. The same happens in reverse in l.18 and l.20. Speakers often vary their vocabulary in this way.

l.7   *Yep*: A very informal version of 'yes'. *Changes* is the title of a book.

l.14   *extent* here is a publishing term meaning 'number of pages'.

l.17   *one-seven-six* is just another way of saying 'a hundred and seventy six'. Since they are discussing numbers of pages, it is not necessary for the speaker to spell out that it is 'hundreds' and 'tens'.

l.22   *stock*: Books in the company's warehouse, ready to send out to booksellers.

l.22   *a bit careful*: *a bit* is much more common in informal spoken language than 'a little' or 'rather/somewhat'. (See also l.60.)

ll.31 −32   Note the ellipses here of the *it* pronoun subject before *shouldn't*. This is frequent in informal responses with modal verbs:

> A: Can we do it by August?
> B: Might be difficult, actually.
>
> A: Who's in charge of that?
> B: Must be Linda, surely.

Notice that ELLIPSIS also happens with the auxiliary *do* in l.35. This is common where the utterance ends in a TAG (*don't I*).

l.34   *gosh* is a rather middle-class exclamation. The same speaker uses *jolly good* in l.93, which has a similar middle-class feel to it.

l.37   *I reckon* is frequent in informal talk, meaning 'I think/guess/estimate'.

l.42   *this is the bit where ...*: This expression is often used to introduce a parody or some sort of joke about the present situation, especially emphasising the predictability of things.

l.42   Note here how *goes* is used instead of 'says'. The verb 'go' is used to report speech in informal contexts (especially narratives), where the speaker wants to dramatise the reported speech, or to emphasise the actual sounds the person made, or any gestures or body language they used:

> A: And then he goes 'a-a-a-gh!' and jumped off the roof. I thought he was going to kill himself!

The simple past tense 'went' can also be used in this way for speech reports.

l.44 Note the ELLIPSIS of *I* in *(I) Don't mean that.* This often happens with frequently occurring FIXED EXPRESSIONS such as this one. In l.62, similarly, *we* is understood before *have to see ...*

Observe also how the speaker uses three DISCOURSE MARKERS together here (*right, fine, great*), to mark the boundary between this bit of business and the next. (See also Unit 6, ll. 36–37.)

l.46 *hang on* is an informal version of 'wait (a moment)'.

l.53 The speaker here says *take **us** to*, rather than 'take **it** to', which personalises the expression more.

ll.55 –56 Here we note that the speakers do not use *a* (or least of all *one*) before *hundred*. This is common in informal situations. Learners of English often overuse *one* before words like hundred, thousand, dozen, etc. which is only used in rather formal contexts or contexts where it is essential to be very precise.

l.58 *hideous* often means 'very ugly', but here it just means 'awful/very bad'.

l.65 *mono*: This is short for 'monochrome', meaning black-and-white, not colour.

l.67 *there was just no way* ...: This is a frequent informal spoken expression meaning '(I) can/could not possibly ...':

> There's just no way I can phone him at 6 o'clock in the morning.

l.69 The collocation 'sort out a problem' is much more frequent in spoken language than '(re) solve a problem'. See also ll.84–85.

l.72 Note the final position of *still*. The position gives it emphasis. This would be very unusual in written style, but often happens in spoken language. In formal writing we would expect 'I am still aiming for the end of May'.

l.75 *basically* here seems to be used to mean 'in a general sense'; it softens the definiteness of 'yes' as an answer.

l.78 The use of *action* as a verb here is typical business language, meaning 'put into action'. We would not use it in everyday conversation.

ll.81 and 83 *bits* is much more informal than 'pieces' would be here.

l.84 *G&E* stands for Goodfellow & Egan, a typesetting company.

l.105 *as we speak*: 'at this very moment'. Compare this with 'as I write' in written language.

Follow-up activity

Note how often throughout the extract the speakers use discourse markers like *you know* and *I mean*. These soften and personalise their remarks, which is very important in a context like this, where consensus is necessary and where the speakers are negotiating their way towards agreement, even though this is 'business English'.

Occurrences of get

Note that the paraphrases of meaning are approximate; it is very difficult to give precise glosses.

line	context	meaning/use
3	I have to erm **get** a confirmed date for the tapescript from the author	obtain/secure
10	and then *Changes* ... which is finally **getting** moving	starting (to move)
18	I think we've **got** spare pages	have
24–25	we must allow time for things to (a) **get** there and (b) **get** into the warehouse	(a) arrive/reach (b) be put into
28–29	we should **get** stock early July	receive/have
29–30	so that's a month to **get** to Italy	reach/travel to
30–31	we've **got** ... Workbook Book Two film okay by the 29th of May	have/have noted down
71	we've **got** yeah film end of May again	have/have noted down
74	have you **got** costs from Tony	obtained/received
77	about **getting** disks of things to Tony	sending/so that he receives
80–89	he's **got** Teacher's Book Two He hasn't **got** the bits of artwork yet He's **got** Workbook Two he's **got** the fonts he needed he hasn't **got** the artwork	has/doesn't have
96–97	I couldn't offer you any intelligent advice on reprints until I actually **get** it	receive
98	it would take me about three months I would think to **get an angle on** it	part of an idiomatic expression: 'to understand its nature'/'have a proper perspective on it'
99	but I'm not **getting** it until June	receiving

Further reading

For a full description of *get* in English see Quirk et al (1985: index).

On the language of business meetings, see Williams (1988).

For more on the problem-solution pattern, see Hoey (1983).

References

Aijmer K. (1989) Themes and tails: the discourse functions of dislocated elements. *Nordic Journal of Linguistics* 12 (2): 137–54

Aston G. (1995) Say 'thank you': some pragmatic constraints in conversational closings. *Applied Linguistics* 16 (1): 57–86

Bauman, R. (1986) *Story, Performance, Event: Contextual Studies of Oral Narrative.* Cambridge University Press

Bennett W. (1989) The structure of English tags. *Word* 40 (3): 315–33

Berry H.M. (1981) Systemic linguistics and discourse analysis: a multi-layered approach to exchange structure. In M. Coulthard and M. Montgomery (eds) *Studies in Discourse Analysis.* London: Routledge 120–45

Bhatia V.K. (1993) *Analysing Genre: Language Use in Professional Settings.* London: Longman

Brazil D. (1995) *A Grammar of Speech.* Oxford University Press

Brown P. and S. Levinson (1987) *Politeness: Some Universals in Language Usage.* Cambridge University Press

Bublitz W. (1988) *Supportive Fellow-Speakers and Cooperative Conversations.* Amsterdam: John Benjamins

Carter R.A. (1987) *Vocabulary: Applied Linguistic Perspectives.* London: Routledge

Carter R.A. and M.J. McCarthy (1988) *Vocabulary and Language Teaching* London: Longman

Carter R.A. and M.J. McCarthy (1995a) Grammar and the spoken language. *Applied Linguistics* 16 (2): 141–58

Carter R.A. and M.J. McCarthy (1995b) Discourse and creativity: bridging the gap between language and literature. In G. Cook and B. Seidlhofer (eds) *Principle and Practice in Applied Linguistics. Studies in Honour of H.G. Widdowson.* Oxford University Press 303–21

Chafe W. (1982) Integration and involvement in speaking, writing, and oral literature. In D. Tannen (ed) *Spoken and Written Language: Exploring Orality and Literacy.* Norwood, New Jersey: Ablex Publishing Corporation 35–53

Channell J. (1994) *Vague Language.* Oxford University Press

Collins COBUILD (1990) *English Grammar.* London: Collins

Cook G. (1992) *The Discourse of Advertising.* London: Routledge

Coulthard R.M. and M. Montgomery (1981) The structure of monologue. In M. Coulthard and M. Montgomery (eds) *Studies in Discourse Analysis.* London: Routledge 31–39

Coulthard R.M. (1995) Explorations in applied linguistics 3: forensic linguistics. In G. Cook and B. Seidlhofer (eds) *Principle and Practice in Applied Linguistics.* Oxford University Press

Crismore A. and R. Farnsworth (1990) Metadiscourse in popular and professional science discourse. In W. Nash (ed) *The Writing Scholar*. Newbury Park, California: Sage Publications 118–36

Crowdy S. (1993) Spoken corpus design. *Literary and Linguistic Computing* 8 (2): 259–65

Crystal D. and D. Davy (1975) *Advanced Conversational English*. London: Longman

Elliot A.J. (1981) *Child Language*. Cambridge University Press

Fairclough N. (1989) *Language and Power*. London: Longman

Farrell T.B. (1985) Narrative in natural discourse: on conversation and rhetoric. *Journal of Communication* 35 (4): 109–27

Fernando C. (1996) *Idioms and Idiomaticity*. Oxford University Press

Fludernik M. (1991) The historical present tense yet again: tense switching and narrative dynamics in oral and quasi-oral storyteller. *Text* 11 (3): 365–98

Fowler R. (1986) *Linguistic Criticism*. Oxford University Press

Fronek J. (1982) *Thing* as a function word. *Linguistics* 20: 633–54

Gardner R. (1987) The identification and role of topic in spoken interaction. *Semiotica* 65 (1/2): 129–41

Gardner, H. and R. Spielman (1980) Funny stories and conversational structures. *Papers in Linguistics* 13 (2) 179–200

Haegeman L. (1989) Be going to and will: a pragmatic account. *Journal of Linguistics* 25 (2): 291–317

Halliday M.A.K. (1989) *Spoken and Written Language*. Oxford University Press

Halliday M.A.K. (1985) It's a fixed word order language is English. *ITL Review of Applied Linguistics* 67/68: 207–18

Halliday M.A.K. (1994) *An Introduction to Functional Grammar*. (2nd edition) London: Edward Arnold

Hintikka J. (1982) Tag questions and grammatical acceptability. *Nordic Journal of Linguistics* 5 (2): 129–32

Hoey M.P. (1983) *On the Surface of Discourse*. London: Allen and Unwin

Hoey M.P. (1991) Some properties of spoken discourse. In R. Bowers and C. Brumfit (eds) *Applied Linguistics and English Language Teaching*. Basingstoke: Macmillan/MEP 65–84

Holmes J. (1983) Speaking English with the appropriate degree of conviction. In C. Brumfit (ed) *Learning and Teaching Languages for Communication: Applied Linguistic Perspectives*. London: CILT

Holmes J. (1988) Doubt and certainty in ESL textbooks. *Applied Linguistics* 9 (1): 21–44

Ishikawa M. (1991) Iconicity in discourse: the case of repetition. *Text* 11 (4): 553–80

Labov W. (1972) *Language in the Inner City*. Oxford: Basil Blackwell

Lerner G.H. (1991) On the syntax of sentences-in-progress. *Language in Society* 20 (3): 441–58

Lewis M. (1993) *The Lexical Approach: The State of ELT and a Way Forward*. Hove: LTP

Loveday L. (1982) Communicative interference: a framework for contrastively analyzing L2 communicative competence exemplified with the linguistic behaviour of Japanese performing in English. *International Review of Applied Linguistics* XX: 1–16

McCarthy M.J. (1984) A new look at vocabulary in EFL. *Applied Linguistics* 5 (1): 12–22

McCarthy M.J. (1988) Some vocabulary patterns in conversation. In R.A. Carter and M.J. McCarthy *Vocabulary and Language Teaching*. London: Longman 181–99

McCarthy M.J. (1992a) Interactive lexis: prominence and paradigms. In R.M. Coulthard (ed) *Advances in Spoken Discourse Analysis*. London: Routledge 197–208

McCarthy M.J. (1992b) English idioms in use. *Revista Canaria de Estudios Ingleses* 25: 55–65

McCarthy M.J. (1994) It, this and that. In R.M. Coulthard (ed) *Advances in Written Text Analysis*. London: Routledge 266–75

McCarthy M.J. (1997) *Spoken Language and Applied Linguistics*. Cambridge University Press

McCarthy M.J. and R.A. Carter (1994) *Language as Discourse: Perspectives for Language Teaching*. London: Longman

McCarthy M.J. and R.A. Carter (1995) What is spoken grammar and how should we teach it? *ELT Journal* 49 (3): 207–18

McCarthy M.J. and R.A. Carter (1997) Grammar, tails and affect: constructing expressive choices in disclosure. *Text* 17, 3

McCarthy M.J. and F. O'Dell (1994) *English Vocabulary in Use*. Cambridge University Press

McGregor W. (1995) The English 'tag question': a new analysis is(n't) it? In P. Hasan and P. Fries (eds) *On Subject and Theme: A Discourse Functional Perspective*. Amsterdam: John Benjamins 91–121

Moon R. (1992) Textual aspects of fixed expressions in learners' dictionaries. In P.J. Arnaud, H. Béjoint (eds) *Vocabulary and Applied Linguistics*. Basingstoke: Macmillan 13–27

Nattinger J.R. and J.S. DeCarrico (1992) *Lexical Phrases and Language Teaching*. Oxford University Press

Norrick N.R. (1988) Binomial meaning in texts. *Journal of English Linguistics* 21 (1): 72–87

Ochs E. (1979) Planned and unplanned discourses. In T. Givón (ed) *Syntax and Semantics 12: Discourse and Semantics*. London: Academic Press

Quirk R., S. Greenbaum, G. Leech, J. Svartvik (1985) *A Comprehensive Grammar of the English Language*. London: Longman

Rundell M. (1995a) The word on the street. *English Today* 11 (3): 29–35

Rundell M. (1995b) The BNC: A spoken corpus. *Modern English Teacher* 4 (2): 13–15

Schiffrin D. (1981) Tense variation in narrative. *Language* 57 (1): 45–62

Schiffrin D. (1987) *Discourse Markers*. Cambridge University Press

Schleppegrell M. (1992) Subordination and linguistic complexity. *Discourse Processes* 15 (1): 117–31

Silva-Corvalán C. (1983) Tense and aspect in oral Spanish narrative: context and meaning. *Language* 59 (4): 760–80

Sinclair J. McH. (1991) *Corpus, Concordance and Collocation*. Oxford University Press

Sinclair J. McH. and R.M. Coulthard (1975) *Towards an Analysis of Discourse*. Oxford University Press

Sinclair J. McH. and A. Renouf (1988) A lexical syllabus for language learning. In R.A. Carter and M.J. McCarthy *Vocabulary and Language Teaching*. London: Longman 140–58

Snow C.E. and C.A. Ferguson (eds) (1977) *Talking to Children: Language Input and Acquisition*. Cambridge University Press

Stenström A.B. (1990) Lexical items peculiar to spoken discourse. In J. Svartvik (ed) *The London-Lund Corpus of Spoken English*. Lund University Press 137–75

Stubbs M. (1983) *Discourse Analysis*. Oxford: Basil Blackwell

Stubbs M. (1986) 'A matter of prolonged fieldwork'; notes towards a modal grammar of English. *Applied Linguistics* 7 (1): 1–25

Swales J. (1990) *Genre Analysis*. Cambridge University Press

Tannen D. (1989) *Talking Voices*. Cambridge University Press

Thavenius C. (1983) *Referential Pronouns in English Conversation*. Lund: Gleerup

Thompson G. (1994) *Reporting.* Collins-Cobuild English Guides no.5. London: HarperCollins

Toolan M. (1988) *Narrative. A Critical Linguistic Introduction.* London: Routledge

Tsui A. (1994) *English Conversation.* Oxford University Press

Ure J. (1971) Lexical density and register differentiation. In G.E. Perren and J.L.M. Trim (eds) *Applications of Linguistics: Selected papers of the Second International Congress of Applied Linguistics, Cambridge, 1969.* Cambridge University Press 443–52

Van de Kopple W.J. (1985) Some exploratory discourse on metadiscourse. *College Composition and Communication* 36: 82–93

Ventola E. (1987) *The Structure of Social Interaction: A Systemic Approach to the Semiotics of Service Encounters.* London: Frances Pinter

White S. (1989) Back-channels across cultures: a study of Americans and Japanese. *Language in Society* 18 (1): 59–76

Williams M. (1988) Language taught for meetings and language used in meetings: is there anything in common? *Applied Linguistics* 9 (1): 45-58

Wolfson N. (1979) The conversational historical present alteration. *Language* 55: 168–82

Yule G., T. Mathis and M. Hopkins (1992) On reporting what was said. *ELT Journal* 46 (3): 245–51

CANCODE publications

CANCODE stands for '<u>C</u>ambridge and <u>N</u>ottingham <u>C</u>orpus of <u>D</u>iscourse in English'. It is a corpus-based applied linguistic research project based in the Department of English Studies at the University of Nottingham. All data collected are the property of Cambridge University Press. The following bibliography is of work published in connection with the project.

Carter, R.A. (1997a) *Investigating English Discourse: language, literacy, literature.* London: Routledge

Carter, R.A. (1997b) Orders of reality: Speaking Englishes, speaking cultures. *ELT Journal* 51, 2

Carter R.A. and M.J. McCarthy (1995a) Grammar and the spoken language. *Applied Linguistics* 16 (2): 141–58

Carter R.A. and M.J. McCarthy (1995b) Discourse and creativity: bridging the gap between language and literature. In G. Cook and B. Seidlhofer (eds) *Principle and Practice in Applied Linguistics.* Oxford University Press 303–21

Carter R.A. and M.J. McCarthy (1997) Written and spoken vocabulary. In N. Schmitt and M.J. McCarthy (eds) *Vocabulary: Description, Acquisition, Pedagogy.* Cambridge University Press

Carter R.A., Hughes, R. and M.J. McCarthy (1997) Telling tails: grammar, the spoken language and materials development. In B. Tomlinson (ed) *Materials Development in L2 Teaching.* Cambridge University Press

Hudson J., R.A. Carter and M.J. McCarthy (1996) Spoken corpus design, mimeo, Department of English Studies, University of Nottingham

Hughes R., R.A. Carter and M.J. McCarthy (1995) Discourse context as a predictor of grammatical choice. In D. Graddol and S. Thomas (eds) *Language in a Changing Europe.* Clevedon: BAAL/Multilingual Matters 47–54

McCarthy M.J. (1995) Conversation and literature: tense and aspect. In J. Payne (ed) *Linguistic Approaches to Literature.* Birmingham: English Language Research 58–73

McCarthy M.J. (1997) *Spoken Language and Applied Linguistics.* Cambridge University Press

McCarthy M.J. and R.A. Carter (1995) Spoken Grammar: what is it and how can we teach it? *ELT Journal* 49 (3): 207–218

McCarthy M.J. and R.A. Carter (1997) Grammar, tails and affect: constructing expressive choices in discourse. *Text* 17, 3

Stanfield C. (1996) English as she is spoke (conversation with CANCODE researcher Jean Hudson). *Cambridge Language Reference News* 2:2